M & M Essential
ANATOMY

D1133688

Majid Alimohammadi, B.Sc (PT), M.Sc., Ph.D.

Instructor
Department of Cellular and Physiological Sciences
University of British Columbia, Faculty of Medicine

Majid Doroudi, B.Sc. (PT), M.Sc., Ph.D.

Senior Instructor
Department of Cellular and Physiological Sciences
University of British Columbia, Faculty of Medicine

Kendall Hunt
publishing company

Kendall Hunt
publishing company
www.kendallhunt.com
Send all inquiries to:
4050 Westmark Drive
Dubuque, IA 52004-1840

Copyright © 2011 by Kendall Hunt Publishing Company

ISBN 978-0-7575-8617-0

Printed in the United States of America
10 9 8 7 6 5 4 3 2

Contents

Introduction

LEARNING OBJECTIVES

Upon completion of this chapter you should be able to:

1. Define anatomy and its three major divisions.
2. Differentiate between regional and systemic approaches in studying anatomy.
3. Explain the standard anatomical position and planes.
4. Define the anatomical terms of position, relation, and direction with an example of usage.
5. Describe anatomical terms of movements and give an example of usage.
6. Name main body systems and indicate their major components and function.
7. Identify major human body regions and important subdivisions.
8. Define body cavities.

···· Anatomy

Anatomy is a branch of science that studies the structure of the body and relationship of different organs with each other. If the subject of this study is the human body, then it is referred to as human anatomy. Human anatomy is deeply intertwined with dissection.

There are three different branches of anatomy:

1. **Macroscopic anatomy:** In this branch, the learning framework focuses on learning about the structure of the body with the naked eye; also called gross anatomy. There are two main approaches in gross anatomy:

   a. In a **systemic approach**, different organ systems are individually studied throughout the entire body, such as skeletal system, cardiovascular system etc. This approach provides a better understanding of the continuity of the systems of the human body and is more suitable in certain learning situations (e.g., if a human cadaver is not available for dissection).

   b. In a **regional approach**, the human body is divided into regions, including head and neck, trunk and limbs, etc., and each region is studied separately. This learning approach works better if it is combined with human cadaver dissection.

This book uses a systemic approach to the study of human anatomy.

2. **Microscopic anatomy:** In this branch, the structure of the body is studied at the tissue and cellular level using a microscope; also known as histology.
3. **Developmental anatomy:** This study includes different phases of human development from fertilization to birth; also known as embryology.

···· Anatomical Position

In order to study the location and relation of different human body structures and to avoid ambiguity, the student needs to assume a standard reference position. This is known as anatomical position. In this position the person is standing upright, arms at the sides with face, palms, and big toes pointed forward (Figure 1.1).

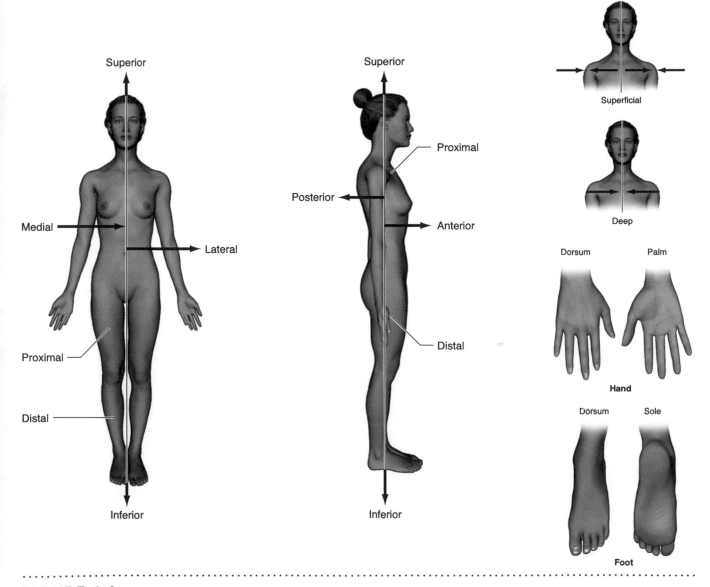

FIGURE 1.1

Commonly Used Terms of Relationship and Comparison

· · · · Anatomical Planes

The various parts of the body can be described in relation to three main groups of anatomical planes (Figure 1.2).

1. **Sagittal planes** are vertical planes that divide the body into left and right parts. If these parts are symmetric, the plane is called **median sagittal plane**, otherwise it will be known as **parasagittal plane**.
2. **Coronal or frontal planes** are vertical planes that divide the body into front and back parts.
3. **Transverse or horizontal planes** are at right angles to the sagittal and coronal planes. These planes divide the body into upper and lower parts.

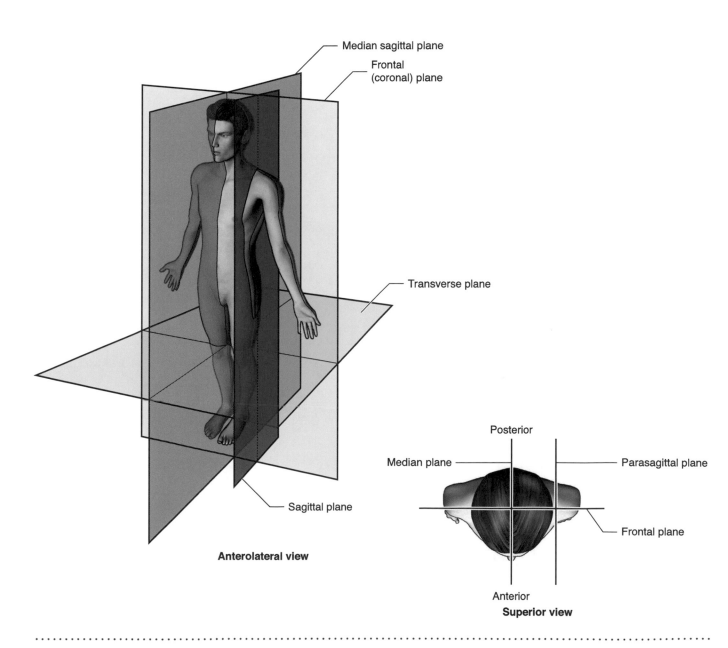

FIGURE 1.2
Planes of Body

Terms of Position, Relation, and Direction

These terms explain the relative position of structures as compared to anatomical planes (Figure 1.1).

TERM	DEFINITION	USAGE
Medial*	closer to midline	left eye is medial to left ear
Lateral*	farther from midline	arms are lateral to trunk
Anterior (ventral)**	closer to front	heart is anterior to vertebral column
Posterior (dorsal)**	closer to back	vertebral column is posterior to stomach
Superior (cranial)***	closer to head	neck is superior to trunk
Inferior (caudal)***	closer to feet (tail)	kidneys are inferior to lungs
Proximal	closer to the root of the structure	arm is proximal to forearm
Distal	farther from the root of the structure	ankle is distal to knee
Superficial	closer to the surface of the body	ribs are superficial to heart
Deep	farther from the surface of the body	lungs are deep to ribs
Palm	palmar aspect of hand	hairs don't grow on the skin of palm
Sole	plantar aspect of foot	skin of the sole is thick
Dorsum	dorsal aspect of hand or foot	superficial veins run deep the skin of the dorsum of hand
Ipsilateral	on the same side of the body	left arm and left leg are ipsilateral
Contralateral	on the opposite side of the body	right elbow and left wrist are contralateral
Internal	inside a body cavity or a hollow structure	internal iliac artery is located inside the pelvic cavity
External	outside a body cavity or a hollow structure	external carotid artery is located outside the cranial cavity

*: in reference to median sagittal plane
**: in reference to coronal (frontal) plane
***: in reference to transverse (horizontal) plane

···· Terms of Movements
1. Standard Movements (Figure 1.3)

TERM	DEFINITION
Flexion*	Bending, or decreasing the angle between parts of the body
Extension*	Straightening, or increasing the angle between parts of the body
Abduction**	Moving away from midline, or axis of the body parts. (Axis of the hand passes through the third finger and metacarpal bone. Axis of the foot passes through the second toe and metatarsal bone.)
Adduction**	Moving toward midline, or axis of the body parts.
Medial rotation***	Turning a body part around its long axis toward the midline
Lateral rotation***	Turning a body part around its long axis away from the midline

*Occurring in sagittal planes   **Occurring in frontal/coronal planes   ***Occurring in transverse/horizontal planes

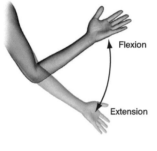

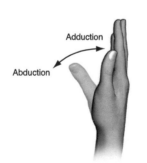

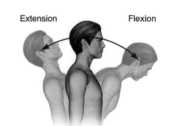

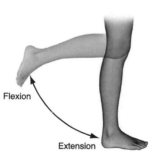

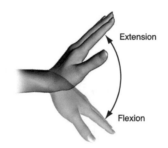

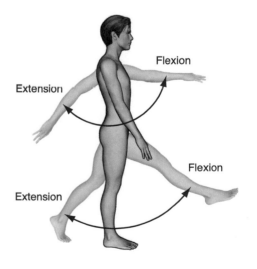

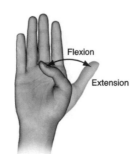

FIGURE 1.3
Standard Movements

2. Special Movements (Figure 1.4)

TERM	DEFINITION
Circumduction	Circular movement of body parts combining flexion, extension, abduction, and adduction
Supination	Rotation of the forearm so that the palm of the hand faces forward
Pronation	Rotation of the forearm so that the palm of the hand faces backward
Eversion	Turning sole of the foot outward
Inversion	Turning sole of the foot inward
Plantar flexion	Moving the foot away from the shin (flexion of the ankle joint)
Dorsi flexion	Moving the foot toward the shin (extension of the ankle joint)
Elevation	Upward movement of a body part
Depression	Downward movement of a body part
Protraction	Forward movement of a body part
Retraction	Backward movement of a body part
Opposition	Movement of the thumb to touch the other fingers' tip

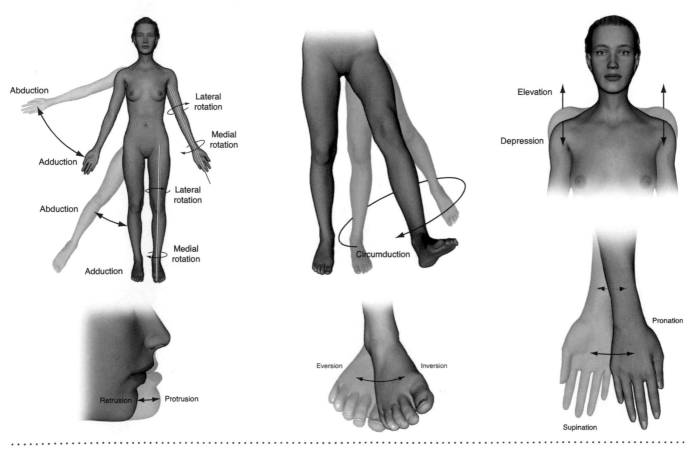

FIGURE 1.4
Special Movements

···· Body Organization

The smallest structural and functional unit of a living organism is the cell. Cells with similar morphology and function will form a tissue. Organs are composed of different tissues. Finally, a coordinated group of several organs will make up an organ system or body system. The human body consists of the following organ systems:

1. Integumentary System

This system is composed of skin and its appendages including hair, nail, sweat gland, sebaceous gland, and erector pilli muscle and other structures. The main functions of this system include but are not limited to protecting the body from fluid loss, injury, and infection. Sweat glands and blood vessels housed in this system contribute in body temperature regulation, and sensory organs embedded in the skin collect information from external environment (Figure 1.5).

- **Skin:**
  The largest organ of the body comprises two microscopic layers (Figure 1.6):
  - **Epidermis** (epithelial tissue) forms a waterproof layer to protect the body. This layer gives rise to nail and hair.
  - **Dermis** (dense connective tissue) supports the epidermis, and contains blood vessels, and nerve fibres. Other structures such as hair follicles, sebaceous glands, and erector pilli muscles are also found in this layer.

  Skin is connected to the underlying structures by a layer of loose connective tissue known as **hypodermis** (subcutaneous tissue). In gross anatomy, hypodermis is referred to as **superficial fascia**. Superficial fascia is usually deposited with fat and contains sweat glands, superficial veins, and cutaneous nerves.

  Underneath the superficial fascia, there is a relatively thick layer of dense connective tissue known as **deep fascia** that covers the entire body (except the head region).

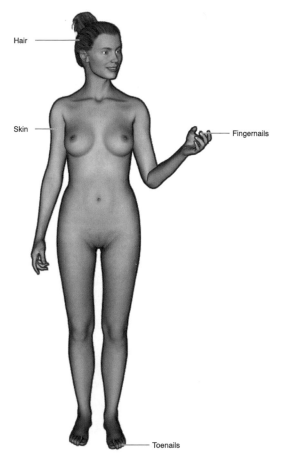

FIGURE 1.5
Integumentary System

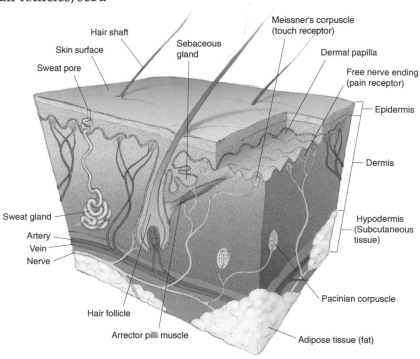

FIGURE 1.6
Skin

2. Skeletal System

This system consists of bones, cartilage, ligaments, and associated structures. Some of the main functions of this system include support and protection of different organs, and body movement (Figure 1.7).

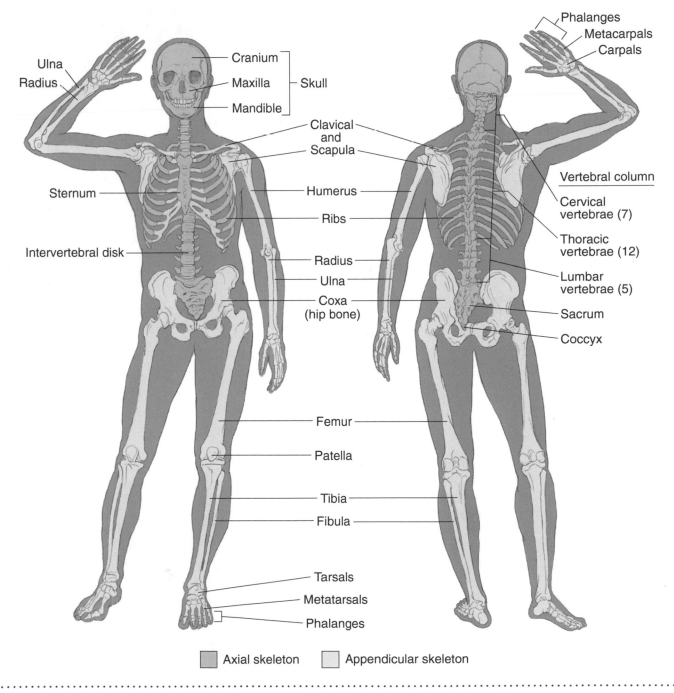

FIGURE 1.7
Skeletal System

3. Nervous System

This system is divided into two components:

   a. Central nervous system, which includes the brain and spinal cord
   b. Peripheral nervous system, which consists of the spinal and cranial nerves

The nervous system is responsible for gathering and processing information both internally and externally (Figure 1.8).

4. Muscular System

Voluntary muscles and tendons are two main constituents of this system. The main function of the muscular system in association with the skeletal system is locomotion—any voluntary movement in any given direction (Figure 1.9).

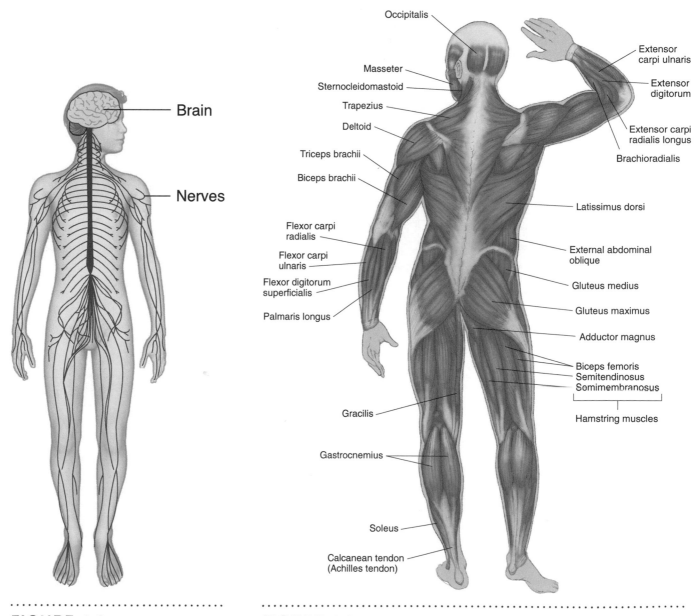

FIGURE 1.8
Nervous System

FIGURE 1.9
Muscular System

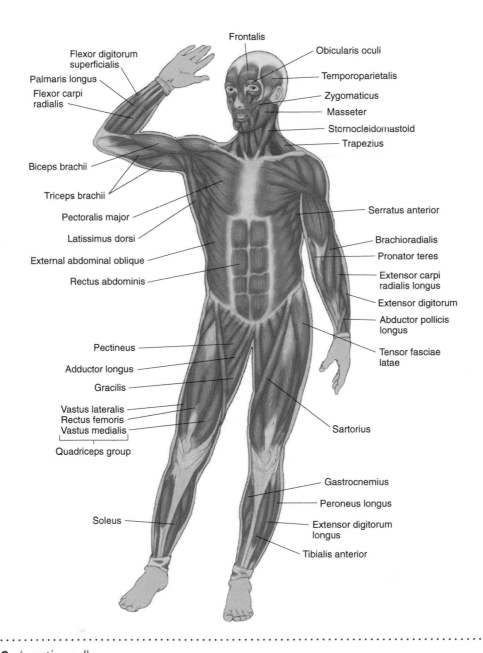

FIGURE 1.9 (continued)
Muscular System

5. Cardiovascular System

The heart and blood vessels are the main components of this system. This system distributes oxygen, nutrients, hormones, and other chemicals to the target tissues and picks up deoxygenated blood and tissue waste materials (Figure 1.10).

6. Lymphatic System

This system is formed by lymphatic organs, such as lymph nodes, spleen, thymus, etc., which are connected by lymphatic vessels. This system acts as the principal defense mechanism of the body. It also absorbs fat from the gastrointestinal tract (Figure 1.11).

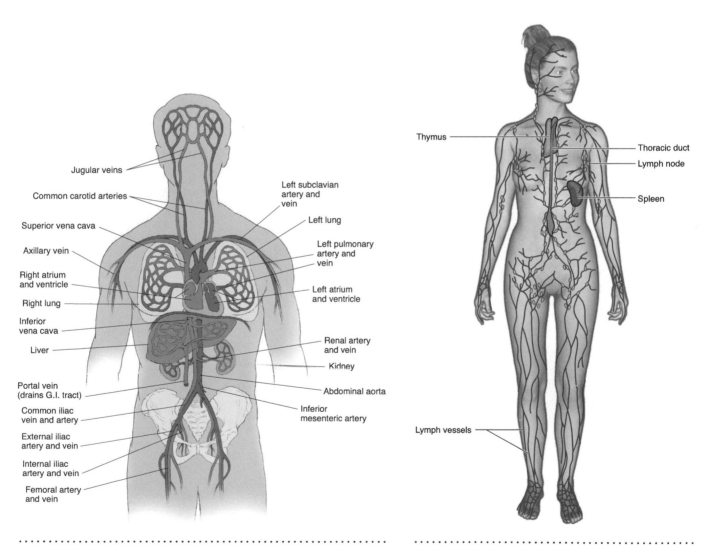

FIGURE 1.10
Cardiovascular System

FIGURE 1.11
Lymphatic System

7. Respiratory System

This system is composed of upper and lower air ways, lungs, and plural membranes. Gaseous exchange between the external environment and the blood is the main function of this system (Figure 1.12).

8. Digestive System

This system, also known as the **gastrointestinal tract**, consists of the alimentary canal and associated organs. Ingestion, digestion, absorption, and elimination of undigested materials are the functions of this system (Figure 1.13).

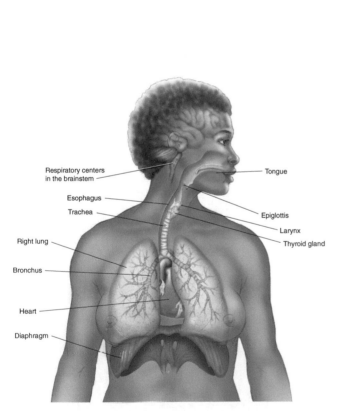

FIGURE 1.12
Respiratory System

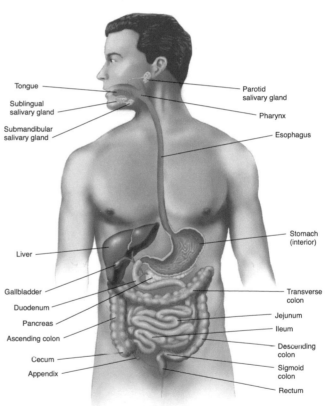

FIGURE 1.13
Digestive System

9. Urinary System

Kidneys, ureters, urinary bladder, and urethra are the main elements of this system. Blood filtration, water maintenance, and ionic balance are considered the main functions of the urinary system (Figure 1.14).

10. Reproductive System

This system in female body consists of internal and external organs. Internal reproductive organs include ovaries, uterine tubes, uterus, vagina, and associated structures. The external organ is referred to the **vulva**.

In male body, the reproductive system is composed of testes, penis, and associated ducts and glands.

Gamete (ovum or sperm) are produced by reproductive systems of both genders; however, the female reproductive system also oversees fertilization, incubation of fertilized egg, and delivery of the fetus (Figure 1.15-a, b).

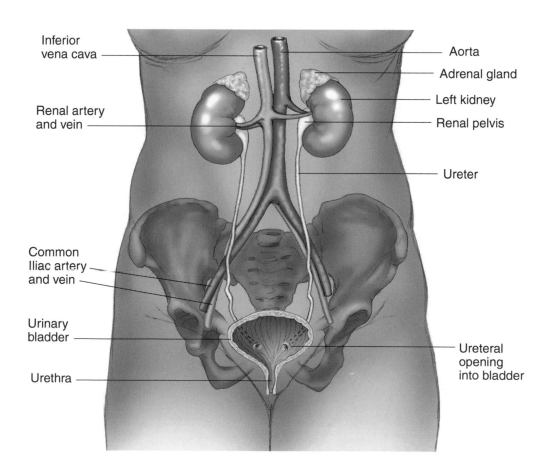

FIGURE 1.14
Urinary System

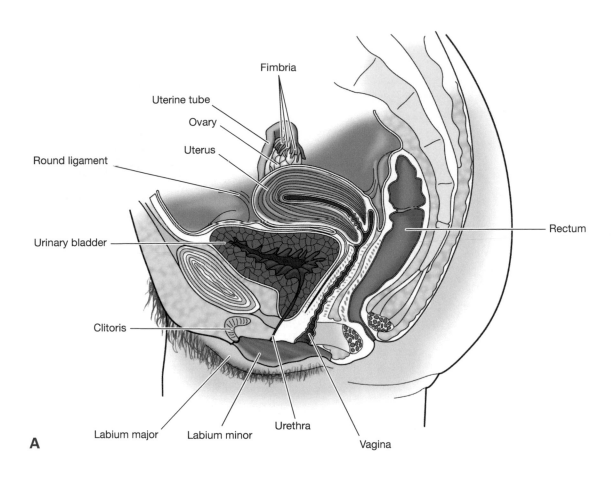

Fimbria

Uterine tube

Ovary

Uterus

Round ligament

Urinary bladder

Rectum

Clitoris

Labium major   Labium minor   Urethra   Vagina

A

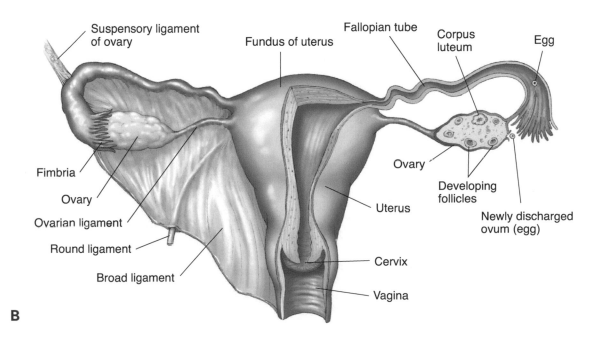

Suspensory ligament of ovary

Fundus of uterus

Fallopian tube

Corpus luteum

Egg

Fimbria

Ovary

Ovarian ligament

Round ligament

Broad ligament

Ovary

Developing follicles

Uterus

Newly discharged ovum (egg)

Cervix

Vagina

B

FIGURE 1.15

Reproductive System

11. Endocrine System

This system is composed of a group of endocrine glands that are located in different regions of the body. These glands include hypophysis (pituitary), thyroid, parathyroid, adrenal, gonads, etc. Some of these glands are associated with other systems (e.g., gonads are also considered as part of the reproductive system).

The endocrine system, along with the nervous system, acts as a regulatory mechanism for chemical functioning within the body (Figure 1.16).

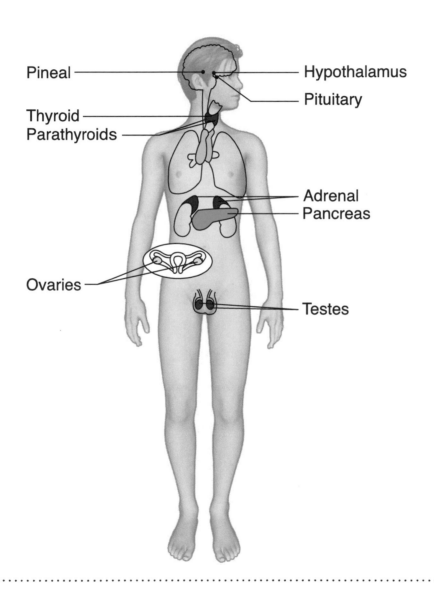

FIGURE 1.16
Endoctrine System

···· # Body Regions

The human body may be divided into several major regions including **head, neck, trunk, upper limb, and lower limb**. These regions are subdivided into smaller areas that are presented in Table 1.1.

TABLE 1.1 *Body Regions and Subdivision*

MAIN REGION	SUBDIVISION	
Head	Cranium Face	
Neck	Anterior neck Posterior neck	
Trunk	Back Thorax Abdomen Pelvis	
Upper limb	Shoulder	Pectoral Scapular Deltoid Axilla
	Arm (brachium) Elbow Forearm (antebrachium)	
	Hand	Carpus (wrist) Metacarpus Digits (fingers)
Lower limb	Gluteal Thigh Knee Leg	
	Foot	Tarsus (ankle) Metatarsus Phalanges (toes)

· · · · **Abdominal Topographic Regions**

In order to describe the location of abdominal viscera, one may divide the anterior abdominal wall into smaller regions. There are two patterns for this classification:

1. In a four-region pattern, a vertical line and a horizontal line cross each other at the belly button, thus dividing the anterior abdominal wall into four quadrants (Figure 1.17):

   - **Right upper quadrant**
   - **Right lower quadrant**
   - **Left upper quadrant**
   - **Left lower quadrant**

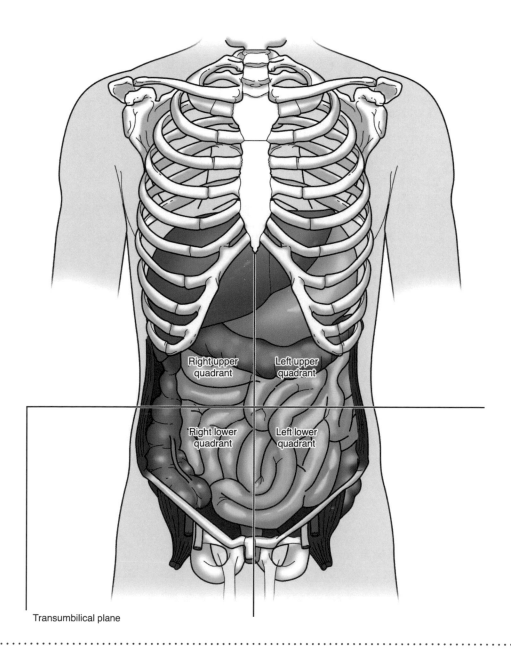

FIGURE 1.17

Four Quadrants of Anterior Abdominal Wall

2. In a nine-region pattern, two vertical lines (midclavicular lines) meet two horizontal lines (subcostal and transtubercular), thus dividing the anterior abdominal wall into nine regions from superior to inferior and from right to left (Figure 1.18):

   - **right hypochondrium, epigastric, left hypochondrium**
   - **right lumbar, umbilical, left lumbar**
   - **right iliac (inguinal), hypogastric, left iliac (inguinal)**

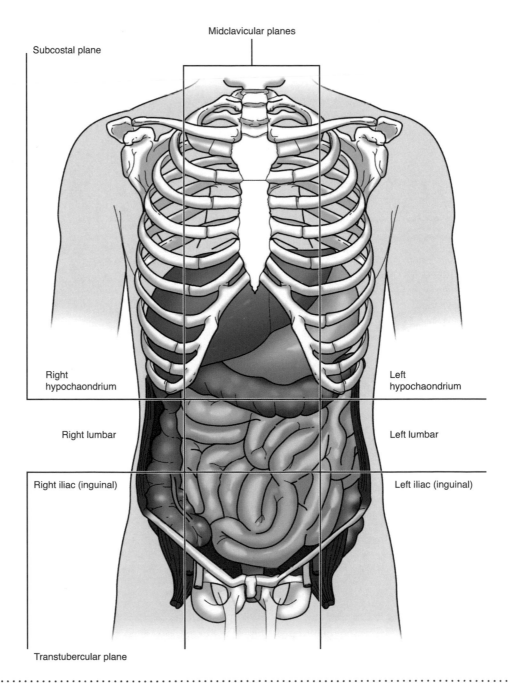

Subcostal plane

Midclavicular planes

Right hypochaondrium

Left hypochaondrium

Right lumbar

Left lumbar

Right iliac (inguinal)

Left iliac (inguinal)

Transtubercular plane

FIGURE 1.18

Nine Regions of Anterior Abdominal Wall

···· Body Cavities

The human body contains confined spaces that hold different organs in order to support and protect them. These spaces include the following (Figure 1.19):

1. **Cranial cavity:** houses the brain.
2. **Vertebral canal:** contains spinal cord.
3. **Thoracic cavity:** holds heart, lungs, and other structures.
4. **Abdominal cavity:** is mostly occupied by the gastrointestinal system and parts of the urinary system.
5. **Pelvic cavity:** houses parts of the gastrointestinal, urinary, and reproductive systems.

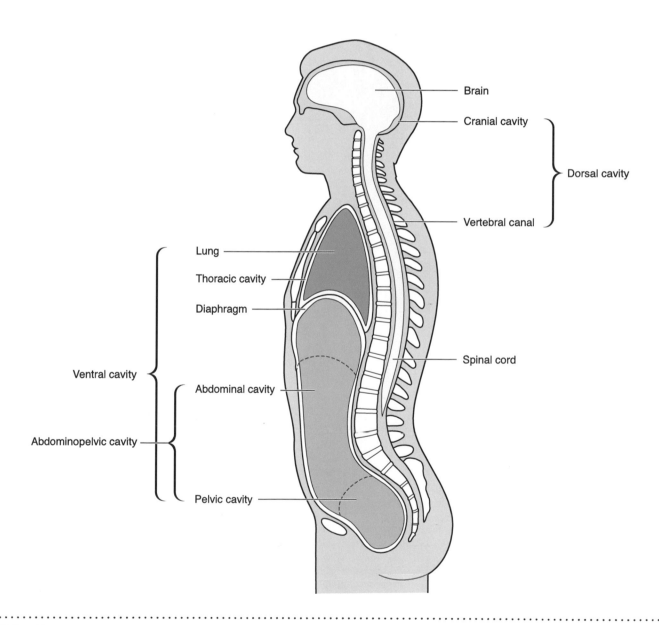

FIGURE 1.19
Body Cavities

CHAPTER 2

Skeletal System

LEARNING OBJECTIVES

Upon completion of this section you should be able to:

1. Explain the principal functions of the skeletal system.
2. Discuss the different types of the bones based on their shape.
3. Describe the structural organization of the skeletal system and list the bones of the axial and appendicular skeleton.
4. Identify the bones of the five regions of the vertebral column and describe the characteristic curves of each region.
5. Explain the bones contributing to the rib cage.
6. Define the bones of the skull in different views.
7. Discuss the bones of the upper and lower limbs.

Introduction

The skeletal system forms the bony framework of the human body and has the following functions:

1. Supports and protects other organs such as the heart and brain
2. Serves as the attachment site for skeletal muscles
3. Stores minerals such as calcium, phosphorus
4. Produces different blood cell lineages (only in red bone marrow)

Bones are classified based on their morphology as follows (Figure 2.1):

1. **Long bones** consist of a long cylindrical body or shaft (diaphysis) and two ends (epiphysis). Diaphysis is primarily formed by compact bone, whereas epiphysis is made up of spongy bone covered by a relatively thin sheet of compact bone. Bones of the arm, forearm, thigh, and leg are examples of this type of bone.
2. **Short bones** are usually cuboidal and formed by spongy bone covered by a layer of compact bone such as wrist and ankle bones.
3. **Flat bones** are composed of two plates of compact bone that sandwich a relatively thick layer of spongy bone such as ribs and some of the skull bones.
4. **Irregular bones** lack any specific shape and are formed by a spongy core covered by compact bone. Vertebrae and facial bones belong to this group of bones.
5. **Sesamoid bones** are partially embedded in some tendons (such as patella) and similar to short bones are made up of a spongy bone covered by a shell of compact bone.

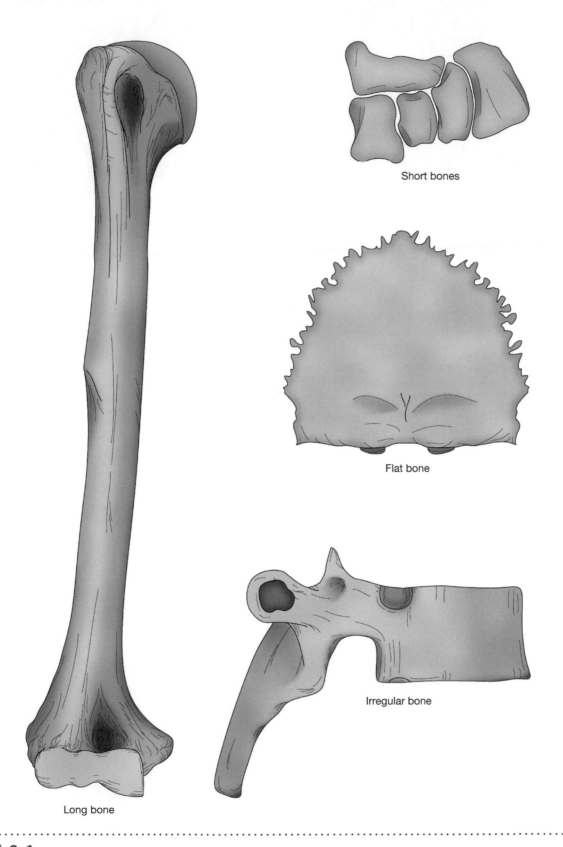

Short bones

Flat bone

Irregular bone

Long bone

FIGURE 2.1
Types of Bones

The skeletal system is composed of 206 bones and is divided in two parts (Figure 2.2).

1. The **axial skeleton** forms the skeleton of the axis of the body (skull, vertebral column, hyoid, ribs, and sternum)
2. The **appendicular skeleton** forms the skeleton of the limbs and is appended to the axial skeleton by shoulder and pelvic girdles. The shoulder girdle consists of clavicle and scapula and the pelvic girdle is formed by hip bones.

   a. The **upper limb skeleton** includes the following bones:
      - Humerus
      - Radius
      - Ulna
      - Carpal bones
      - Metacarpals
      - Phalanges

   b. The **lower limb skeleton** includes the following bones:
      - Femur
      - Patella
      - Tibia
      - Fibula
      - Tarsal bones
      - Metatarsals
      - Phalanges

· · · · Vertebral Column

The vertebral column forms the axis of the skeleton and starts from the base of the skull and rests on the pelvis. This column is composed of 33 pieces of irregular bones called **vertebrae** that are mainly joined together by an intervertebral disc to form a flexible but rigid column for bearing and transferring body weight. The average length of the vertebral column is about 60 centimeters in females and 70 centimeters in males. The intervertebral discs height counts for one-fourth of the total length of the vertebral column. In older adults, the length of the vertebral column decreases because of shrinkage of the intervertebral disc and increased vertebral column curvatures (Fig. 2.3).

Vertebral column is divided into five regions:

1. Cervical region: 7 vertebrae (CI–CVII)
2. Thoracic region: 12 vertebrae (TI–TXII)
3. Lumbar region: 5 vertebrae (LI–LV)
4. Sacral region including 5 fused segments called the sacrum (SI–SV)
5. Coccygeal region including 3 to 4 fused segments called the **coccyx**.

In a lateral view, the vertebral column has four curvatures. Two of these curvatures are present at birth and are known as **primary curvatures**. The primary curvatures are convex posteriorly and are found in the thoracic and sacral regions (Figure 2.3).

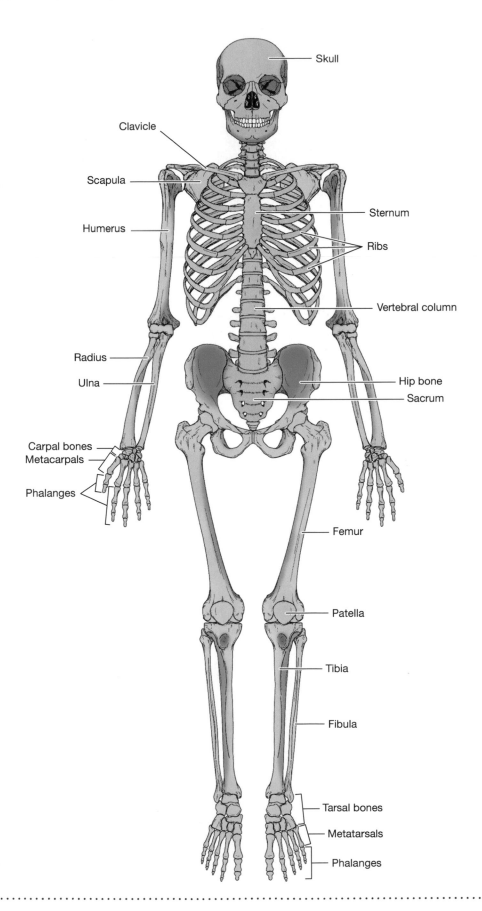

Skull

Clavicle

Scapula

Humerus

Sternum

Ribs

Vertebral column

Radius

Ulna

Hip bone

Sacrum

Carpal bones
Metacarpals

Phalanges

Femur

Patella

Tibia

Fibula

Tarsal bones

Metatarsals

Phalanges

FIGURE 2.2

Axial and Appendicular Skeleton

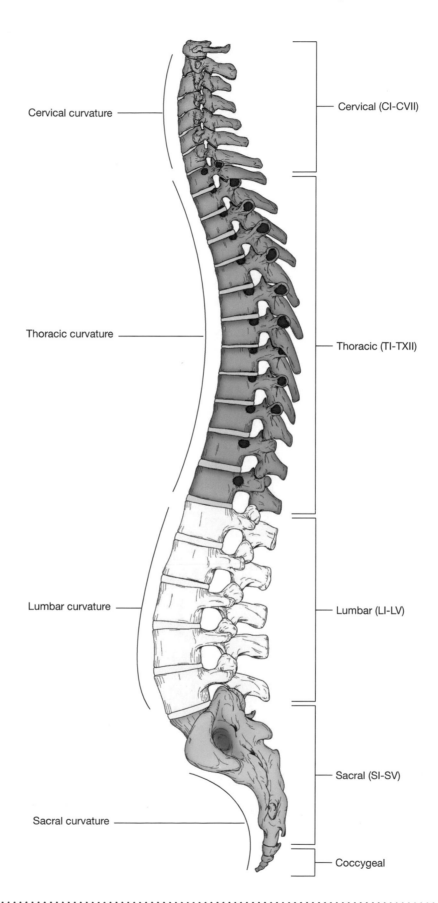

Cervical curvature

Thoracic curvature

Lumbar curvature

Sacral curvature

Cervical (CI-CVII)

Thoracic (TI-TXII)

Lumbar (LI-LV)

Sacral (SI-SV)

Coccygeal

FIGURE 2.3

Vertebral Column (lateral view)

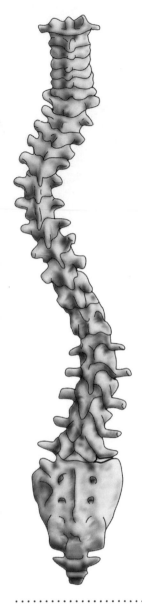

FIGURE 2.4

Scoliosis

The other two curvatures are acquired after birth thus referred to as **secondary curvatures**. The secondary curvatures are convex anteriorly and are found in the cervical and lumbar regions.

In an anterior or posterior view, there is no deviation in the vertebral column. Abnormal lateral deviations are known as **scoliosis** (Figure 2.4).

Characteristics of a Typical Vertebra

A typical vertebra consists of a body anteriorly and a vertebral arch posteriorly. The body and vertebral arch surround a space known as the **vertebral foramen**. In an articulated vertebral column, these foramina will form a longitudinal canal called the **vertebral canal** that houses the spinal cord and associated structures. The vertebral arch in turn is made up of pedicles, laminae, spinous process, transverse processes, and articular processes (Figures 2.5 and 2.6).

Vertebral body: Almost cylindrical but its shape varies in different regions. The size of the vertebral body gradually increases in lower segments of the vertebral column in order to accommodate the increasing forces applied by body weight.

Pedicles: Two bony projections that extend posterolaterally from the vertebral body. Superior and inferior margins of each pedicle carries a notch called the **vertebral notch**. The vertebral notches of the adjacent vertebrae form an **intervertebral foramen** that acts as a passage for spinal nerves and associated vessels.

Laminae: Two bony ridges extend posteromedially from pedicles to join together in the midline.

Transverse processes: Extend laterally from the junction of the pedicles and laminae.

Spinous process: Extends posteriorly from the junction of laminae.

Articular processes: Arise from the junction of the pedicles and laminae. **Superior articular processes** extend superiorly to articulate with inferior articular processes of the vertebra above. **Inferior articular processes** extend inferiorly to articulate with the superior articular processes of the vertebra below.

Cervical Vertebrae

A typical cervical vertebra (CIII to CVI) presents the following features (Figure 2.7):

- Small square-shaped body
- Large triangular vertebral foramen
- Transverse foramen on the transverse process (foramen transversarium)
- Bifurcated spinous process

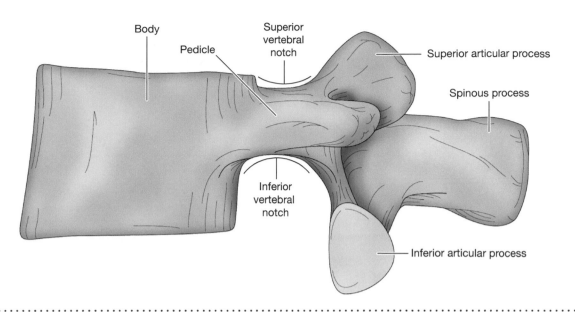

FIGURE 2.5

A Typical Lumbar Vertebra (lateral view)

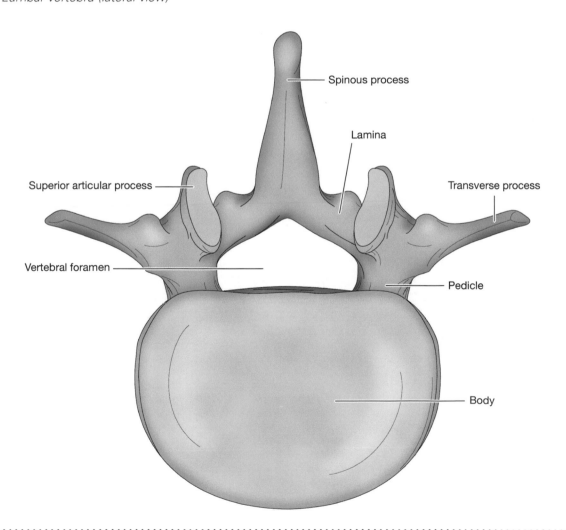

FIGURE 2.6

A Typical Lumbar Vertebra (superior view)

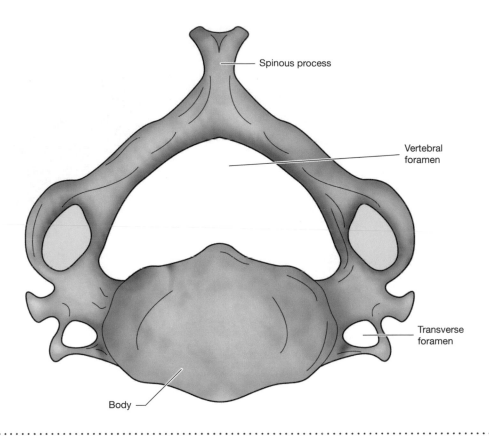

Spinous process

Vertebral foramen

Transverse foramen

Body

FIGURE 2.7
A Typical Cervical Vertebra

Atlas (CI)

The first cervical vertebra consists of two lateral masses connected together by anterior and posterior arches. The superior surface of the lateral masses articulates with the occipital condyles, whereas the inferior surface articulates with vertebra CII (axis). The posterior surface of the anterior arch of atlas carries an articular surface to articulate with the odontoid process (dens) of vertebra CII. Posterior surface of the posterior arch presents a small projection called the posterior tubercle that is equivalent to the spinous process of the other vertebrae. Similar to the other cervical vertebrae, atlas has the transverse foramen on its transverse process (Figure 2.8).

Axis (CII)

The second cervical vertebra acts as a pivot for rotational movements of the head. On the superior surface of the body, there is a tooth-like vertical projection called the **odontoid process (dens axis)** that articulates with the anterior arch of atlas. There are two articular processes lateral to the odontoid process that articulate with the lateral masses of the atlas. Axis also has a bifid spinous process and a transverse foramen on each of its transverse processes (Figures 2.9 and 2.10).

Vertebra CVII

The seventh cervical vertebra has the longest spinous process that is not bifurcated, hence the name **prominent vertebra** (Figure 2.11).

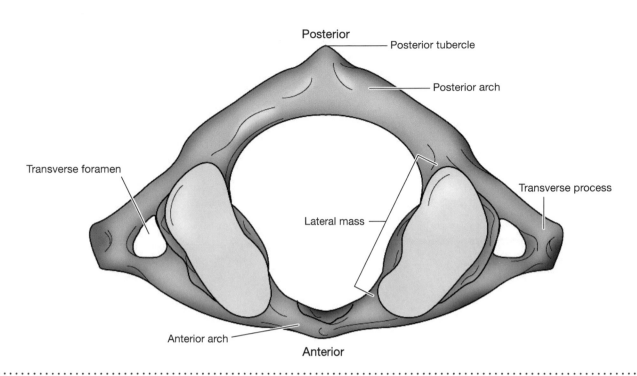

FIGURE 2.8
Atlas (superior view)

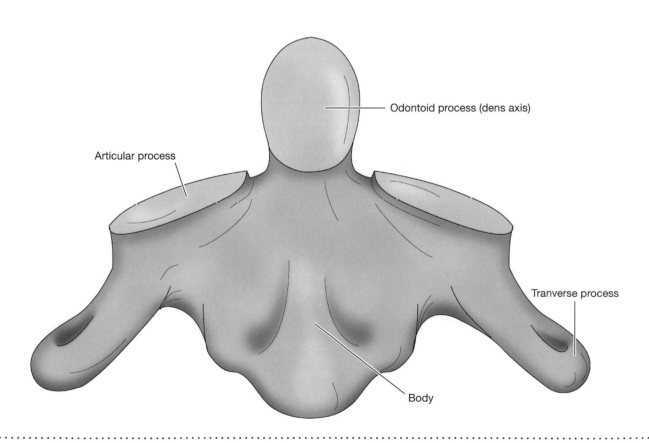

FIGURE 2.9
Axis (anterior view)

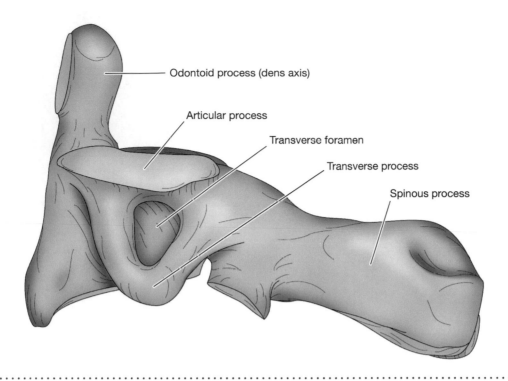

Odontoid process (dens axis)

Articular process

Transverse foramen

Transverse process

Spinous process

FIGURE 2.10
Axis (lateral view)

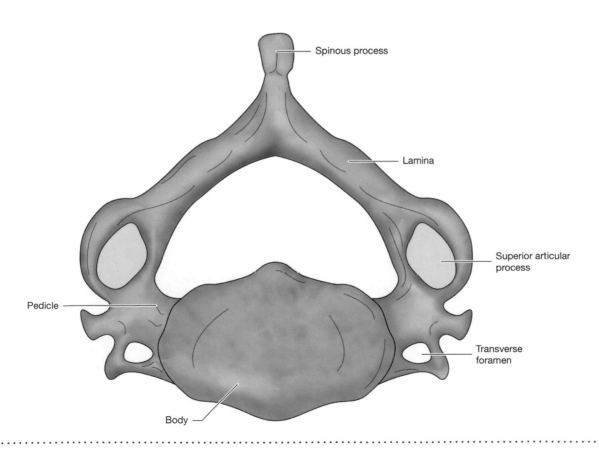

Spinous process

Lamina

Superior articular
process

Pedicle

Transverse
foramen

Body

FIGURE 2.11
Vertebra CVII

Thoracic Vertebrae

A thoracic vertebra (TI to TXII) presents the following features (Figures 2.12 and 2.13).

- Costal facets on the sides of the body for articulation with the head of the ribs
- Costal facets on the transverse processes for articulation with the tubercle of the ribs (vertebra TXI and TXII do not have this costal facet)
- Heart-shaped body
- Small round vertebral foramen
- Long spinous process that is inclined inferiorly

Lumbar Vertebrae

A lumbar vertebra (LI–LIV) is characterized by (Figures 2.5 and 2.6):

- Large kidney-shaped body
- Triangular vertebral foramen
- Long and slender transverse processes
- Short and thick spinous process

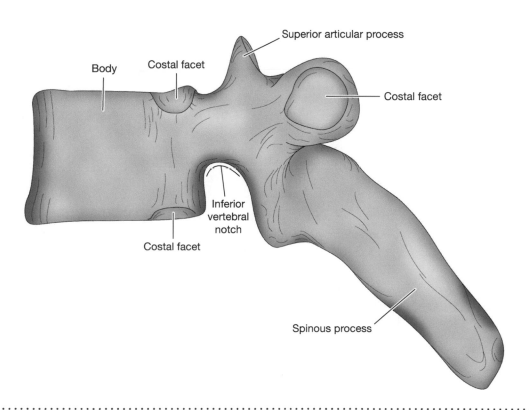

FIGURE 2.12

A Typical Thoracic Vertebra (lateral view)

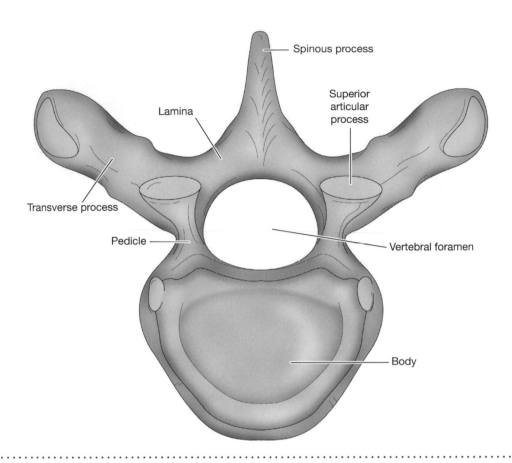

FIGURE 2.13

A Typical Thoracic Vertebra (superior view)

···· Sacrum

This is a wedge-shaped bone formed by the fusion of five sacral vertebrae (Figures 2.14 and 2.15).

The apex of the bone is pointing inferiorly and articulates with coccyx, whereas the base faces superiorly and articulates with the fifth lumbar vertebra.

The lateral surfaces of the bone carry an L-shaped articular surface known as the **auricular surface**. This surface articulates with similar articular surfaces on the hip bone.

The anterior surface of the bone is relatively smooth and concave. There are four pairs of anterior sacral foramina on this surface for the passage of the anterior rami of sacral spinal nerves.

The posterior surface is convex and the remnants of the sacral vertebral processes are presented as sacral crests. There are also four pairs of posterior sacral foramina for passage of the posterior rami of sacral spinal nerves.

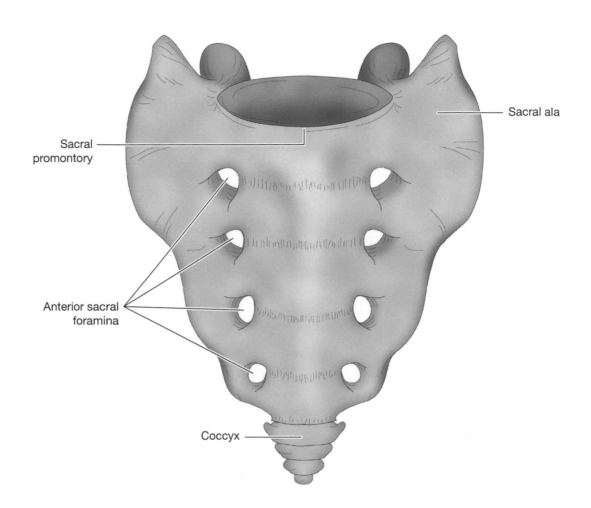

Sacral ala

Sacral promontory

Anterior sacral foramina

Coccyx

FIGURE 2.14
Sacrum (anterior view)

The anterior margin of the superior surface of the vertebra SI bulges anteriorly and is known as the **sacral promontory**. In a female pelvis, sacral promontory is used as a landmark in pelvimetry. On either side of the promontory there is a triangular surface known as **sacral ala** (Figure 2.14).

The sacral canal is the continuation of the vertebral canal in sacrum. At the end of this canal the laminae of vertebra SV fail to fuse together, thus forming an opening known as **sacral hiatus** (Figure 2.15).

· · · · Coccyx

This is a small triangular bone that is formed by the fusion of four to five coccygeal vertebrae. Base of the bone articulates with vertebra SV and the apex is free (Figure 2.15).

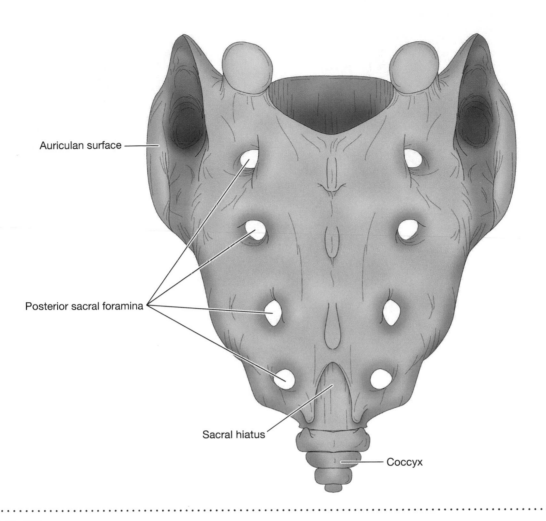

Auriculan surface

Posterior sacral foramina

Sacral hiatus

Coccyx

FIGURE 2.15

Sacrum (posterior view)

· · · · **Sternum**

Sternum is a flat bone that contributes to the formation of the anterior thoracic wall. This bone is composed of manubrium, body, and xiphoid process (Figure 2.16).

Manubrium is a trapezoid bony plate that forms the proximal end of the sternum. On the superior border there is a notch known as the **jugular notch (suprasternal notch)**. On either side of this notch one can find an articular surface for articulation with the medial end of clavicle. There is also another articular surface on the lateral margins for the first costal cartilage.

Inferior margin of the manubrium articulates with the superior border of the body and forms an angle known as the **sternal angle (of Louis)**. This angle is an important clinical landmark and is presented as a prominent transverse ridge that indicates the site of articulation of the second costal cartilage with the sternum.

Body of the sternum is slightly convex anteriorly and there are articular surfaces on either side for articulation with the costal cartilages of ribs III through VI.

Xiphoid process comes in a variety of shapes and articulates with the inferior margin of the body of the sternum to form the xiphisternal joint. The seventh costal cartilage articulates with the sides of this joint.

· · · · Ribs (Costae)

The ribs are twelve pairs of flat curved bones that form most of the thoracic cage wall. The posterior end (head) of the ribs articulates with the thoracic vertebrae. The anterior end of the first seven pairs of ribs articulate with the sternum via their costal cartilages and are termed as **true ribs**. The remaining five pairs are **false ribs**; of these, the first three pairs articulate with the sternum through the seventh costal cartilage, whereas the last two pairs that do not articulate with sternum or other ribs are known as **free ribs (floating ribs)**.

Characteristics of a Typical Rib

A typical rib (III to IX) has the following characteristics (Figures 2.17 and 2.18):

- The head of the rib articulates with the costal facets on the body of the thoracic vertebrae at the corresponding level and the vertebra above.
- The neck of the rib is stretched between the head and costal tubercle.
- The tubercle of the rib is a small bony elevation that carries an articular surface for articulation with the costal facet on the transverse process of the corresponding thoracic vertebra.
- The body (shaft) of the rib is a thin flat bony plate that curves anterolaterally. This curve is most prominent at the point of the costal angle. On the inferior border of the internal surface of the body, there is a bony groove termed as **costal groove** that houses the intercostal nerves and vessels.

NOTE: Ribs I, II, X, XI, and XII are considered atypical as they lack some of the above-mentioned features.

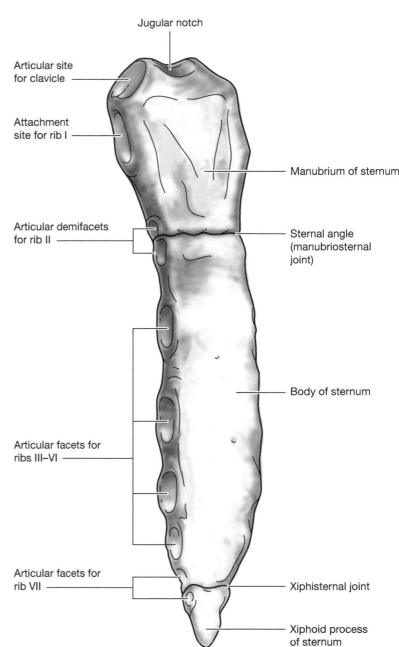

FIGURE 2.16
Sternum

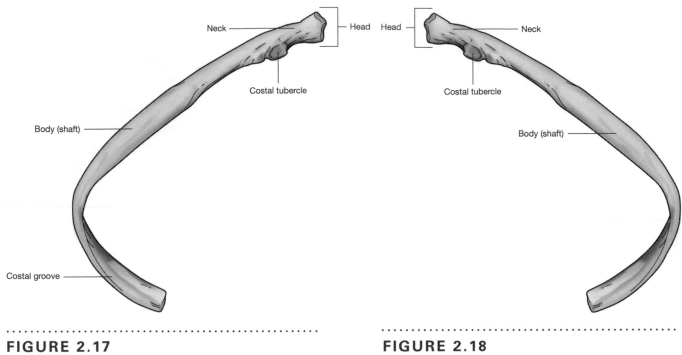

FIGURE 2.17
A Typical Rib (left, posterior view)

FIGURE 2.18
A Typical Rib (right, posterior view)

Thoracic Cage

The thoracic cage protects vital organs such as the heart and lungs. It is a conical bony cavity formed by thoracic vertebrae, ribs, costal cartilages, and sternum (Figure 2.19). The apex of the cone is located at the root of the neck and is bounded by vertebra TI, the first ribs, and the superior border of manubrium. This bean-shaped opening is called the **superior thoracic aperture**.

The base of the cone or **inferior thoracic aperture** is bounded by vertebra TXII, the eleventh and twelfth ribs, the **costal margin**, and xiphoid process. The costal margin is formed by the costal cartilages of the ribs VII to X. The inferior thoracic aperture is sealed by the diaphragm.

Ribs are separated by spaces known as **intercostal spaces**, which contain intercostal muscles, nerves, and vessels.

The thoracic cavity contained inside the thoracic cages is divided into three main compartments: two **pleural cavities** on the sides that hold the lungs and **mediastinum** in between those cavities that houses the heart and other thoracic viscera (Figure 5.1).

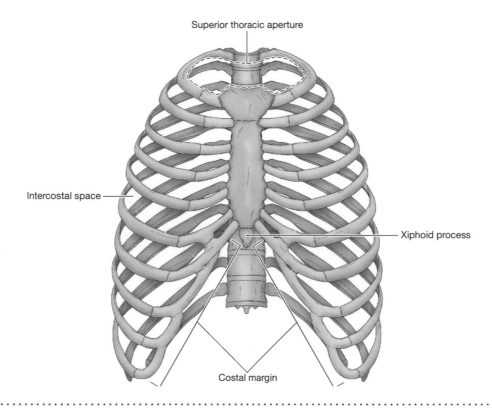

FIGURE 2.19

Thoracic Cage

· · · · Skull

Skull, the skeleton of the head, supports facial structures and protects the brain. It consists of 22 bones, 14 of which form the framework of the face (**viscerocranium**), and the other 8 bones form a bony box (**neurocranium**) to hold the brain (Table 2.1a and b). These bones are held together by immobile joints known as **sutures** except the lower jaw (mandible), which articulates with the temporal bone to form a mobile joint.

It is worth mentioning that skull without the mandible is known as the **cranium**.

TABLE 2.1A: *Viscerocranium*

Viscerocranium	Paired	Lacrimal bone
		Nasal bone
		Zygomatic bone
		Maxilla
		Inferior nasal concha
		Palatine bone
	Unpaired	Vomer
		Mandible

TABLE 2.1B: *Neurocranium*

Neurocranium	Paired	Parietal bone
		Temporal bone
	Unpaired	Frontal bone
		Occipital bone
		Sphenoid bone
		Ethmoid bone

To avoid unnecessary details, it's better to study the skull in different views.

Anterior View of the Skull

In this view, one can observe the following bones from superior to inferior: **frontal bone, nasal bones, zygomatic bones, maxillae,** and **mandible.** There are also five bony cavities in this view, including two orbital cavities, two nasal cavities, and an oral cavity (Figure 2.20).

Each **orbital cavity** is a four-sided pyramidal space, with the apex pointing posteriorly. There are three openings in each orbital cavity that serve as passages for blood vessels and nerves. These openings are known as the **optic canal, superior orbital fissure,** and **inferior orbital fissure.** There is also a bony channel that connects the medial corner of the orbital cavity to the nasal cavity known as the **nasolacrimal duct** (Figure 2.21).

The bony **nasal cavities** are separated from each other by a vertical bony septum. On the lateral wall of each nasal cavity there are three curved bony plates known as the **superior, middle,** and **inferior nasal conchae.** The inferior nasal concha is an individual bone. The anterior opening of each nasal cavity is known as the **anterior nasal aperture,** and the posterior opening of each nasal cavity is referred to as the **choana** (Figure 2.24).

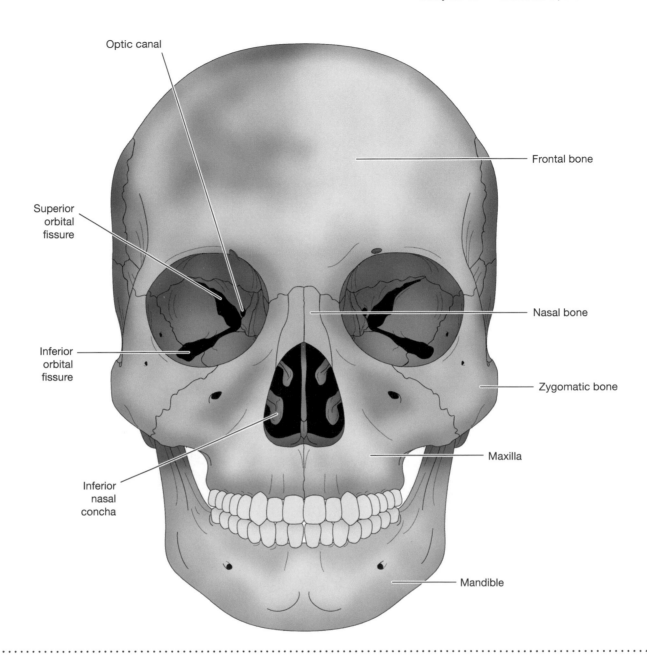

Optic canal

Superior
orbital
fissure

Inferior
orbital
fissure

Inferior
nasal
concha

Frontal bone

Nasal bone

Zygomatic bone

Maxilla

Mandible

FIGURE 2.20

Skull (anterior view)

Lateral View of the Skull

The parietal bone, frontal bone, occipital bone, temporal bone, zygomatic bone, maxilla, and mandible are the main bones seen in this view of the skull (Figwure 2.21).

Some of the most prominent bony features in the lateral view include the following:

- External acoustic (auditory) meatus and mastoid process on the temporal bone
- Zygomatic arch formed by processes of the zygomatic and temporal bones
- Coronoid and condylar processes of the mandible

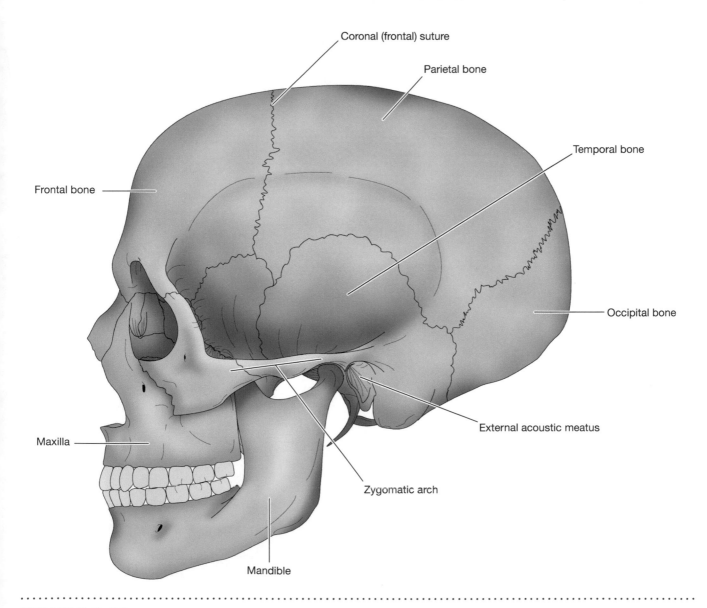

FIGURE 2.21

Skull (lateral view)

Posterior View of the Skull

Most of the posterior view of the skull is formed by the occipital and two parietal bones. The suture between the parietal bones and the occipital bone, called the **lambdoid suture**, can be seen in this view. There is a bony projection on the occipital bone known as the **external occipital protuberance** that indicates the border between the head and neck (Figure 2.22).

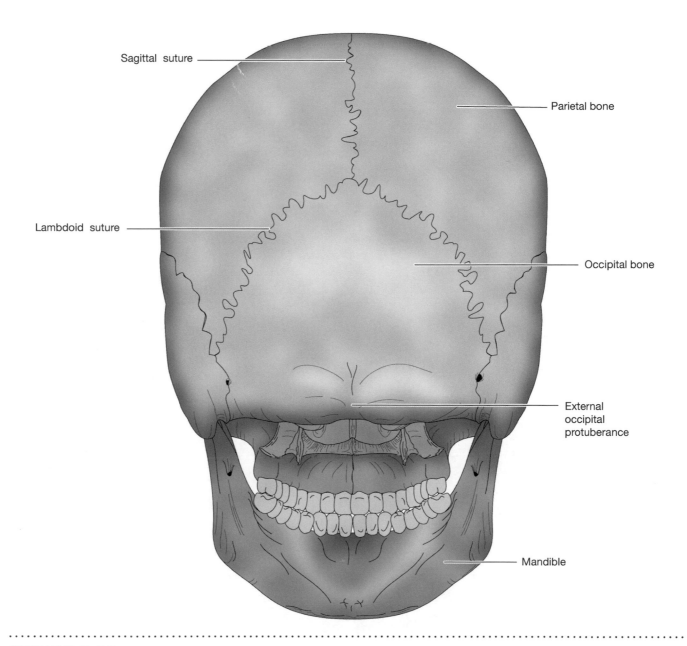

FIGURE 2.22

Skull (posterior view)

Superior View of the Skull

The superior view is mainly formed by the frontal bone, parietal bones, and occipital bone. These bones make a dome-like roof for the skull known as the **calvaria** (vault). The coronal suture (between the frontal bone, and parietal bones), the sagittal suture (between the left and right parietal bones), and the lambdoid suture (between the parietal bones and occipital bone) are visible on this view. The junction of the coronal and sagittal sutures is called the **bregma**, and the intersection between the sagittal and lambdoid sutures is called the **lambda**. These areas in infants are known as anterior and posterior fontanels respectively. Fontanels are membranes of connective tissue that allow the skull to grow proportionately (Figure 2.23).

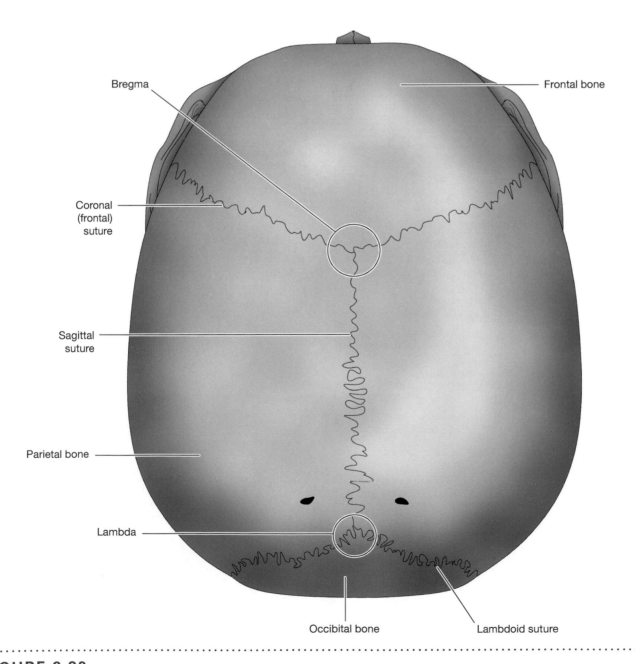

FIGURE 2.23

Skull (superior view)

Base of the Skull (External View)

After removing the mandible, the following bones are seen on this view (from anterior to posterior): maxillae, palatine bones, sphenoid bone, temporal bones, and occipital bone. Some of the main bony features of the skull on this view include, but are not limited to, the hard palate formed by maxillae and palatine bones, the pterygoid processes of the sphenoid bone, the posterior nasal openings (choanae) separated by vomer bone, the styloid and mastoid processes of the temporal bones, foramen magnum, and occipital condyles for articulation with vertebra CI (Figure 2.24).

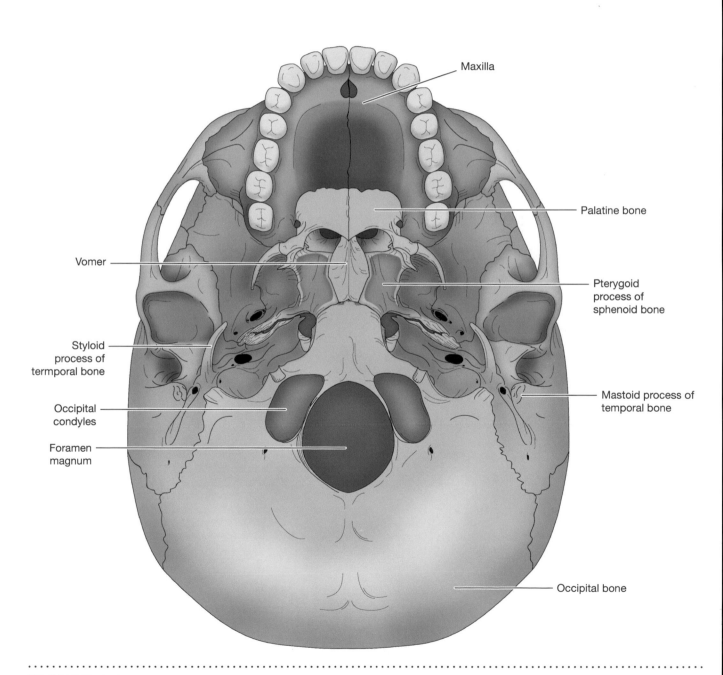

FIGURE 2.24

Base of the Skull (external view)

Base of the Skull (Internal View)

This view of the skull is divided into three fossae known as the **anterior, middle, and posterior cranial fossae** (Figure 2.25).

Anterior cranial fossa is formed by the frontal bone, ethmoid bone, and lesser wings of the sphenoid bone.

Middle cranial fossa is mainly made by the sphenoid and parts of the temporal bones.

Posterior cranial fossa is mainly formed by the occipital bone and parts of the temporal bones.

The boundary between anterior and middle cranial fossae is primarily formed by lesser wings of the sphenoid bone; the boundary between the middle and posterior cranial fossae is demarcated by the petrous part of the temporal bone.

There are some openings on the floor of the cranial fossae that serve as passages for nerves and blood vessels (Table 2.2) and (Figure. 2.25)

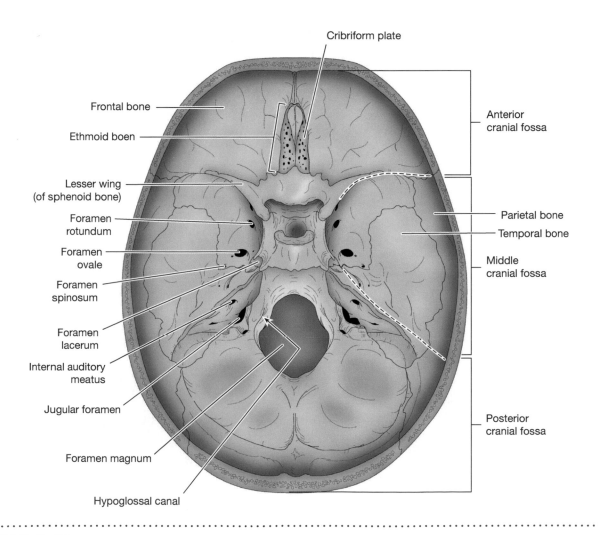

FIGURE 2.25

Base of the Skull (internal view)

TABLE 2.2 *Main Openings on the Floor of the Cranial Fossae*

OPENING	PASSING STRUCTURES
Anterior cranial fossa	
Openings on cribriform plate	Olfactory nerves (CN I)
Optic canal	Optic nerve (CN II)
Middle cranial fossa	
Superior orbital fissure	Occulomotor nerve (CN III), trochlear nerve (CN IV), ophthalmic division (V1) of trigeminal nerve (CN V), abducent nerve (CN VI) and ophthalmic veins
Foramen rotundum	Maxillary division (V2) of trigeminal nerve (CN V)
Foramen ovale	Mandibular division (V3) of trigeminal nerve (CN V)
Foramen spinosum	Middle meningeal artery
Foramen lacerum	Internal carotid artery
Posterior cranial fossa	
Internal auditory (acoustic) meatus	Facial nerve (CN VII), and vestibulecochlear nerve (CN VIII)
Jugular foramen	Glossopharyngeal nerve (CN IX), vagus nerve (CN X), and accessory nerve (CN XI)
Foramen magnum	Medulla oblongata, and vertebral arteries
Hypoglossal canal	Hypoglossal nerve (CN XII)

···· Upper Limb Skeleton

The upper limb skeleton is composed of 32 bones on each side.

Clavicle

The clavicle (collar bone) is an S-shaped long bone that provides the only bony attachment (articulation) between the upper limb and axial skeleton. It is subcutaneous and thus palpable throughout its length. Clavicle has two ends and a body (shaft). There are two curves along the body of the clavicle. The medial curve is convex anteriorly, whereas the lateral curve is concave anteriorly (Figure 2.26).

The **medial (sternal) end** is relatively rounded and articulates with the manubrium of the sternum to form the sternoclavicular joint. The **lateral (acromial) end** is rather flat and articulates with the acromion of the scapula to form the acomioclavicular joint.

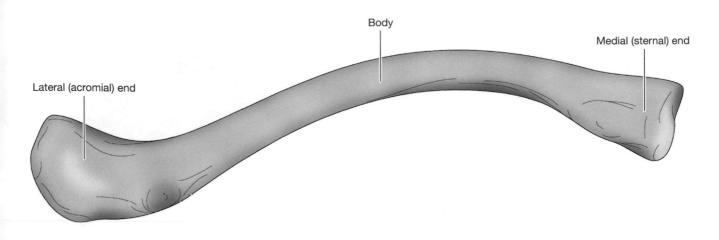

FIGURE 2.26
Right Clavicle (inferior view)

Scapula

The scapula (shoulder blade) is a flat triangular bone overlying ribs II to VII on the posterolateral aspect of thorax. It has two surfaces (anterior and posterior), three borders (lateral, medial, and superior), three angles (superior, inferior, and lateral), and two processes (acromion and coracoid).

The anterior surface is concave and is known as the **subscapular fossa**. A bony ridge, the **spine of scapula**, divides the posterior surface into two fossae. The smaller fossa above the spine is known as the **supraspinous fossa**, whereas the larger fossa below the spine is called the **infraspinous fossa** (Figures 2.27 and 2.28).

The lateral angle of scapula carries an oval articular surface, the **glenoid cavity (fossa)**, which articulates with the head of the humerus to form the glenohumeral (shoulder) joint. Supraglenoid and infraglenoid tubercles are two small bony elevations located above and below the glenoid cavity respectively.

The lateral extension of the spine of scapula forms a flat bony plate known as the **acromion**. There is a beak-like bony projection on the superior border of scapula known as the **coracoid process**. This process is pointing anteriorly and laterally.

The clavicle and scapula form the shoulder (pectoral) girdle.

Humerus

Humerus (arm bone) is a long bone with a body (shaft) and two ends (proximal and distal).

The proximal end is composed of the following (Figure 2.29):

- The **head**: a smooth spherical surface directed medially and superiorly that articulates with the glenoid cavity of the scapula to form the glenohumeral (shoulder) joint.
- The **anatomical neck**: a narrow part immediately below the head.

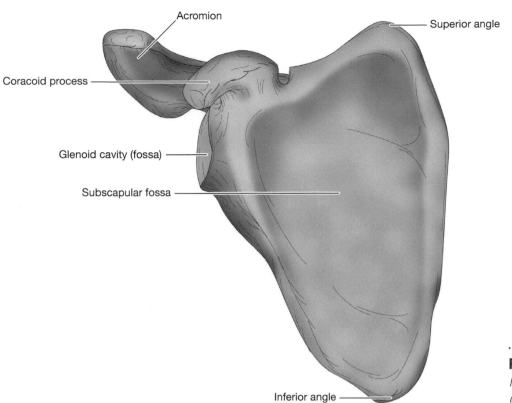

FIGURE 2.27
*Right Scapula
(anterior view))*

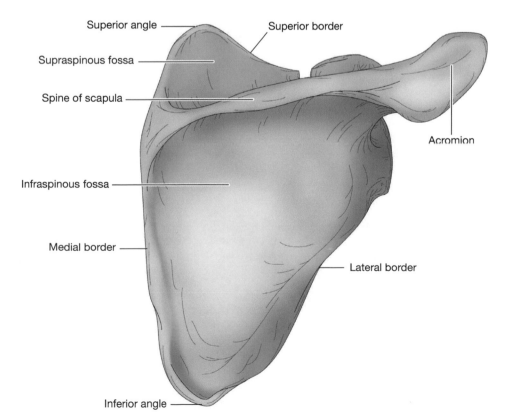

FIGURE 2.28
*Right Scapula
(posterior view)*

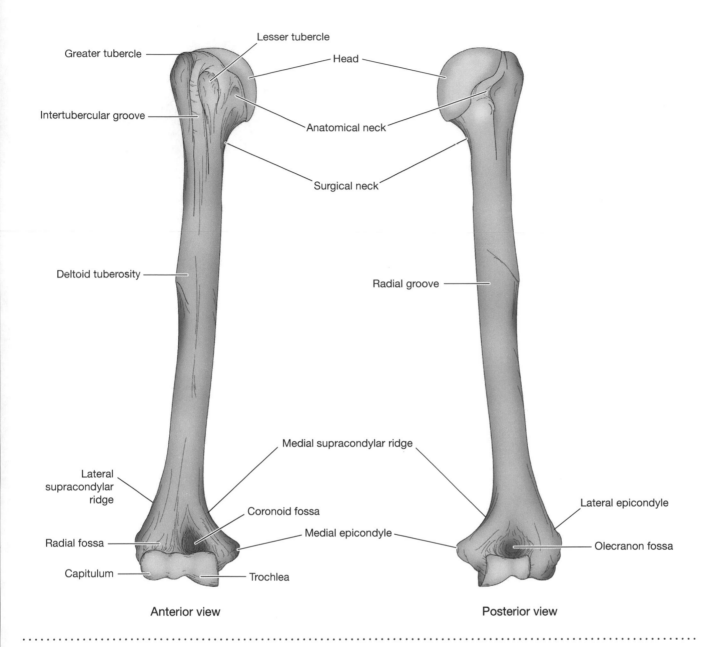

Greater tubercle

Lesser tubercle

Head

Intertubercular groove

Anatomical neck

Surgical neck

Deltoid tuberosity

Radial groove

Medial supracondylar ridge

Lateral supracondylar ridge

Coronoid fossa

Lateral epicondyle

Radial fossa

Medial epicondyle

Olecranon fossa

Capitulum

Trochlea

Anterior view

Posterior view

FIGURE 2.29
Right Humerus

- **Greater** and **lesser tubercles**: two bony prominences separated by a vertical groove known as the **intertubercular (bicipital) groove**. The greater tubercle is located on the lateral side of the proximal end, while the lesser tubercle is located anteriorly.
- **Surgical neck**: narrow part of the proximal end directly distal to the greater and lesser tubercles. The surgical neck is the most common site for proximal end fractures.

The body of the humerus carries a flat bony elevation on the lateral side known as the **deltoid tuberosity**. Behind and below the deltoid tuberosity there is a shallow groove running inferolaterally known as the **radial (spiral) groove**.

The distal end of the humerus consists of the following:

- **Capitulum**: a rounded articular surface that articulates with the superior surface of the head of the radius.
- **Trochlea**: a pulley-shaped articular surface that articulates with the trochlear notch of the ulna.
- **Lateral** and **medial epicondyles**: two prominent bony elevations located adjacent and proximal to the capitulum and trochlea, respectively.
- **Medial** and **lateral supracondylar** ridges: two sharp bony ridges proximal to medial and lateral epicondyles, respectively.
- **Radial fossa**: superior to capitulum on the anterior view.
- **Coronoid fossa**: superior to trochlea on the anterior view.
- **Olecranon fossa**: superior to trochlea on the posterior view.

Radius

Radius is a long bone on the lateral side of the forearm. It is composed of two ends (proximal and distal) and a body (Figures 2.30 and 2.31).

The proximal end of the bone carries head, neck, and radial tuberosity. The **head** is in the form of a short cylinder and articulates with the capitulum of humerus at its superior surface. It also articulates with the radial notch of the ulna at its periphery. The neck is the narrow part located below the head. The **radial tuberosity** is located inferior and medial to the neck.

The body of radius is triangular in cross-section and possesses a medial border known as the **interosseous border**.

The distal end of the radius is larger than the proximal end and carries the **styloid process** on its lateral aspect. The inferior surface of this end articulates with some of the bones in the proximal row of carpal bones. The **ulnar notch** located on the medial side of the distal end articulates with the head of the ulna.

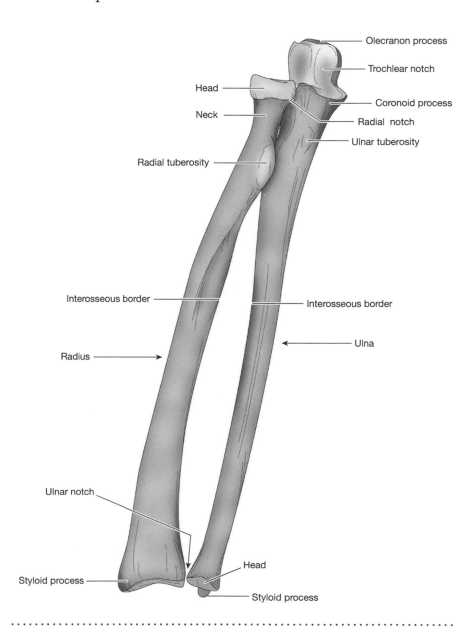

FIGURE 2.30

Right Radius and Ulna (anterior view)

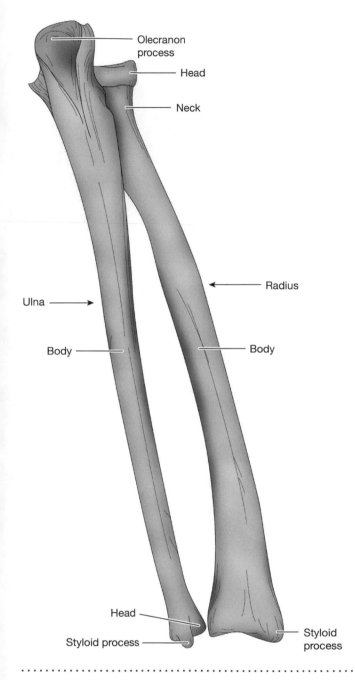

FIGURE 2.31
Right Radius and Ulna (posterior view)

Ulna

Ulna is a long bone on the medial side of the forearm. This bone is composed of two ends (proximal and distal) and a body (Figures 2.30 and 2.31).

The proximal end is larger and looks like a wrench. This end carries two processes and two notches. The **olecranon process** is located posteriorly, while the **coronoid process** is located anteriorly. These two processes are separated by the **trochlear notch** that articulates with trochlea of the humerus. Lateral to the coronoid process there is another notch known as the **radial notch** that articulates with the circumference of the radial head.

The body of ulna is triangular in cross-section and possesses a lateral border known as the **interosseous border**.

The distal end is composed of a round **head** and the **styloid process**. The head of the bone articulates with the ulnar notch of the radius laterally and some of the bones of the proximal row of carpal bones inferiorly.

Bones of the Hand

These bones are located in three regions of the hand including the carpus (wrist), the metacarpus, and the digits (fingers).

The wrist bones or **carpal bones** are eight in number. These short bones are arranged in a proximal and a distal row. The proximal row from lateral to medial includes the **scaphoid, lunate, triquetrum,** and **pisiform**. The distal row from lateral to medial includes the **trapezium, trapezoid, capitates,** and **hamate**. The proximal row articulates with the distal ends of the radius and ulna, while the distal row articulates with the proximal end of the metacarpal bones (Figure 2.32).

The **metacarpal bones** are five in number. These small long bones are composed of a proximal end (base), body (shaft), and a distal end (head) and are numbered from lateral to medial. The base of a metacarpal bone articulates with the distal row of the carpal bones and the head of a metacarpal bone articulates with the proximal end of the proximal phalanx of the corresponding finger (Figure 2.32).

Each finger has three **phalanges** (proximal, middle, and distal) except the thumb, which only has two phalanges (proximal and distal). Each phalanx is composed of a base, body, and head (Fig. 2.32).

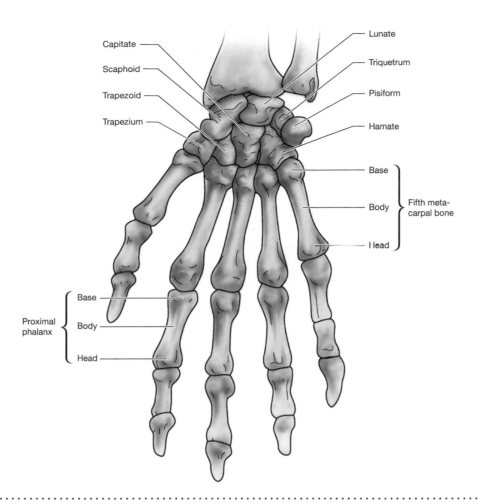

FIGURE 2.32
Bones of the Right Hand (palmar view)

· · · · Lower Limb Skeleton

The lower limb skeleton is composed of 31 pieces on each side.

Hip Bone

Hip bone is a flat bone that forms the pelvic girdle and transfers the body weight to the lower limbs. This bone is composed of three parts—ilium, ischium, and pubis—fused together in the **acetabulum**, a cup-like cavity on the lateral surface of the bone (Figure 2.33).

The hip bone has two surfaces (lateral and medial), five borders (superior, inferior, anterior, posterior, and medial), one foramen (obturator), and a cavity (acetabulum).

The **lateral surface** presents the following features from superior to inferior (Figure 2.33):

a. Gluteal surface
b. Acetabulum: articulates with the head of the femur
c. Obturator foramen: in life it is almost completely sealed by a fibrous membrane (obturator membrane).

The **medial surface** is divided by the medial border of the bone into two parts (Figure 2.34). The superior part carries the **iliac fossa** anteriorly, which forms the lateral wall of the **false pelvis (greater pelvis)**, and the **auricular surface** posteriorly, which articulates with the sacrum. The inferior part carries the obturator foramen and forms the lateral wall of the **true pelvis (lesser pelvis)**.

The **superior border** forms the **iliac crest**, which ends anteriorly to the anterior superior iliac spine and posteriorly to the posterior superior iliac spine (Figure 2.33).

The **anterior border** presents the following features from superior to inferior (Figure 2.34):

 a. Anterior superior iliac spine
 b. Anterior inferior iliac spine
 c. Superior pubic ramus
 d. Pubic tubercle
 e. Pubic crest

The **inferior border** is formed by the ischiopubic ramus stretched between the pubic body and the ischial tuberosity (Figures 2.33 and 2.34).

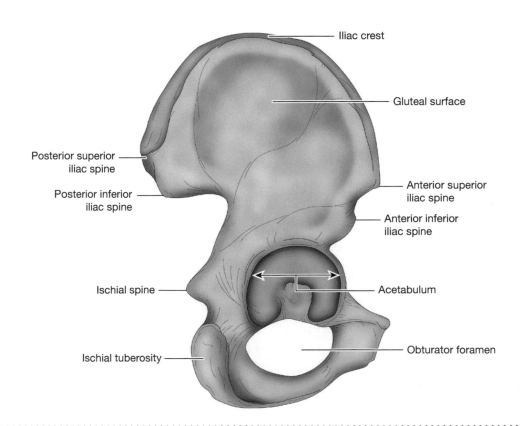

FIGURE 2.33

Right Hip Bone (lateral view)

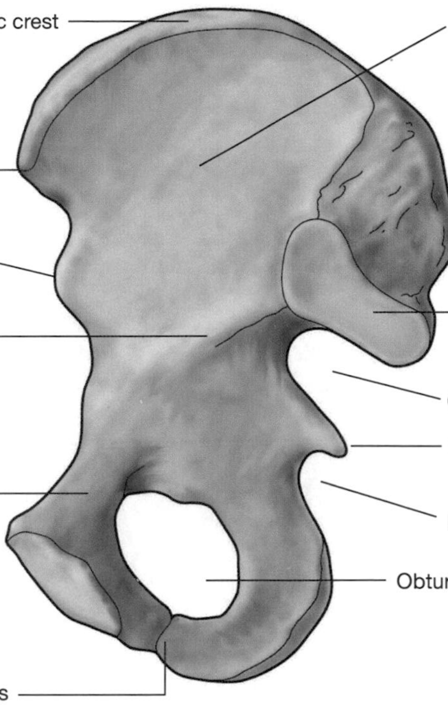

FIGURE 2.34
Right Hip Bone (medial view)

The **posterior border** presents the following features from superior to inferior (Figures 2.33 and 2.34):

  a. Posterior superior iliac spine (PSIS)
  b. Posterior inferior iliac spine (PIIS)
  c. Greater sciatic notch
  d. Ischial spine
  e. Lesser sciatic notch
  f. Ischial tuberosity

Bony Pelvis

The bony pelvis resembles a big funnel formed by four bones (two hip bones, sacrum, and coccyx). It is divided into false and true pelvises by the superior pelvic aperture (Figure 2.35).

The superior pelvic aperture (inlet) is a round or oval bony ring formed from posterior to anterior by the promontory of sacrum, sacral alae, medial border of the left and right hips bones, pectineal line of the superior pubic rami, and pubic crest of the left and right pubic bones (Figure 2.36).

The inferior pelvic aperture (outlet) is a diamond-shaped opening formed from posterior to anterior by the coccyx, sacrotuberous ligaments, ischiopubic rami, and pubic symphysis (Figure 2.37).

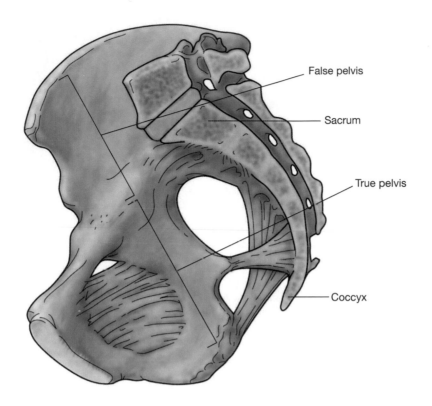

FIGURE 2.35
True and False Pelvises (sagittal section)

The false pelvis is that part of the bony pelvis located above the superior pelvic aperture and is bounded by the iliac fossa on each side. The false pelvis contains parts of the digestive system (Figure 2.35).

The true pelvis is located between the superior and inferior pelvic apertures and is bounded anteriorly by pubic bones, laterally by pelvic surfaces of the pubis, ischium, and obturator membrane, and posteriorly by sacrum. True pelvis mostly contains parts of the urinary and reproductive systems (Fig. 2.35).

Femur

The femur is the longest bone in human body and is composed of two ends (proximal and distal) and a body (shaft).

The proximal end of the bone presents a spherical articular surface known as the **head** that articulates with the acetabulum of the hip bone (Figures 2.38 and 2.39). The **neck** is the cylindrical narrow part of the proximal end directed inferolaterally from the head. There are also two bony projections termed as the **lesser and greater trochanters**. The greater trochanter is located on the lateral side of the proximal end, whereas the lesser trochanter is located on the posteromedial aspect the proximal end. Between the trochanters there is an **intertrochanteric line** anteriorly and an **intertrochanteric crest** posteriorly.

The **body of femur** is almost cylindrical and has a prominent posterior border known as the **linea aspera** (rough line).

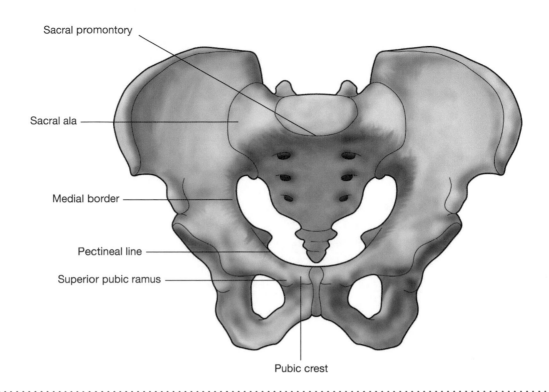

FIGURE 2.36
Superior Pelvic Aperture

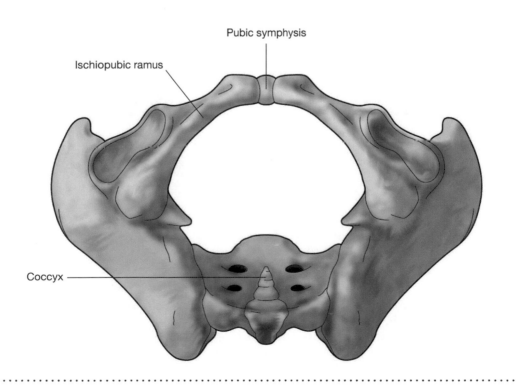

FIGURE 2.37
Inferior Pelvic Aperture

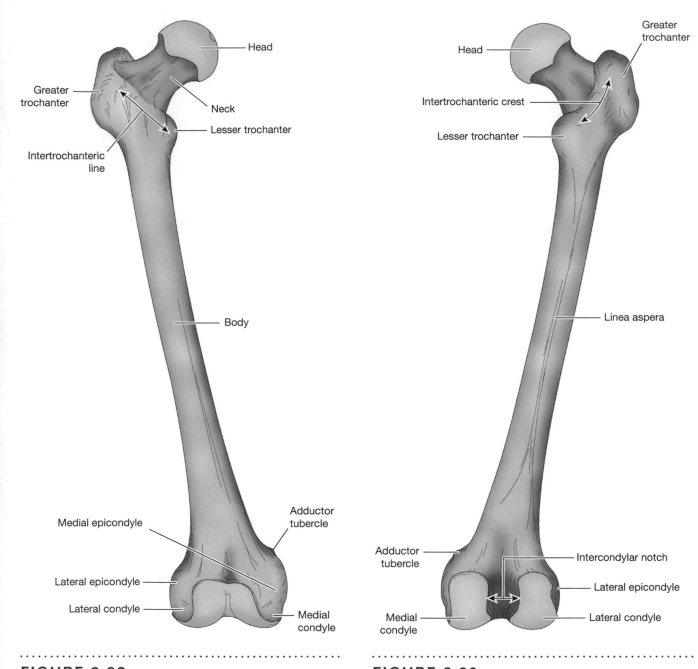

FIGURE 2.38
Right Femur (anterior view)

FIGURE 2.39
Right Femur (posterior view)

The distal end of the bone has two **condyles (medial and lateral)** carrying articular surfaces that articulate with corresponding condyles of tibia to form the knee joint. A patellar articular surface separates the femoral condyles anteriorly and articulates with the patella. The condyles are separated posteriorly by a U-shaped notch known as the **intercondylar notch**. There is a bony projection on each side of the distal end and superior to condyles known as the **epicondyle (medial and lateral)**. The **adductor tubercle** is located above the medial epicondyle.

Patella

The patella is the largest sesamoid bone and is located in front of the knee joint. It is a triangular bone with its apex pointing inferiorly. It has an anterior and a posterior surface, the latter carries an articular surface to articulate with the patellar surface of the femur. The anterior surface is rather rough and is the insertion of quadriceps muscle tendon (Figure 2.40).

Tibia

The tibia is a long bone on the medial side of the leg and is composed of two ends (proximal and distal) and a body (shaft).

The **proximal end** is large and has two **condyles (medial and lateral)** and a bony elevation on its anterior surface known as the **tibial tuberosity** that serves as the attachment site for patellar ligament (Figure 2.41). Each tibial condyle carries an articular surface on its superior aspect that articulates with the corresponding articular surface of the femoral condyles.

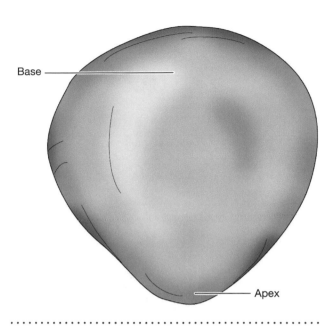

Base —
Apex

FIGURE 2.40
Right Patella (anterior view)

The **body** of the tibia is triangular in cross-section. Its anterior border and medial surface are both readily palpable through the skin. The posterior surface carries a rough line known as the **soleal line** on its upper half (Figure 2.42).

The **distal end** of the bone carries a bony projection on its medial side called the **medial malleolus** and a notch on its lateral side termed as the **fibular notch** The inferior surface of the distal end and the medial malleolus articulate with the trochlear surface of the talus bone (Figures 2.41 and 2.42).

Fibula

The fibula is a long slender bone on the lateral side of the leg and is composed of two ends (proximal and distal) and a body (shaft).

The **proximal end** of fibula is composed of the head and neck. The head articulates with the lateral tibial condyle (Figures 2.41 and 2.42).

The **body** of the bone mainly serves as the attachment site for the muscles of the leg.

The **distal end** of the bone enlarges to form the **lateral malleolus** that articulates with the talus.

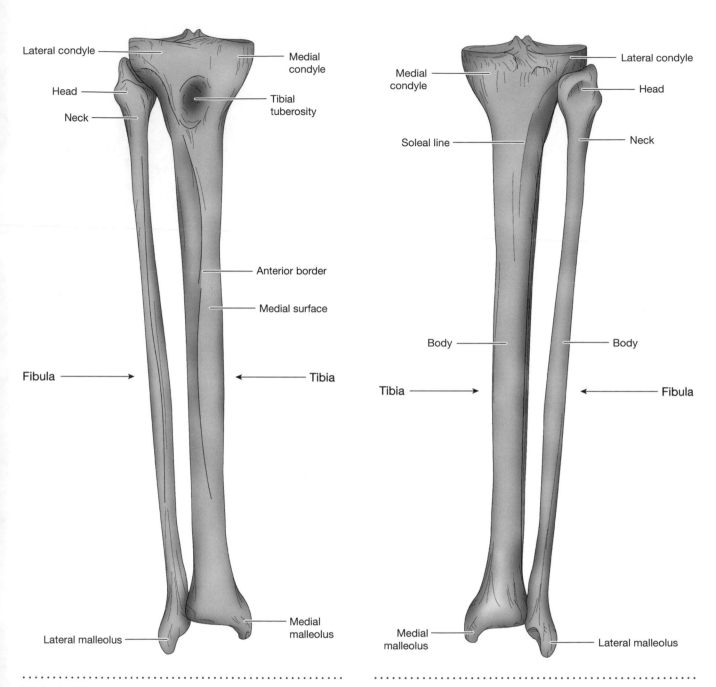

FIGURE 2.41
Right Tibia and Fibula (anterior view)

FIGURE 2.42
Right Tibia and Fibula (posterior view)

Foot Bones

The foot bones are located in three regions of the foot, including the tarsus, metatarsus and phalanges (digits).

The short tarsal bones are seven in number and are arranged in three groups (Figure 2.43). The proximal group includes the **calcaneus** and **talus**. The middle group only consists of the **navicular** and the distal group is composed of the **cuboid** and the **cuneiforms (medial, intermediate, and lateral)**.

Calcaneus is larger than other tarsal bones. **Talus** has a body, neck, and a head. The body of the bone articulates with the tibia and the fibula and transfers the body weight to the calcaneus and the forefoot (Figure 2.43).

The **metatarsal** bones are similar to metacarpal bones and are small long bones that are numbered from medial to lateral. Each bone has a proximal end (base), a distal end (head), and a body (shaft). The bases of the metatarsal bones are articulated with cuboid or cuneiforms and their heads articulate with the bases of the proximal phalanges of the toes (Figure 2.43).

Each toe has three **phalanges** (proximal, middle, and distal) except the big toe, which only has two phalanges (proximal and distal). Each phalanx is composed of a base, a body, and a head (Figure 2.43).

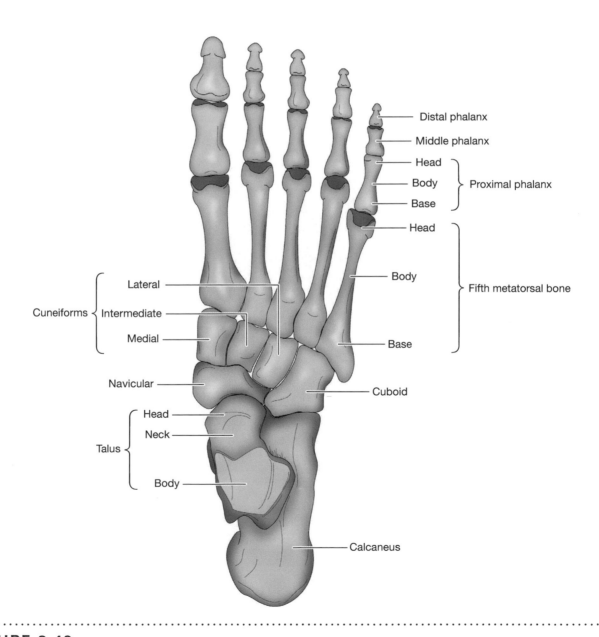

FIGURE 2.43

Bones of the Right Foot (dorsal view)

LEARNING OBJECTIVES

Upon completion of this section you should be able to:

1. Explain the classification of the joints from anatomical and functional points of view.
2. Identify the different types of the solid joints.
3. Explain the major characteristics of a typical synovial joint.
4. Describe the different types of the synovial joints.
5. Discuss the associated structures of the joints.
6. Explain the joints contributing of the trunk.
7. Define the joints of the skull.
8. Discuss the joints of the upper and lower limbs.

···· Joint

The joint is also known as **articulation** and is defined as the site in which two or more bones meet each other.

The joints are classified based on their structure (anatomical classification) or range of motion (functional classification). From a structural point of view, joints are divided into two categories: synovial and solid. Considering the range of motion, the joints may be classified as freely movable (**diarthrosis**), slightly movable (**amphiarthrosis**), and immovable (**synarthrosis**).

Solid Joints

In the solid joints, the bones are held together by connective tissue. Depending on the type of the connective tissue (dense connective tissue or cartilage) the solid joints are classified as **fibrous** or **cartilaginous**. These joints are classified as slightly movable (amphiarthrosis) or immovable (synarthrosis).

A. **Fibrous joints:** In these joints the bones are linked together by dense connective tissue. These joints are subdivided into three groups:

1. **Sutures** are formed between the bones of the skull. In the early years of life the bones are held together by a thin layer of dense connective tissue that later will be replaced by bony tissue (Figure 2.44-a).
2. **Gomphoses** are formed between the roots of the teeth and the bony socket in the maxilla and mandible by an intervening ligament (periodontal ligament) (Figure 2.44-b).

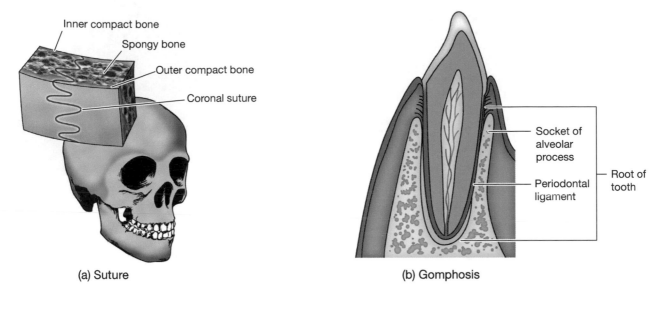

(a) Suture

(b) Gomphosis

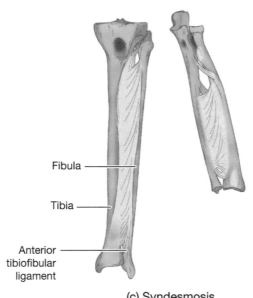

(c) Syndesmosis

FIGURE 2.44

Fibrous Joints

      3. Syndesmoses are joints in which the bones are connected to each other by means of a membrane or ligament (Figure 2.44-c).

  B. Cartilaginous joints: In this type of joint, the bones are tightly connected to each other by cartilage. These joints have limited movements and are divided into two groups:

      1. Synchondroses are joints in which the bones are linked together by hyaline cartilage. These joints are usually ossified before puberty (Figure 2.45-a).

      2. Symphyses are joints in which a fibrocartilage disc connects the bones (Figure 2.45-b).

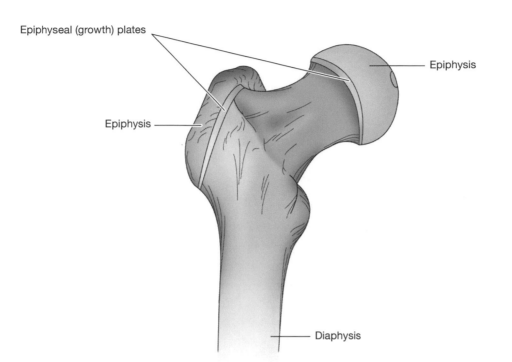

Epiphyseal (growth) plates

Epiphysis

Epiphysis

Diaphysis

A

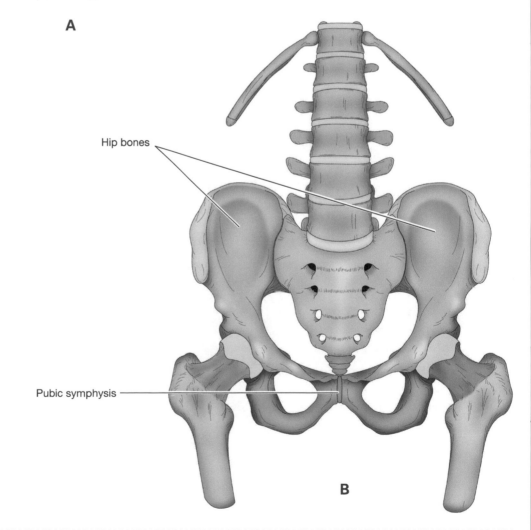

Hip bones

Pubic symphysis

B

FIGURE 2.45
Cartilaginous Joints

Synovial Joints

The main characteristic of the synovial joints is the presence of a cavity between the bones. The bones are held together by means of a fibrous capsule (Figure 2.46). All synovial joints are of diarthrosis type. A typical synovial joint is composed of the following:

Joint capsule: a fibrous sleeve-like structure that completely invests the joint and is supported by the ligaments around the joint.

Joint (articular) cavity: a space enclosed by the joint capsule.

Synovial membrane: the inner surface of the joint cavity (except the articular surfaces of the bones) is covered by a specialized layer of connective tissue known as synovial membrane. The space enclosed by synovial membrane is called the **synovial cavity**.

Synovial fluid: a watery fluid secreted by the synovial membrane and contained within the synovial cavity. The synovial fluid not only nourishes the articular cartilage but also lubricates it and reduces the friction in order to facilitate the joint movement.

Articular cartilage: a thin layer of hyaline cartilage that covers the articular surfaces of the bones. Some of the synovial joints carry ligaments.

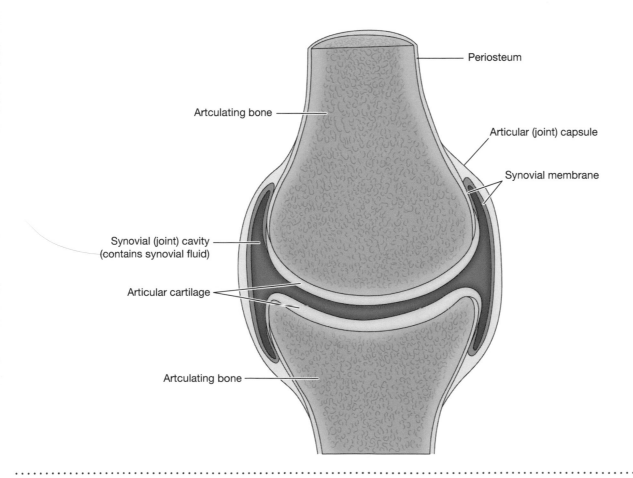

FIGURE 2.46

Synovial Joint

Types of Synovial Joints

1. **Monaxial joints:**

   a. **Hinge joint:** It is similar to the door hinge that can only move around one axis. These joints can perform flexion and extension movements (Figure 2.47-a).

   b. **Pivot joint:** In pivot joints, the rotational movements occur around a longitudinal axis (Figure 2.47-b).

2. **Biaxial joints:**

   a. **Ellipsoid or condyloid joint:** In this type of joint an oval convex articular surface of one bone meets the oval concave articular surface of another bone. Flexion, extension, abduction, adduction, and limited circumduction are the possible movements of this joint (Figure 2.47-c).

   b. **Bicondylar joint:** It is a type of joint in which two convex articular surfaces of one bone are received by two concave articular surfaces of the other bone. This joint allows flexion, extension, and limited range of rotation (Figure 2.47-d).

   c. **Saddle joint:** In this type of joint the articular surfaces of both bones resemble a saddle. Flexion, extension, abduction, adduction, and limited circumduction are the possible movements at this joint (Figure 2.47-e).

3. **Multiaxial joints:**

   a. **Ball and socket joint:** In this joint the spherical articular surface of one bone fits with the cup-shape articular surface of the other bone. This joint permits flexion, extension, abduction, adduction, medial and lateral rotations, and circumduction (Figure 2.47-f).

4. **Nonaxial joints:**

   a. **Plane (planar) joint:** In this type of joint the articular surfaces are almost flat. This joint is capable of performing sliding or gliding movements in different directions (Figure 2.47-g).

Associated Structures of the Joints

There are some structures associated with different joints. The main function of these structures is to facilitate the movements of the soft tissues surrounding the joints or to support the joints. These include but are not limited to the following:

1. **Ligaments:** They are thick bands of dense connective tissue that join the bones to each other. Some of the ligaments are thickenings of the joint capsule, whereas others are individual structures (Figure 2.47-d).
2. **Bursae:** These are small sacs of connective tissue separating the moving structures around the joints (e.g., bursae between skin and joint capsule, muscles and joint capsule). The bursae are lined by a synovial membrane and filled with synovial fluid (Figure 2.48.)
3. **Menisci:** They are incomplete fibrocartilage rings attached to the articular surfaces to increase their congruency (Figure 2.47-d).
4. **Labrums:** These are fibrocartilage rings attached to the circumference of the articular surfaces to enhance their depth (Figure 2.48).
5. **Intra-articular discs:** They are cushions of fibrocartilage found within the joints to absorb shocks and/or increase the congruency.

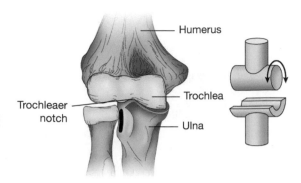

(a) Hinge joint between trochlea of humerus and trochlear notch of ulnar at the elbow

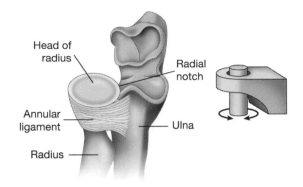

(b) Pivot joint between head of radius and radial notch of ulna

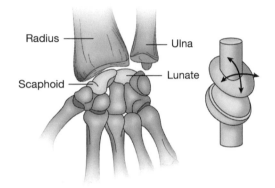

(c) Condyloid joint between radius and scaphoid and lunate bones

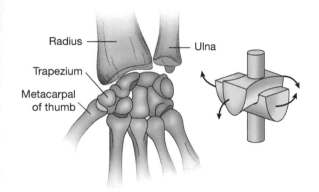

(e) Saddle joint between trapezium and first metacarpal

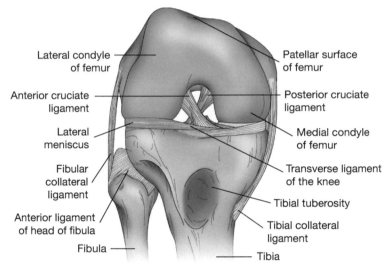

(d) Bicondylar joint between femoral condyles and tibial condyles

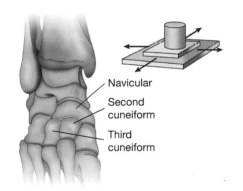

(g) Plane joints between tarsal bones

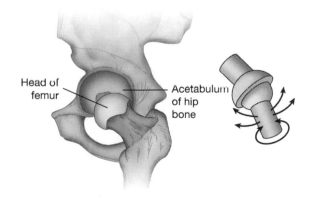

(f) Ball-and-socket joint between head of femur and acetabulum of hip bone

FIGURE 2.47

Types of Synovial Joints

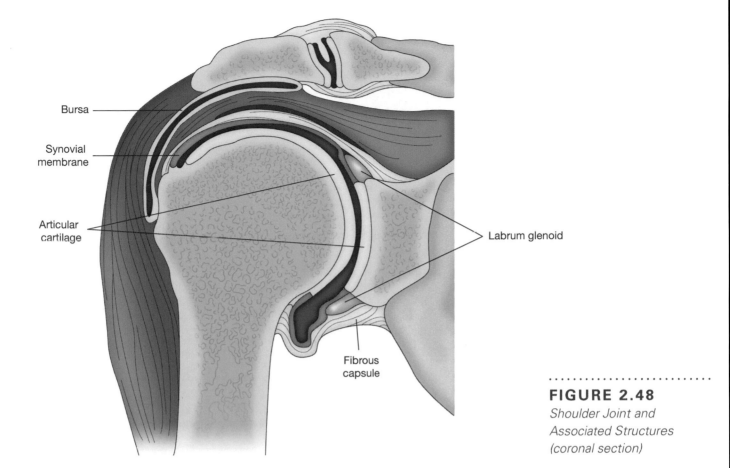

Bursa

Synovial
membrane

Articular
cartilage

Labrum glenoid

Fibrous
capsule

FIGURE 2.48
*Shoulder Joint and
Associated Structures
(coronal section)*

· · · · Joints of the Trunk

1. **Joints of the vertebral column:** Typical vertebrae are articulated with each other at three points (Figure 2.49).

   a. Joints between the superior and inferior articular processes on each side known as **zygapophysial joints**. They are synovial plane joints.

   b. Joints between the vertebral bodies via the intervertebral discs (Figure 2.50). These joints are of symphysis type. An intervertebral disc is composed of a centrally located gelatinous substance (**nucleous pulposus**) surrounded by concentric layers of dense connective tissue (**annulus fibrosus**).

   The joint between the anterior arch of atlas (CI) and odontoid process of axis (CII) is a synovial pivot joint.

   The joints between the atlas (CI) and condyles of occipital bone are classified as synovial condylar joints.

   The joints of the vertebral column are supported by a series of ligaments including but not limited to the following (Figure 2.49):

   - An **anterior longitudinal ligament** is stretched along the anterior surfaces of the vertebral bodies.
   - A **posterior longitudinal ligament** attaches the posterior surfaces of the vertebral bodies to each other.
   - **Flava ligaments** join the laminae of the adjacent vertebrae to each other.

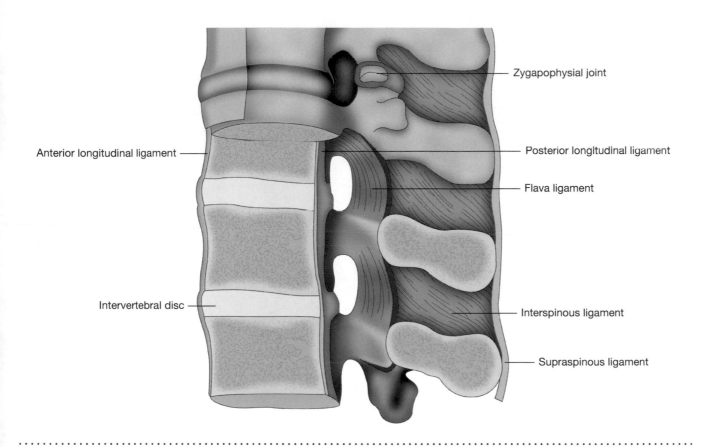

Zygapophysial joint

Anterior longitudinal ligament

Posterior longitudinal ligament

Flava ligament

Intervertebral disc

Interspinous ligament

Supraspinous ligament

FIGURE 2.49

Joints of the Vertebral Column (lateral view, sagittal section)

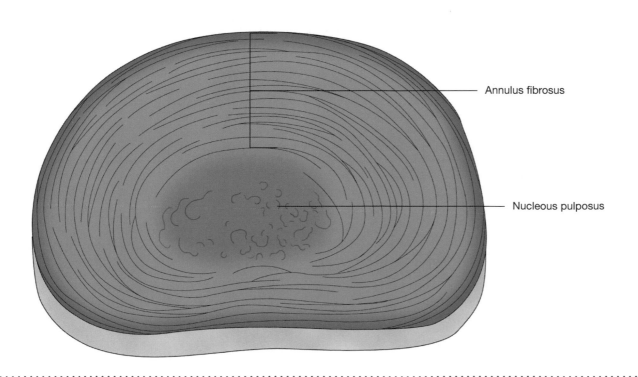

Annulus fibrosus

Nucleous pulposus

FIGURE 2.50

Intervertebral Disc

- **Interspinous ligaments** are stretched between the spinous processes of the adjacent vertebrae.
- **Supraspinous ligament** joins the tips of the spinous processes of the adjacent vertebrae. This ligament in neck region widens and thickens in sagittal plane to attach to occipital bone. This part of the ligament is called the **nuchal ligament**.

2. **Joints of the thoracic cage:**

   a. **Costovertebral joints:** The head of a typical rib articulates with the vertebral bodies of the typical thoracic vertebra at the corresponding level and the vertebra above. The tubercle of a typical rib articulates with the costal facet on the transverse process of the corresponding typical thoracic vertebra (Figure 2.51).

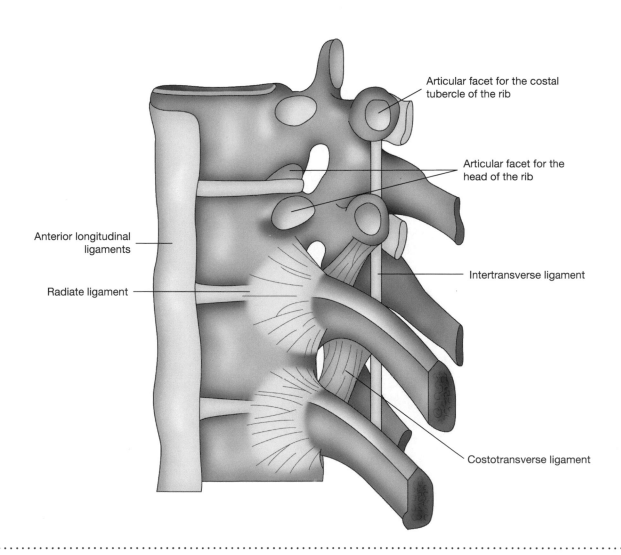

FIGURE 2.51

Joints of the Thoracic Region (lateral view)

b. **Sternocostal joints:** The anterior end of the first seven pairs of ribs articulate with the sternum via their costal cartilages. The next three pairs of ribs articulate with the sternum via the costal cartilage of the seventh rib (Figure 2.52).

All the costovertebral and sternocostal joints are of synovial planar type except the first pair of sternocostal joints that are cartilaginous joints.

c. **Manubriosternal joint:** This is a symphysis type of joint formed between the manubrium and body of the sternum.

d. **Xiphisternal joint:** This joint is formed between the body of the sternum and xyphoid process and is considered as a symphysis type of the joint.

The manubristernal and xiphisternal joints often become ossified with age.

e. **Sternoclavicular joints:** A pair of synovial saddle joints formed between the medial (sternal) end of the clavicle and the manubrium of the sternum. There is a fibrocartilage disc (articular disc) separating the articular surfaces of this joint (Figure 2.52).

This is the only joint that anchors the upper limb to the axial skeleton.

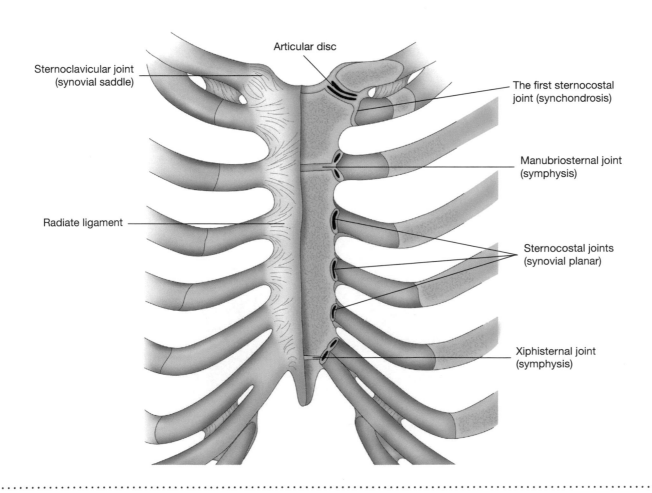

FIGURE 2.52

Joints of Thoracic Cage (anterior view, coronal section)

3. **Joints of the pelvis:**

    a. **Sacroiliac joints:** They are formed between the auricular surfaces of the sacrum and hip bones. These are the synovial planar type of joints that often become fibrous with age. The sacroiliac joints are supported by anterior and posterior sacroiliac ligaments (Figure 2.53). These joints transfer the body weight to the lower limb.

    b. **Pubic symphysis:** This is a symphysis type of joint formed between the pubic parts of the right and left hip bones (Figure 2.53).

      The sacrum and hip bones are connected together by means of two strong ligaments known as **sacrotuberous** and **sacrospinous ligaments**. The sacrotuberous ligament is stretched between the sacrum and ischial tuberosity of the hip bone, whereas the sacrospinous ligament connects the sacrum to the ischial spine of the hip bone. These two ligaments convert the greater and lesser sciatic notches of the hip bones into the greater and lesser sciatic foramina, respectively (Figure 2.54).

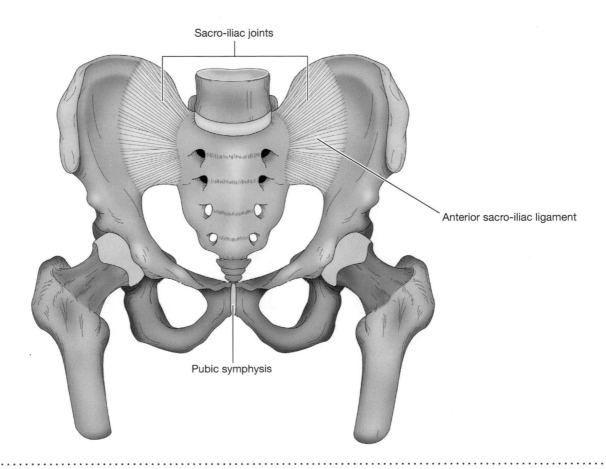

Sacro-iliac joints

Anterior sacro-iliac ligament

Pubic symphysis

FIGURE 2.53
Joints of the Pelvis (anterior view)

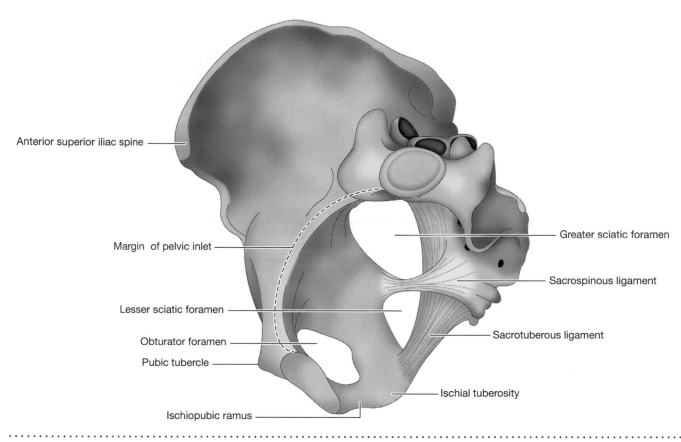

Anterior superior iliac spine

Margin of pelvic inlet

Lesser sciatic foramen

Obturator foramen

Pubic tubercle

Ischiopubic ramus

Greater sciatic foramen

Sacrospinous ligament

Sacrotuberous ligament

Ischial tuberosity

FIGURE 2.54

Sacrotuberous and Sacrospinous Ligaments

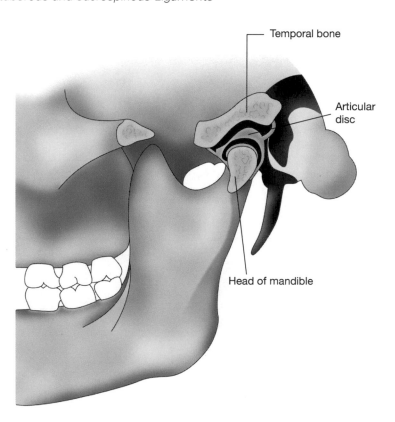

Temporal bone

Articular disc

Head of mandible

Joints of the Skull

All of the skull bones articulate together via sutures except the mandible that articulates with the temporal bone to form a condylar synovial joint known as **temporomandibular joint (TMJ)**. An articular disc intervenes between the articular surfaces (Figure 2.55).

FIGURE 2.55

Temporomandibular Joint

···· Joints of the Upper Limb

1. **Sternoclavicular joints:** A pair of synovial saddle joints formed between the medial (sternal) end of the clavicle and the manubrium of the sternum. There is a fibrocartilage disc (articular disc) separating the articular surfaces of this joint (Figure 2.52).
2. **Acromioclavicular joint:** This is a planar synovial joint between the lateral (acromial) end of the clavicle and the acromion of the scapula. This joint is supported by the **coracoclavicular ligament** (Figure 2.56).
3. **Glenohumeral (shoulder) joint:** It is formed between the head of the humerus and the glenoid cavity of the scapula. The glenoid cavity of the scapula is surrounded by a fibrocartilage ring, **labrum glenoid**, that deepens the cavity for a better congruency with the head of the humerus (Figure 2.48). The shoulder joint is a ball and socket synovial joint. This joint is mainly supported by superior, middle, and inferior glenohumeral ligaments. These ligaments are the thickened parts of the joint capsule (Figure 2.57)

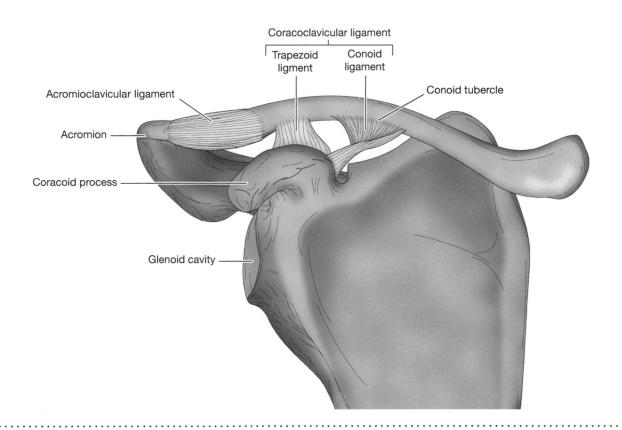

FIGURE 2.56
Right Acromioclavicular Joint

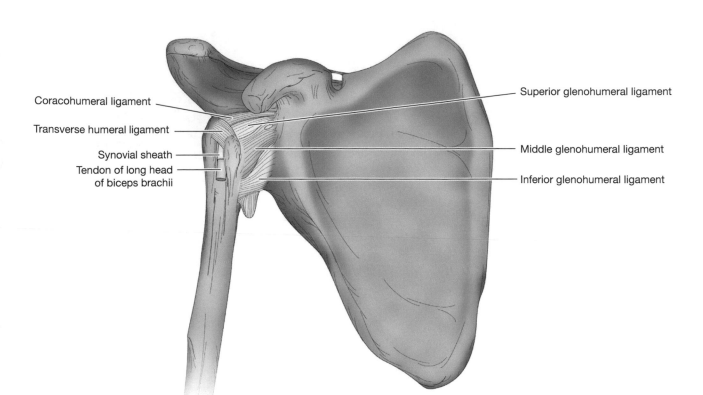

Coracohumeral ligament

Transverse humeral ligament

Synovial sheath

Tendon of long head of biceps brachii

Superior glenohumeral ligament

Middle glenohumeral ligament

Inferior glenohumeral ligament

FIGURE 2.57

Right Shoulder Joint (anterior view)

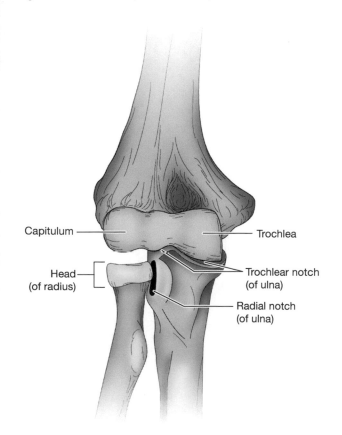

Capitulum

Head (of radius)

Trochlea

Trochlear notch (of ulna)

Radial notch (of ulna)

4. **Elbow joint:** This is a complex joint composed of three components, two of which are formed between the distal end of the humerus and the proximal ends of the ulna and radius. The third component, however, is formed between the proximal end of the ulna and the proximal end of the radius. All these three components are invested by the same fibrous capsule. The articular surfaces of the first two components include the trochlea and capitulum of the humerus that articulate with the trochlear notch of the ulna and the superior surface of the head of the radius respectively. These two components act as a hinge synovial joint (Figure 2.58). The elbow joint is mainly supported by the medial (ulnar) collateral and lateral (radial) collateral ligaments (Figure 2.59).

FIGURE 2.58

Right Elbow Joint, Articular Surfaces (anterior view)

5. **Radioulnar joints:**

   a. **Proximal (superior) radioulnar joint:** It is a pivot synovial joint between the circumference of the head of the radius and the radial notch of the ulna. The head of the radius is held against the radial notch of the ulna by annular ligament. This joint as the third component of the elbow joint shares its capsule with the rest of the elbow joint (Figure 2.60).

   b. **Middle radioulnar joint:** This is a syndesmosis fibrous joint in which an interosseous membrane connects the interosseous borders of the ulna and radius.

   c. **Distal (inferior) radioulnar joint:** It is a pivot synovial joint between the head of the ulna and the ulnar notch of the radius. This joint shares its capsule with the wrist joint.

   All three radioulnar joints are involved in supination and pronation movements of the forearm.

6. **Radiocarpal (wrist) joint:** It is formed between the distal end of the radius and the proximal row of the carpal bones (except pisiform) and is of ellipsoid synovial type. Medial (ulnar) and lateral (radial) collateral ligaments assist in providing the stability for the joint (Figure 2.60).

7. **Intercarpal joints:** These are a series of small planar synovial joints formed between the carpal bones (Figure 2.60).

8. **Carpometacarpal joints:** The first carpometacarpal joint is a saddle synovial joint formed between the trapezium and the proximal end of the first metacarpal bone, whereas the rest of the carpometacarpal joints are planar synovial joints formed between the rest of the distal carpal bones and the proximal end of the medial four metacarpal bones (Figure 2.60).

9. **Metacarpophalangeal joints:** These are condylar synovial joints between the distal end of the metacarpal bones and the proximal end of the proximal phalanges (Figure 2.60).

10. **Interphalangeal joints:** These are hinge synovial joints between the phalanges. The **proximal interphalangeal** joints are formed between the proximal and middle phalanges while the **distal interphalangeal** joints are formed between the middle and distal phalanges. Thumb has only one interphalangeal joint between its proximal and distal phalanges (Figure 2.60).

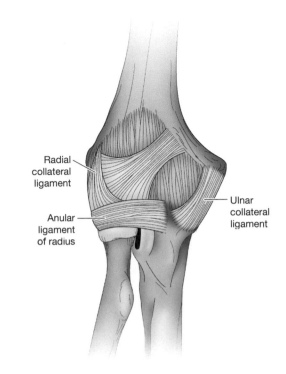

FIGURE 2.59
Right Elbow Joint, Ligaments (anterior view)

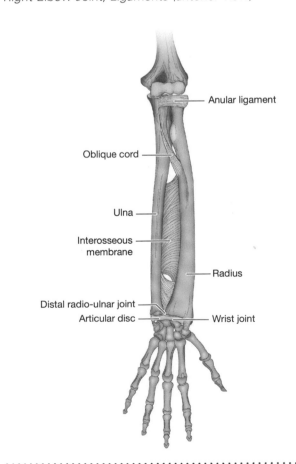

FIGURE 2.60
Joints of the Right Forearm and Hand (anterior view)

· · · · **Joints of the Lower Limb**

1. **Hip joint:** It is formed between the head of the femur and the acetabulum of the hip bone. The acetabulum of the hip is surrounded by a fibrocartilage ring, **labrum acetabulum**, that deepens the cavity for a better congruency with the head of the femur. The hip joint is a ball and socket synovial joint. An intracapsular ligament known as the **round ligament of the head of the femur** assists in stability of the joint (Figure 2.61). This joint is also supported by three ligaments called **iliofemoral, pubofemoral, and ischiofemoral**. These ligaments are the thickened parts of the joint capsule (Figure 2.62).

2. **Knee joint:** This is a complex joint composed of two components, one of which is formed between the femoral condyles and the superior surface of the tibial condyles. The other component is formed between the patellar surface of femur and the posterior surface of the patella. The first component is a bicondylar synovial joint. Two crescent shape fibrocartilage structures known as **medial and lateral menisci**, act not only as shock absorber but also improve the congruency between the articular surfaces (Figures 2.47b and 2.63). The medial (tibial) and lateral (fibular) collateral ligaments provide side-to-side stability of the joint while the anterior and posterior cruciate ligaments provide antero-posterior stability of the joint. The cruciate ligaments are located inside the joint capsule (Figures 2.63 and 2.64).

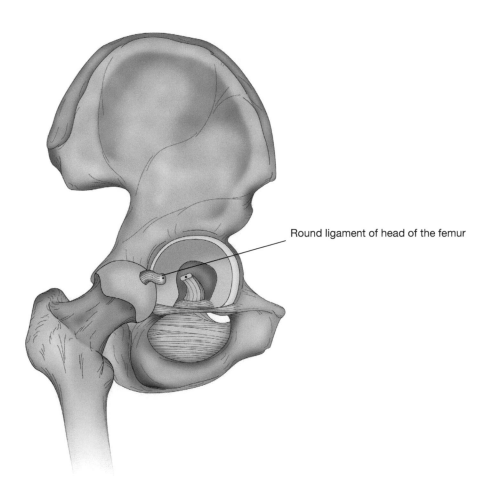

Round ligament of head of the femur

FIGURE 2.61

Right Hip Joint

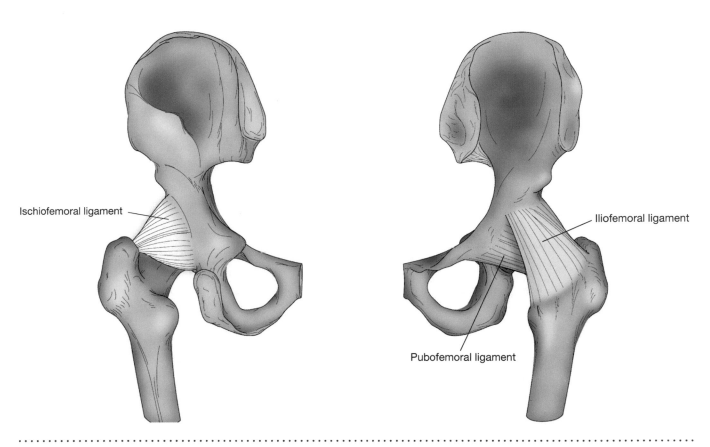

FIGURE 2.62
Left Hip Joint, Ligaments

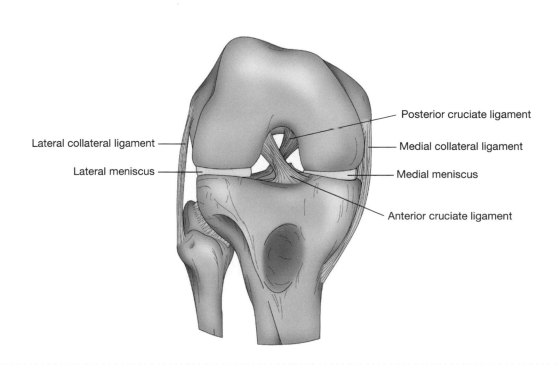

FIGURE 2.63
Right Knee Joint (anterior view)

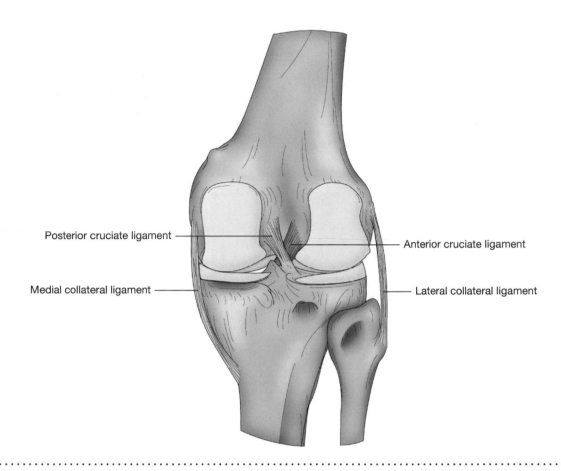

Posterior cruciate ligament

Anterior cruciate ligament

Medial collateral ligament

Lateral collateral ligament

FIGURE 2.64

Right Knee Joint (posterior view)

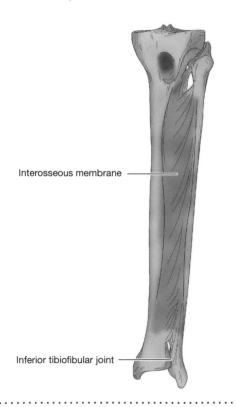

Interosseous membrane

Inferior tibiofibular joint

FIGURE 2.65

Left Tibiofibular Joints (anterior view)

3. **Tibiofibular joints:**

   a. **Proximal (superior) tibiofibular joint:** It is a planar synovial joint between the head of the fibula and lateral condyle of the tibia (Figure 2.65).

   b. **Middle tibiofibular joint:** This is a syndesmosis fibrous joint in which an interosseous membrane connects the interosseous borders of the tibia and fibula.

   c. **Distal (inferior) tibiofibular joint:** It is a syndesmosis fibrous joint between the distal ends of the tibia and fibula.

4. **Talocrural (ankle) joint:** It is formed between the distal end of the tibia and fibula and the body of talus and is of hinge synovial type (Figure 2.66). Medial (deltoid) and lateral ligaments assist in providing the stability for the joint (Figure 2.67 and 2.68).

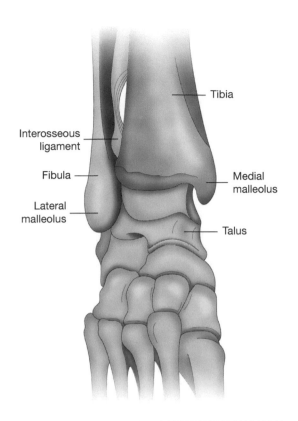

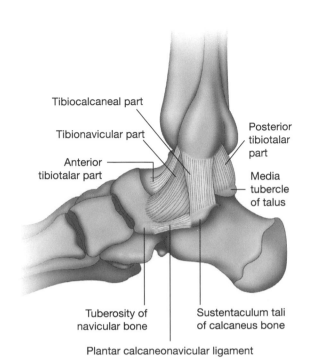

FIGURE 2.66
Right Ankle Joint (anterior view)

FIGURE 2.67
Right Ankle Joint, Ligaments (medial view)

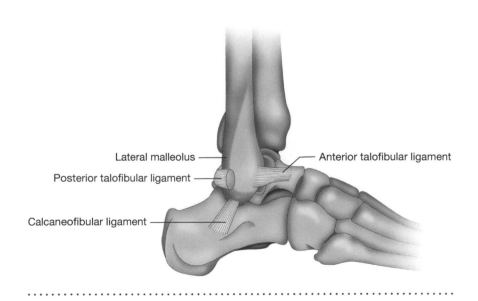

FIGURE 2.68
Right Ankle Joint, Ligaments (lateral view)

5. **Intertarsal joints:** These are a series of small planar synovial joints formed between the tarsal bones (Figure 2.69).
6. **Tarsometatarsal joints:** They are planar synovial joints formed between the distal tarsal bones and the proximal end of the metatarsal bones (Figure 2.69).
7. **Metatarsophalangeal joints:** These are condylar synovial joints between the distal end of the metatarsal bones and the proximal end of the proximal phalanges (Figure 2.69).
8. **Interphalangeal joints:** These are hinge synovial joints between the phalanges. The **proximal interphalangeal** joints are formed between the proximal and middle phalanges while the **distal interphalangeal** joints are formed between the middle and distal phalanges. The big toe has only one interphalangeal joint between its proximal and distal phalanges (Figure 2.69).

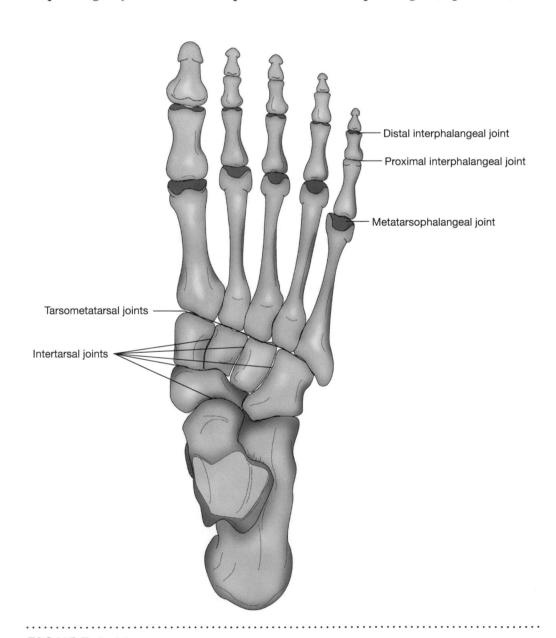

Distal interphalangeal joint

Proximal interphalangeal joint

Metatarsophalangeal joint

Tarsometatarsal joints

Intertarsal joints

FIGURE 2.69

Right Foot Joints (dorsal view)

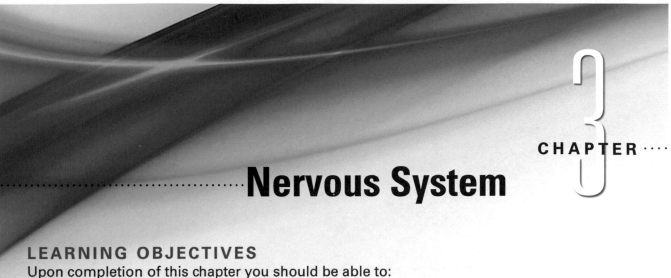

CHAPTER ···· 3

···· **Nervous System**

LEARNING OBJECTIVES

Upon completion of this chapter you should be able to:

1. Explain the classification of the nervous system.
2. Identify the main components of the central nervous system.
3. Briefly discuss the main anatomical features of the spinal cord, brainstem, cerebellum, diencephalon, and cerebral hemispheres.
4. Name the different parts of the peripheral nervous system.
5. Describe and compare the cranial nerves and spinal nerves.
6. Explain the formation and distribution of the somatic plexuses.
7. Discuss the components of the autonomic nervous system and their distribution.

···· Introduction

The nervous system is responsible for receiving and processing impulses from the environment (internal or external) and initiating an appropriate response. From structural point of view, it is divided into the central nervous system (CNS) and the peripheral nervous system (PNS) (Figure 3.1); however, from functional point of view, it is composed of the somatic and visceral (autonomic) nervous systems.

1. **The central nervous system (CNS)** includes the brain and spinal cord. This system processes the incoming and outgoing messages and is also involved in higher mental activities, such as learning, memory, reasoning, and so on. The components of this system are enclosed and protected by bony cavities, for example, the cranial cavity (brain) and the vertebral canal (spinal cord).

The nervous tissue in the CNS is organized as gray and white matters. The **gray matter** is composed of nerve cell bodies, bundles of unmyelinated nerve fibers, and neuroglia (non-neuronal supportive cells). The **white matter** mainly consists of bundles of myelinated nerve fibers known as **tracts** (Figure 3.2).

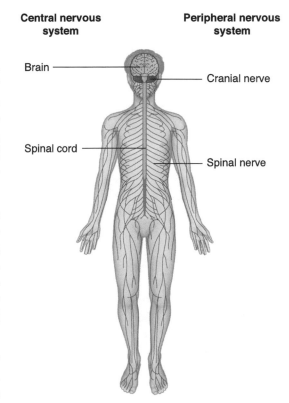

Central nervous system

Brain

Spinal cord

Peripheral nervous system

Cranial nerve

Spinal nerve

FIGURE 3.1
Divisions of the Nervous System

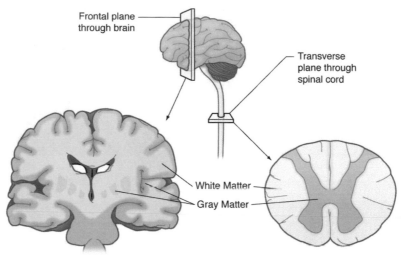

FIGURE 3.2
Gray and White Matters

In the spinal cord the gray matter forms an H-shaped inner core surrounded by white matter. In the brain, a thin outer shell of gray matter (**cortex**) covers the core of white matter.

A cluster of nerve cell bodies embedded within the CNS is called a **nucleus**, whereas an aggregation of nerve cell bodies outside the CNS is referred to as a **ganglion**.

2. **The peripheral nervous system (PNS)** includes the spinal and cranial nerves and associated ganglia. Table 3.1 demonstrates the classification of the nervous system.

TABLE 3.1: *Nervous Systems Classification*

NERVOUS SYSTEM	DIVISIONS	SUBDIVISION	
Central nervous system (CNS)	Brain	Forebrain (Prosencephalon)	Telencephalon (cerebral hemispheres)
			Diencephalon (thalamus, etc.)
		Midbrain (Mesencephalon)	—
		Hindbrain (Rhombencephalon	Metencephalon (pons and cerebellum)
			Myelencephalon (medulla oblongata)
	Spinal cord	—	
Peripheral nervous system (PNS)	Cranial nerves: 12 pairs		
	Spinal nerves: 31 pairs		

···· Spinal Cord

The spinal cord is the terminal cord-like part of the CNS located in the vertebral canal. Its length is about 43 to 45 cm occupying the upper two-thirds of the vertebral canal. The spinal cord starts at the level of CI and ends at the level of LI/LII. However, in children, it extends as low as the level of LIII. The spinal cord has an enlargement in its cervical region and another enlargement in its lumbosacral region. The spinal nerves forming the brachial plexus and lumbosacral plexus emerge from these enlargements respectively. The spinal cord tapers down inferior to the lumbosacral enlargement forming the **conus medullaris** (Figure 3.3).

On the surface of the spinal cord six grooves can be identified. A deep groove on its anterior surface is called the **anterior median fissure** and a less prominent groove on its posterior surface is known as the **posterior median sulcus**. On either side of the anterior median fissure there is a shallow groove known as the **anterolateral sulcus** from which the anterior rootlets (motor) of the spinal nerves emerge. On either side of the posterior median sulcus there is a **posterolateral** sulcus from which the posterior rootlets (sensory) of the spinal nerves emerge (Figure 3.4).

The anterior rootlets join to form the anterior root (motor) of the spinal nerve. In the same way, the posterior rootlets merge to form the posterior root (sensory) of the spinal nerve. Each posterior root of the spinal nerve has a sensory ganglion known as the **dorsal root ganglion** housing the cell bodies of the sensory neurons. A typical mixed (motor and sensory) spinal nerve is formed by the union of the anterior and posterior roots. A section of the spinal cord that gives rise to a certain pair of spinal nerve is known as a **spinal cord segment**, thus there are 31 spinal cord segments.

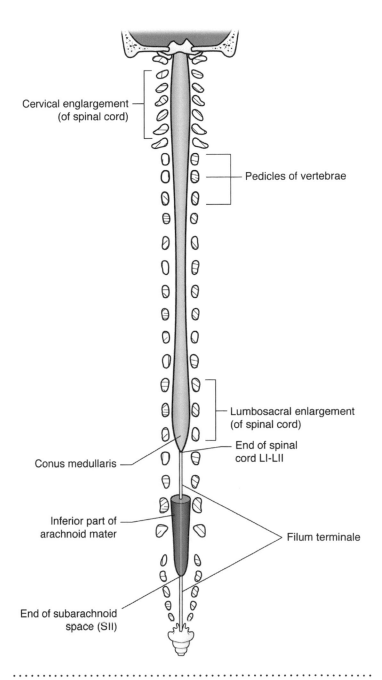

Cervical englargement
(of spinal cord)

Pedicles of vertebrae

Lumbosacral enlargement
(of spinal cord)

End of spinal
cord LI-LII

Conus medullaris

Inferior part of
arachnoid mater

Filum terminale

End of subarachnoid
space (SII)

FIGURE 3.3

Spinal Cord (external features)

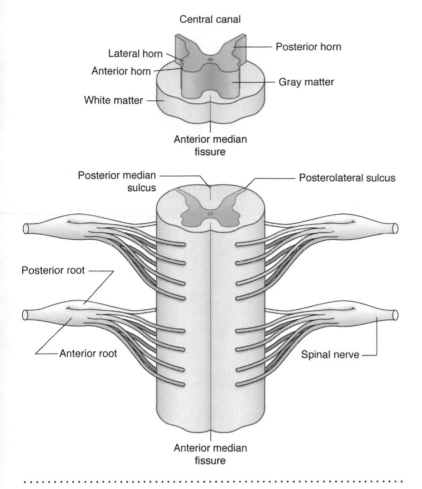

FIGURE 3.4
Spinal Cord (internal feature)

Internal Structure of the Spinal Cord

The spinal cord, like the other parts of the CNS, contains the white and gray matter. The gray matter of the spinal cord looks like the letter H with an **anterior horn** and a **posterior horn** on each side. The right and left halves of the gray matter are connected by a narrow strip containing the central canal. In some segments of the spinal cord (from T1 to L2 and from S2 to S4) there is a third horn between the anterior and posterior horns known as the **lateral horn** (Figure 3.4). The lateral horns contain the cell bodies of the autonomic neurons.

The anterior horns contain the cell bodies of the motor neurons that their axons form the motor (anterior) roots of the spinal nerves. The posterior horns contain the cell bodies of the sensory neurons. The neurons of the posterior horn receive sensory information from the neurons residing in the dorsal root ganglion.

The white matter surrounds the gray matter of the spinal cord and is organized as three columns (anterior, lateral, and posterior) on each half of the spinal cord. These columns contain bundles of myelinated nerve fibers (dendrites and axons) that travel as **tracts** along the length of the spinal cord. There are two main groups of tracts in the white matter of the spinal cord:

1. **The ascending (sensory) tracts** convey the messages from the periphery to the upper centers of the nervous system.
2. **The descending (motor) tracts** convey the messages from the upper centers of the nervous system to the periphery.

· · · · Medulla Oblongata

The medulla oblongata is pyramidal in shape separated from pons by a transverse sulcus (ponto-medullary) superiorly, and continuous with the spinal cord inferiorly. The cranial nerve IX, X, XI, and XII emerge from the anterolateral surface of the medulla oblongata (Figures 3.5 and 3.6).

The medulla oblongata as a part of the CNS is composed of gray and white matters and the arrangement is the same as the spinal cord in the inferior half of the medulla. However, in the superior half of the medulla the gray matter is embedded within the white matter as clusters of nuclei. These nuclei are associated with cranial nerve V, VIII, IX, X, XI, and XII. The white matter contains the sensory and motor tracts.

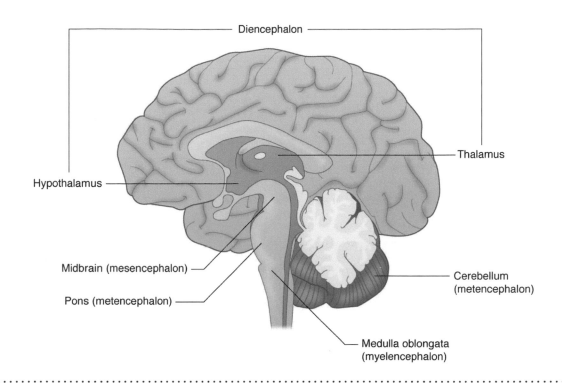

FIGURE 3.5
Sagittal Section of the Brain

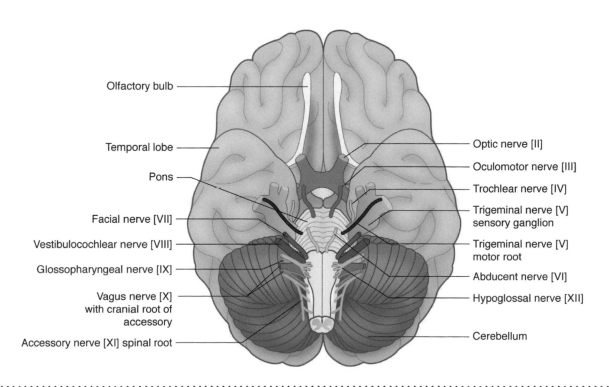

FIGURE 3.6
Inferior View of the Brain (cranial nerves)

Pons

The pons is related to the cerebellum (posteriorly), medulla oblongata (inferiorly), and midbrain (superiorly). The anterior surface is convex and carries a longitudinal sulcus (basilar sulcus) occupied by the basilar artery. The cranial nerves VI, VII, and VIII emerge from the ponto-medullary sulcus, whereas cranial nerve V appears at the anterolateral surface of the pons (Figures 3.5 and 3.6).

The white matter of the pons is formed by the ascending and descending tracts. The gray matter is organized as nuclei embedded in the white matter. These nuclei are mostly related to cranial nerves V, VI, VII, and VIII.

Midbrain

The midbrain is stretched between the pons and diencephalon. The anterior aspect of the midbrain presents two columns (**cerebral peduncles**) between which the cranial nerve III emerges. These columns convey descending (motor) tracts. On the posterior aspect of the midbrain there are four elevations known as **superior** and **inferior colliculi**. The superior colliculi are a relay center for the visual reflexes, whereas the inferior colliculi are a relay center for the auditory reflexes (Figures 3.5 and 3.6).

Ascending (sensory) tracts occupy the white matter of the midbrain behind the cerebral peduncles. There are several nuclei embedded within the white matter, some of which are associated with the cranial nerves III, IV, and V.

NOTE: The combination of the medulla oblongata, pons, and midbrain is known as the **brainstem**.

Cerebellum

The cerebellum is contained within the posterior cranial fossa and behind the medulla oblongata and pons. It is responsible for coordination of voluntary movements. The cerebellum is composed of two **hemispheres** and the **vermis** between (Figure 3.5). The cerebellum is connected to the midbrain, pons, and medulla by three peduncles known as **superior**, **middle**, and **inferior peduncles**, respectively (Figure 3.7). These peduncles are mostly formed by myelinated nerve fibers that travel between cerebellum and other centers of the CNS.

The gray matter occupies the surface of the cerebellar hemispheres (cerebellar cortex) and surrounds the white matter in which some nuclei are located.

Diencephalon

The diencephalon is located between the cerebral hemispheres and includes the thalami and all other structures surrounding the third ventricle (Figure 3.5).

The thalamus is an egg-shaped structure consisting of a group of nuclei, most of which are sensory. The thalamus receives all the senses (except smell) and relay them to the certain sensory areas of cerebral hemisphere (Figure 3.9).

The hypothalamus is located inferior and medial to the thalamus and functions as a center of the autonomic nervous system.

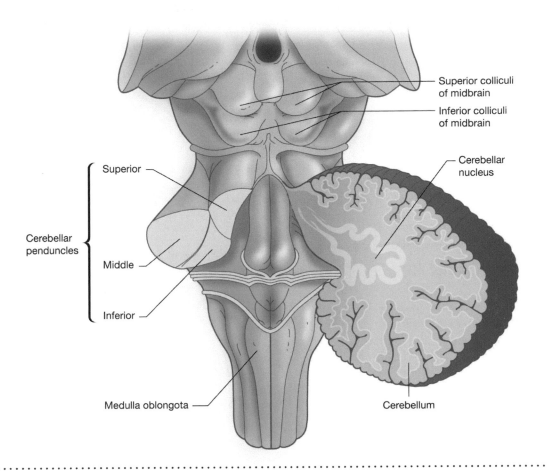

FIGURE 3.7
Brainstem (posterior view)

Cerebral Hemispheres

The left and right cerebral hemispheres are contained within the anterior and middle cranial fossae. The cerebral hemispheres have medial, lateral and inferior surfaces (Figures 3.5, 3.6, and 3.8).

Each cerebral hemisphere is a highly convoluted structure that can be divided into four main lobes: **frontal**, **parietal**, **occipital**, and **temporal**. Each lobe is responsible for different aspects of the brain functions; however, the main role of these lobes is to initiate motor impulse (frontal lobe), to receive general sensory stimuli (parietal lobe), and to receive auditory (temporal lobe) or visual (occipital lobe) impulses (Figure 3.8).

The outer surface of the cerebral hemisphere represents folds (Gyri), separated by furrows (Sulci). There are three main sulci on each cerebral hemisphere.

1. **Central sulcus** separates the frontal lobe from the parietal lobe.
2. **Lateral sulcus** is the superior boundary of the temporal lobe and separates the frontal and parietal lobes from the temporal lobe.
3. **Parieto-occipital sulcus** separates the parietal lobe from the occipital lobe.

The gray matter occupies the surface of each cerebral hemisphere to form the cerebral cortex. It also forms clusters of nuclei within the white matter that are collectively known as **basal ganglia**. These nuclei are involved in coordination of the motor function (Figure 3.9).

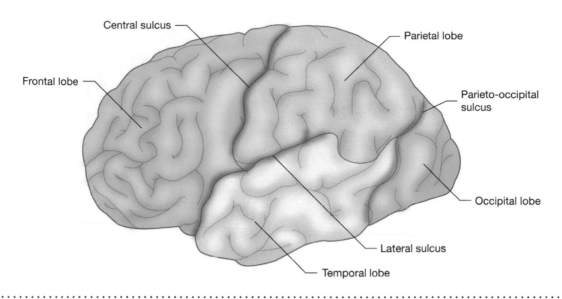

FIGURE 3.8

Cerebral Lobes (lateral view)

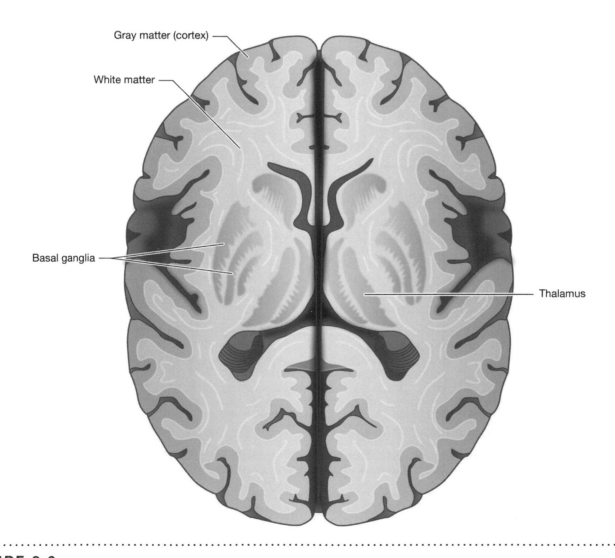

FIGURE 3.9

Cerebral Hemispheres (horizontal section)

The white matter is located deep to the cortex and is formed by myelinated nerve fibers. These nerve fibers can be classified into three groups based on the parts of the CNS that they connect together (Figure 3.10).

1. **Association** fibers join the different parts of the same cerebral hemisphere.
2. **Commissural** fibers connect the different lobes of the two hemispheres together.
3. **Projectional** fibers include the ascending (sensory) or descending (motor) fibers connecting the cortex to the lower centers of the CNS.

···· Cerebral Ventricles

The nervous system is developed from embryonic neural tube. The caudal part of the neural tube forms the spinal cord and the cephalic part of that forms the cerebral vesicles. The lumen of the neural tube in the brain is larger and develops into cerebral ventricles. This lumen in the spinal cord remains narrow and forms the central canal.

The cerebral ventricles house a specialized vascular plexus known as the **choroid plexus**. This plexus is responsible for secretion of cerebrospinal fluid (CSF) that circulates in all cerebral ventricles, central canal of the spinal cord, and subarachnoid space.

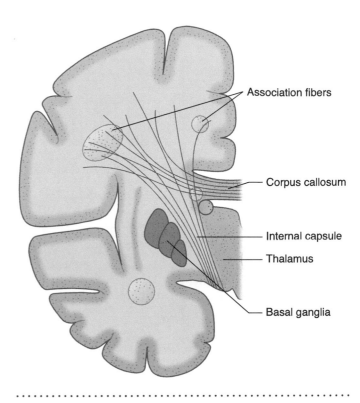

FIGURE 3.10
Coronal Section of Cerebral Hemisphere (white matter organization)

Labels: Association fibers, Corpus callosum, Internal capsule, Thalamus, Basal ganglia

There are four ventricles within the brain (Figure 3.11).

1. **Lateral ventricles:** In each cerebral hemisphere there is an amorphous space that is known as the lateral ventricle. Each lateral ventricle is connected to the third ventricle through the **interventricular foramen of Monro**.
2. **Third ventricle:** The third ventricle is an irregular and narrow space located within the diencephalon between the left and right thalami. This ventricle is connected to the fourth ventricle through the **cerebral aqueduct**. This duct passes through the midbrain.
3. **Fourth ventricle:** This ventricle is a diamond shaped space that is located within the hindbrain and is related to pons and medulla oblongata anteriorly and cerebellum posteriorly. The fourth ventricle is connected to the central canal of the spinal cord (inferiorly), to the third ventricle (superiorly), and through the lateral apertures (foramen of Luschka) and the median aperture (foramen of Magendi) to the subarachnoid space (Figure 3.16).

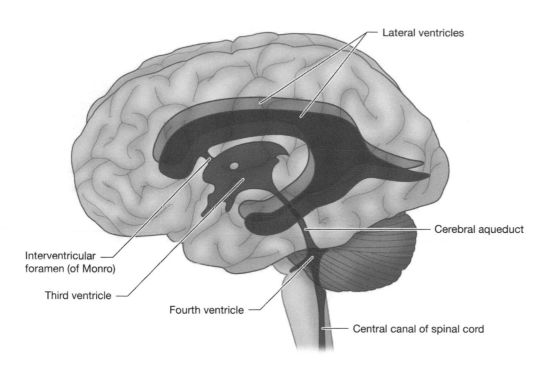

Ventricles of Brain
Left Lateral Phantom View

FIGURE 3.11
Cerebral Ventricles

···· The Meninges

The CNS is surrounded by three membranes or meninges: the **dura mater, the arachnoid**, and **the pia mater** from outside to inside (Figure 3.12).

Dura Mater

The dura mater is a thick layer of dense connective tissue that attaches to the inner surface of the neurocranium in the skull, but is separate from the walls of the vertebral canal to form the **epidural space** (Figure 3.13). The dura mater surrounding the spinal cord ends at the level of SII. The dura mater within the skull is composed of an outer **periosteal** layer and an inner **meningeal** layer. The periosteal layer is attached to the inner surface of the cranial cavities. The meningeal layer separates from the periosteal layer in several locations to form two distinct structures:

1. **Dural reflections** that form incomplete partitions to divide the cranial cavity into several compartments. These reflections include (Figure 3.14):

   a. **Falx cerebri:** is a sagittal sickle shape reflection of the dura mater that partially separates the cerebral hemispheres.

   b. **Tentorium cerebelli:** is a tent-like horizontal sheet that intervenes between the cerebellum and occipital lobe of the cerebral hemispheres. The tentorium cerebelli is notched anteriorly to provide a passage for the midbrain.

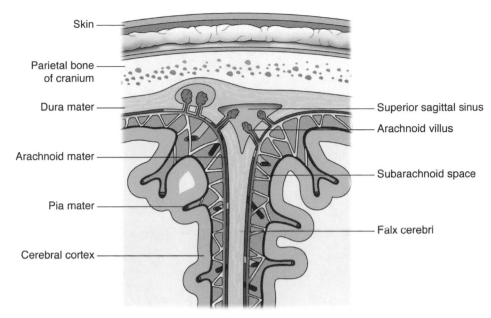

Frontal section through skull showing
the cranial meninges

FIGURE 3.12

Brain and Meninges (coronal section)

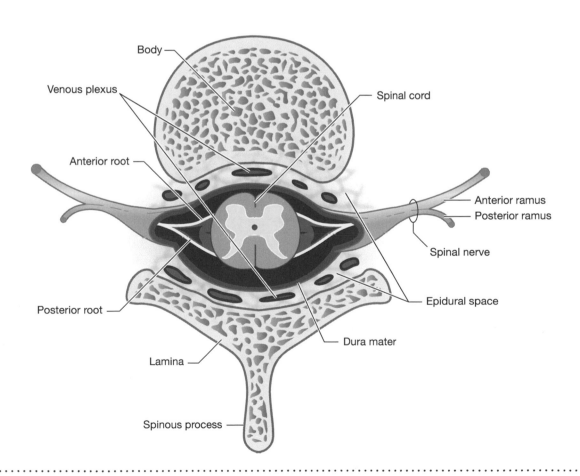

FIGURE 3.13

Vertebral Canal and Spinal Cord (transverse section)

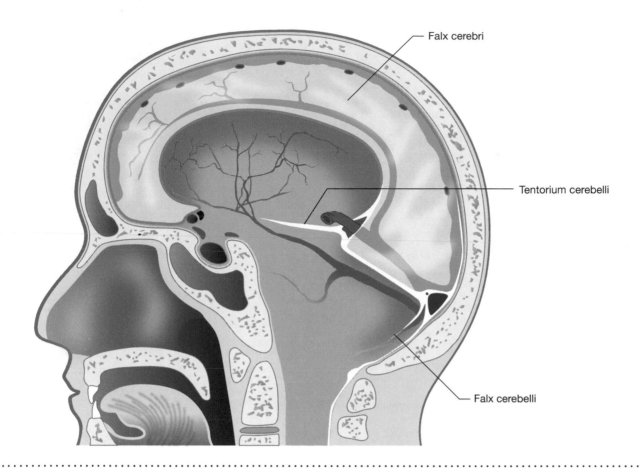

FIGURE 3.14

Dural Reflections (sagittal section of the cranium)

    c. **Falx cerebelli:** is a less prominent sagittal reflection of the dura that partially separates the cerebellar hemispheres.

  2. **Dural sinuses** are channels between the two layers of dura matter that drain the venous blood of the brain to the circulatory system (Chapter 5).

Arachnoid

The arachnoid is a thin layer of loose connective tissue attached to the deep surface of the dura mater. The arachnoid is separated from pia mater by **subarachnoid** space that mainly contains the CSF. There are small finger-like projections (**arachnoid granulations** or **villi**) of the arachnoid entering the dural sinuses. The CSF returns to the dural sinuses via the arachnoid granulations (Figure 3.12). The complete pathway of CSF circulation is shown in Figures 3.15 and 3.16.

Pia Mater

The pia mater is a delicate and thin layer of connective tissue that is in direct touch with the surface of the brain and spinal cord. This layer follows the contours of the brain and spinal cord and carries the blood vessels to the depth of the nervous tissue (Figure 3.12).

The pia mater of the spinal cord has some triangular extensions to the deep surface of the arachnoid and dura mater. These extensions are called **denticulate ligament** and suspend the spinal cord within the vertebral canal (Figure 3.17). The continuation of the pia mater after the spinal cord has ended is known as **filum terminale** (Figure 3.3). The filum terminale extends inferiorly to merge with the arachnoid and dura mater and anchors the spinal cord to the coccyx.

· · · · Peripheral Nervous System

The peripheral nervous system (PNS) is a collection of nerve fibers (axons and dendrites) and aggregations of neuronal cell bodies within the ganglia. This system is composed of 12 pairs of cranial nerves, 31 pairs of spinal nerves, and associated ganglia (Figure 3.1).

Cranial Nerves

There are 12 pairs of cranial nerves; the nuclei of which (except the first two) are located in the brainstem. These nuclei are either sensory, or motor, or autonomic (parasympathetic). The sensory nuclei of the cranial nerves are equivalent to the posterior horn of the spinal cord, whereas the motor nuclei of the cranial nerves are equal to the anterior horn of the spinal cord. The parasympathetic nuclei of the cranial nerves are comparable to the lateral horn (only S2-S4) of the spinal cord. It's worth mentioning that the sensory ganglia of the cranial nerves are like the dorsal root ganglion of the spinal nerves (Figure 3.18).

The cranial nerves pass through different openings at the base of the neurocranium. All of the cranial nerves are distributed in the head and neck except the CN X (vagus), which distributes in the thorax and abdomen as well. Table 3.2 presents the names and the main features of the cranial nerves.

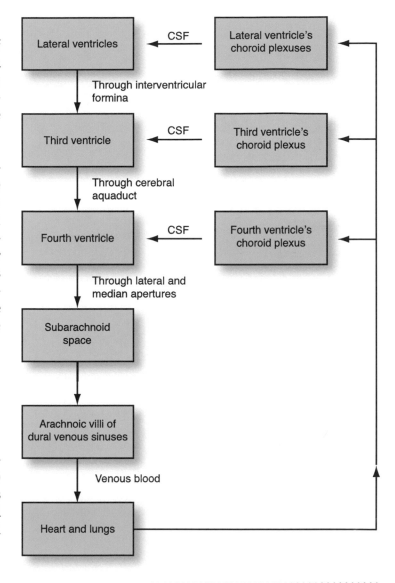

FIGURE 3.15
Cerebrospinal Fluid Circulation

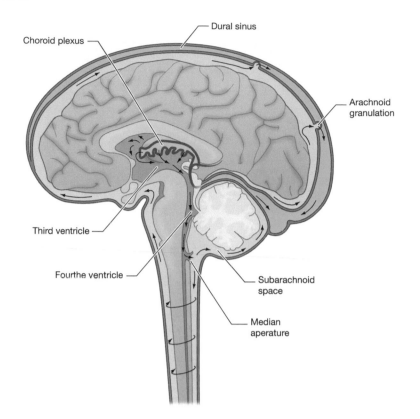

FIGURE 3.16

Circulation of Cerebrospinal Fluid

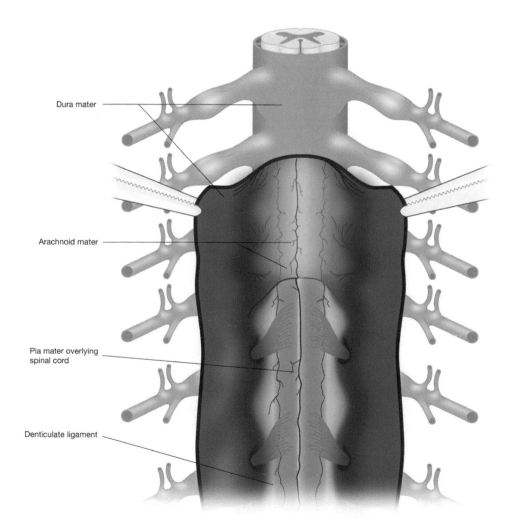

FIGURE 3.17

Spinal Cord

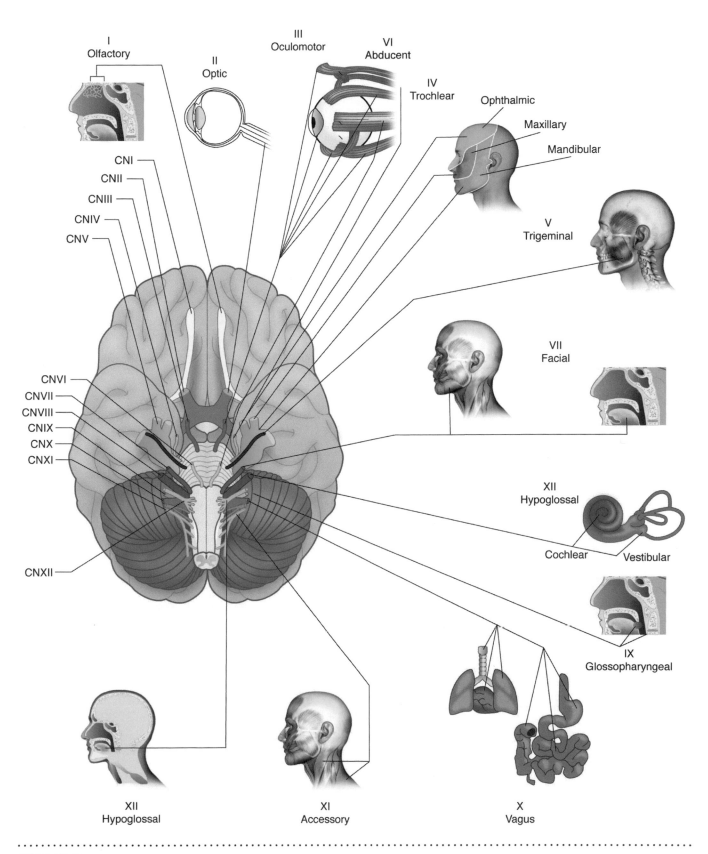

FIGURE 3.18
Cranial Nerves

TABLE 3.2: *The Main Characteristics of the Cranial Nerves*

NUMBER	NAME		COMPONENTS	FUNCTION	OPENING TO SKULL
I	Olfactory		Sensory	Olfaction	Cribriform plate of the ethmoid bone
II	Optic		Sensory	Vision	Optic canal
III	Oculomotor		Motor/autonomic	Some of the extra ocular muscles, ciliary muscle, and sphincter pupil	Superior orbital fissure
IV	Trochlear		Motor	One of the extra ocular muscles	
V	Trigeminal	Ophthalmic division	Sensory	Mainly cornea, skin of the forehead, upper eyelids	
		Maxillary division	Sensory	Mainly skin of the face between the lower eyelid and upper lip, nasal cavity, upper teeth, and palates	Foramen rotundum
		Mandibular division	Sensory/motor	Mainly skin covering the mandible, lower teeth, oral cavity (except palates), and the muscles of mastication	Foramen ovale
VI	Abducent		Motor	One of the extra ocular muscles	Superior orbital fissure
VII	Facial		Sensory/motor/autonomic	Taste of the anterior two-thirds of the tongue, muscles of facial expression, submandibular, sublingual, and lacrimal glands	Internal acoustic (auditory) meatus
VIII	Vestibulocochlear		Sensory	Hearing and balance	

IX	Glossopharyngeal	Sensory/motor/ autonomic	Taste and general sensation of the posterior one third of the tongue, a muscle of the pharynx, and general sensation of the oro-pharynx	Jugular foramen
X	Vagus	Sensory / motor / autonomic	Pharyngeal and palatine muscles, larynx, trachea, lungs, heart, and parts of the gastrointestinal tract	
XI	Accessory	Motor	Sternocleidomastoid and trapezius (spinal root)	
XII	Hypoglossal	Motor	Muscles of the tongue (except palatoglossus)	Hypoglossal canal

The Spinal Nerves

There are 31 pairs of the spinal nerves that leave the vertebral canal through the intervertebral foramina. Each spinal nerve is connected to the spinal cord by an anterior and a posterior root (Figure 3.19). The anterior root arises from the anterior horn of the spinal cord and carries motor (efferent) fibers. The posterior root ends to the posterior horn of the spinal cord and carries sensory (afferent) fibers. Since a spinal nerve is formed by the union of the motor (anterior) and the sensory (posterior) roots, thus a spinal nerve is a mixed (motor and sensory) nerve (Figure 3.4).

The spinal nerves split immediately after emerging from the intervertebral foramina into an **anterior** and a **posterior ramus** (branch). The anterior rami are thicker and form somatic nerve plexuses in cervical, lumbar, and sacral regions. The anterior rami of the thoracic region are known as **intercostal** nerves and do not form a distinct nerve plexus. The posterior rami supply the paravertebral musculature and the overlying skin.

Because the spinal cord is shorter than the vertebral canal, the anterior and posterior roots of the lumbar, sacral, and coccygeal spinal nerves travel further inferiorly to the corresponding intervertebral foramen to exit the vertebral canal (Figure 3.19). This bundle of roots is known as **cauda equina** (horse's tail).

Spinal Nerves Nomenclature

The spinal nerves are named after the spinal segments that give rise to them (Figure 3.20).

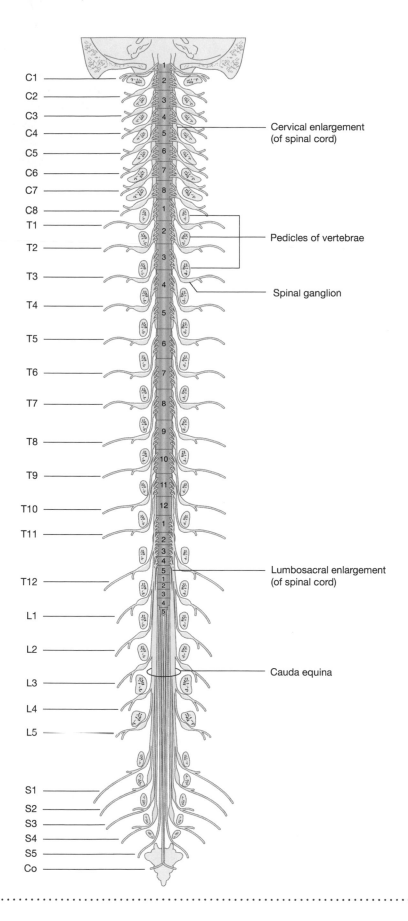

C1
C2
C3
C4 — Cervical enlargement (of spinal cord)
C5
C6
C7
C8
T1 — Pedicles of vertebrae
T2
T3 — Spinal ganglion
T4
T5
T6
T7
T8
T9
T10
T11
T12 — Lumbosacral enlargement (of spinal cord)
L1
L2
L3 — Cauda equina
L4
L5
S1
S2
S3
S4
S5
Co

FIGURE 3.19

Spinal Nerves

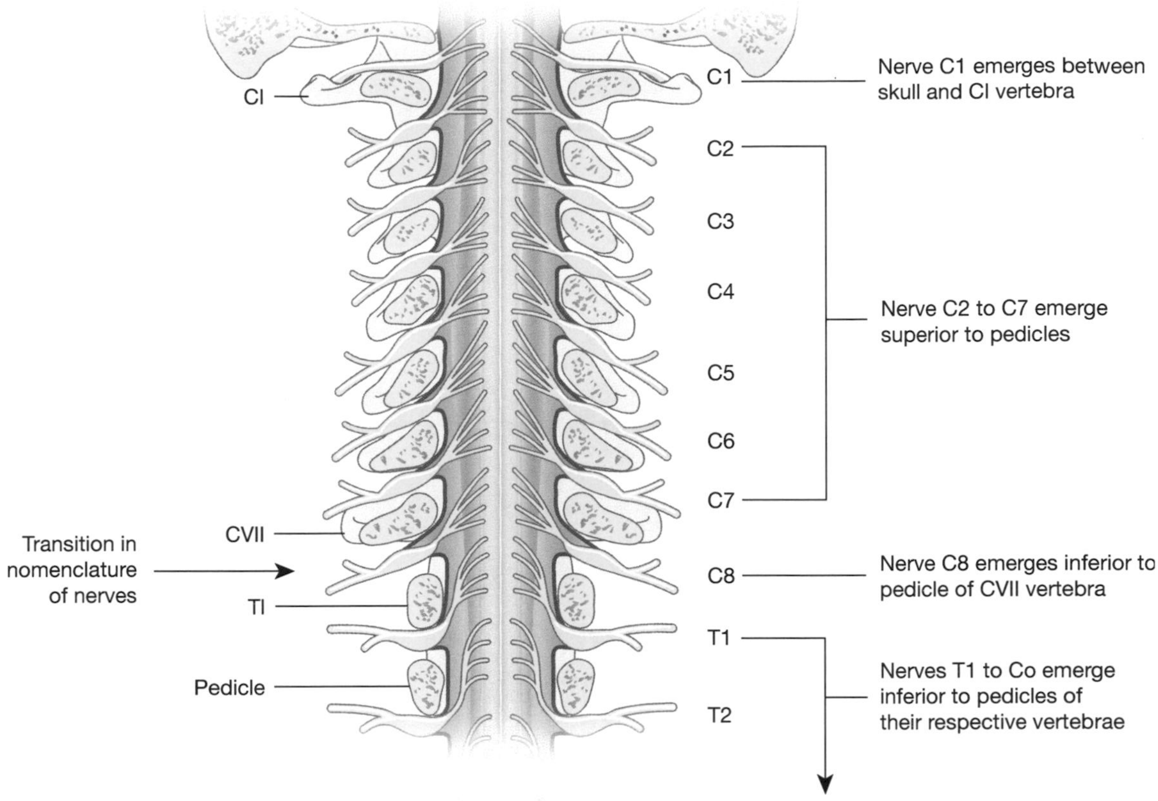

FIGURE 3.20
Spinal Nerve Nomenclature

1. **Cervical spinal nerves** (C1–C8): They emerge from the vertebral canal above the corresponding cervical vertebrae. Because there are only 7 cervical vertebrae, the cervical nerve C8 passes between the vertebra CVII and TI. The anterior rami of these nerves form either the cervical (C1–C4) or brachial (C5–T1) plexuses.
2. **Thoracic spinal nerves** (T1–T12): the anterior rami of these nerves are located in the intercostal spaces and mainly supply the intercostal and abdominal muscles, and the skin of the anterior aspect of the trunk. The spinal nerve T1 contributes in the brachial plexus as well.
3. **Lumbar spinal nerves** (L1–L5): These nerves form the lumbar plexus (L1–L4) and contribute in sacral plexus.
4. **Sacral spinal nerves** (S1–S5): They form the sacral plexus (L4–S4) and contribute in coccygeal plexus.
5. **Coccygeal spinal nerves** (Co): there is only one pair of coccygeal nerves that form the coccygeal plexus with contribution from the sacral nerves S4 and S5.

The area of the skin that is innervated by a single spinal nerve (spinal cord segment) is known as **dermatome**. A part of the skeletal muscle that is innervated by a single spinal nerve (spinal cord segment) is known as **myotome**.

Cervical Plexus

The cervical plexus is composed of a number of nerve loops formed by the anterior rami of the spinal nerves C1-C4 (Figure 3.21). The branches of this plexus are summarized in Table 3.3.

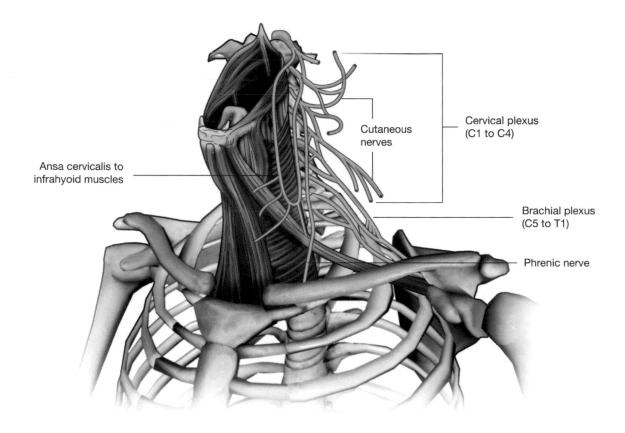

Cutaneous
nerves

Cervical plexus
(C1 to C4)

Ansa cervicalis to
infrahyoid muscles

Brachial plexus
(C5 to T1)

Phrenic nerve

FIGURE 3.21

Cervical Plexus

TABLE 3.3: *Branches of the Cervical Plexus and Their Distribution*

BRANCHES	DISTRIBUTION
1. Cutaneous	Parts of the scalp, auricle, anterior and lateral aspects of the neck
2. Motor	Ansa cervicalis: most of the infrahyoid muscles
	Phrenic nerve: diaphragm

Brachial Plexus

The brachial plexus is a major nerve network that supplies the upper limb (Figures 3.21 and 3.22). It is formed by the union of the anterior rami of the spinal nerves C5–T1, which are considered as the roots of the plexus. These roots join to form three trunks (superior, middle, inferior). Each trunk divides into an anterior and a posterior division. These divisions unite to form three cords (lateral, medial, and posterior) of the brachial plexus. The roots and trunks of the brachial plexus are located in neck region whereas the divisions and cords are mainly contained within the axilla. The main branches of the brachial plexus are summarized in Table 3.4.

Lumbar Plexus

The lumbar plexus is formed by the anterior rami of the spinal nerves L1-L4 deep to psoas major muscle in the abdominal cavity (Figure 3.23). The branches of this plexus contribute in innervations of the muscles and skin of the lower limb. The main branches of the lumbar plexus are summarized in Table 3.5.

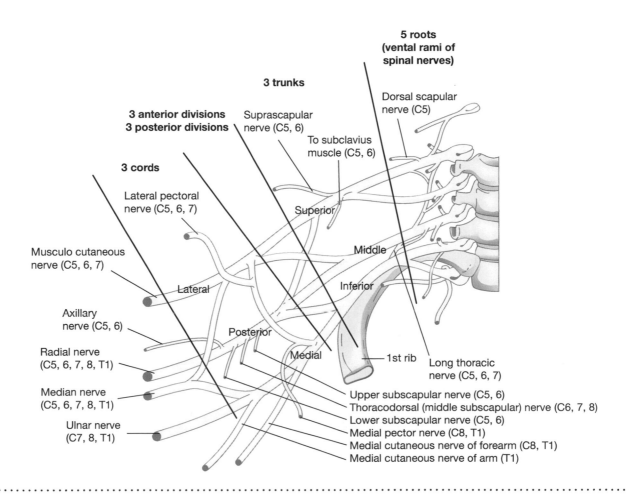

FIGURE 3.22
Brachial Plexus

TABLE 3.4: *The Main Branches (Nerves) of the Brachial Plexus and Their Distribution*

NERVE	ORIGIN	COURSE	DISTRIBUTION
Long thoracic	Roots (C5–C7)	Runs on the lateral aspect of the thoracic wall	Serratus anterior muscle
Dorsal scapular	Root C5	Descends on the medial border of the scapula	Rhomboids and levator scapula muscles
Suprascapular	Superior trunk	Enters supraspinous fossa and passes to infraspinous fossa	Supraspinatous and infraspinatous muscles
Lateral pectoral	Lateral cord	Pierces pectoralis minor muscle and enters pectoralis major muscle	Pectoralis major and minor muscles
Musculocutaneous	Lateral cord	Penetrates coracobrachialis muscle and descends in anterior arm	Muscles of the anterior compartment of the arm, and the skin of the lateral aspect of the forearm
Median	Medial and lateral cords	Passes the anterior arm, cubital fossa, anterior forearm, and through the carpal tunnel to enter hand	Most of the muscles of the anterior compartment of the forearm, thenar muscles, and the first and second lumbricals The skin of the lateral two-thirds of the palm of the hand and most of the lateral three and a half fingers.
Medial pectoral	Medial cord	Pierces pectoralis minor muscle and enters pectoralis major muscle	Pectoralis major and minor muscles
Medial cutaneous nerve of arm	Medial cord	Runs along medial side of arm	Most of the skin of medial side of arm
Medial cutaneous nerve of forearm	Medial cord	Descends on medial side of forearm	Skin of medial side of forearm
Ulnar	Medial cord	Travels on medial side of arm, passes behind the medial epicondyle, descends on medial side of forearm, passes in front of carpal tunnel and enters hand	Some of the muscles in anterior forearm, hypothenar and interosseous muscles, third, and fourth lumbricals. The skin of the medial one third of the palmar and dorsal aspects of the hand, medial one and a half fingers.

Upper subscapular		Run on the posterior wall of axilla	Subscapularis muscle
Lower subscapular			Subscapularis and teres major muscles
Thoracodorsal			Latissimus dorsi muscle
Axillary	Posterior cord	Winds around the surgical neck of the humerus	Deltoid and teres minor muscles.
			Lower part of the skin covering the deltoid muscle
Radial		Travels through the radial groove, enters the cubital fossa, divides into a deep (motor) and a superficial (cutaneous) branch	Muscles of the posterior compartments of arm and forearm.
			Skin of posterior arm and forearm, plus lateral two-thirds of the posterior aspect of the hand

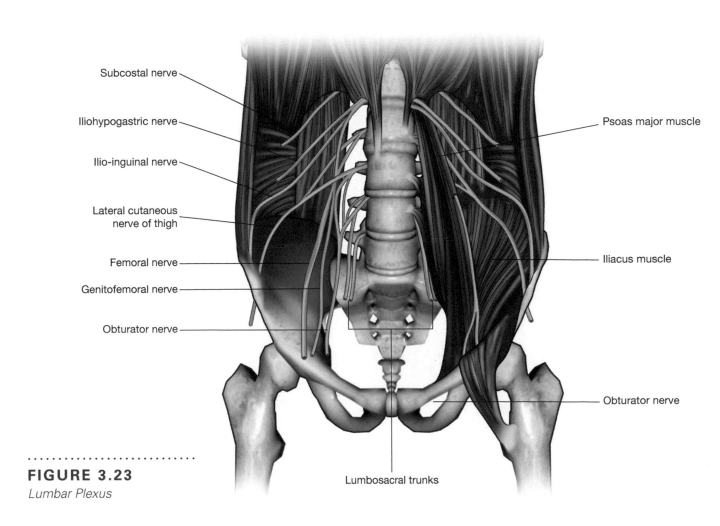

FIGURE 3.23
Lumbar Plexus

Subcostal nerve

Iliohypogastric nerve

Ilio-inguinal nerve

Lateral cutaneous nerve of thigh

Femoral nerve

Genitofemoral nerve

Obturator nerve

Psoas major muscle

Iliacus muscle

Obturator nerve

Lumbosacral trunks

TABLE 3.5: *The Main Branches (Nerves) of the Lumbar Plexus and Their Distribution*

NERVE	COURSE	DISTRIBUTION
Iliohypogastric & Ilioinguinal	Follows the abdominal wall from posterior to anterior	Small contribution in innervations of anterolateral abdominal muscles Skin of the pubic and inguinal regions
Genitofemoral	Descends anterior to psoas major muscle	Cremaster muscle Skin of the upper anterior thigh
Lateral cutaneous nerve of thigh	Passes medial to the anterior superior iliac spine to enter the lateral thigh	Skin of the lateral thigh
Obturator	Descends medial to the psoas major muscle	Muscles of the medial compartment of the thigh and skin of the medial side of the thigh
Femoral	Descends lateral to the psoas major muscle and deep to the inguinal ligament to enter the thigh	Muscles of the anterior compartment of the thigh and iliacus muscle. Skin of the anterior and medial thigh, medial leg, and foot

Sacral Plexus

The sacral plexus is formed by the union of the anterior rami of the spinal nerves L4-S4 in front of the posterior pelvic wall (Figure 3.24). Part of anterior ramus of spinal nerve L4 and the entire of anterior ramus of spinal nerve L5 unite to form the **lumbosacral trunk** that contributes in sacral plexus. The branches of this plexus supply majority of the lower limb muscles and skin. The main branches of the sacral plexus are summarized in Table 3.6.

Coccygeal Plexus

The coccygeal plexus is formed by the ventral rami of spinal nerves S5 and Co and minor contribution from S4 (Figure 3.24). This plexus is located above the pelvic floor and supplies part of the pelvic floor musculature and skin between the tip of the coccyx and anus.

Autonomic Nervous System

The autonomic nervous system is responsible for involuntary functions in human body. This system consists of **sympathetic** and **parasympathetic** components, both of which carry afferent and efferent fibers.

The sympathetic component prepares the person for emergencies (fight or flight), thus it increases the heart beat and respiratory rate, constricts the peripheral blood vessels, and increases the blood pressure. It also changes the distribu-

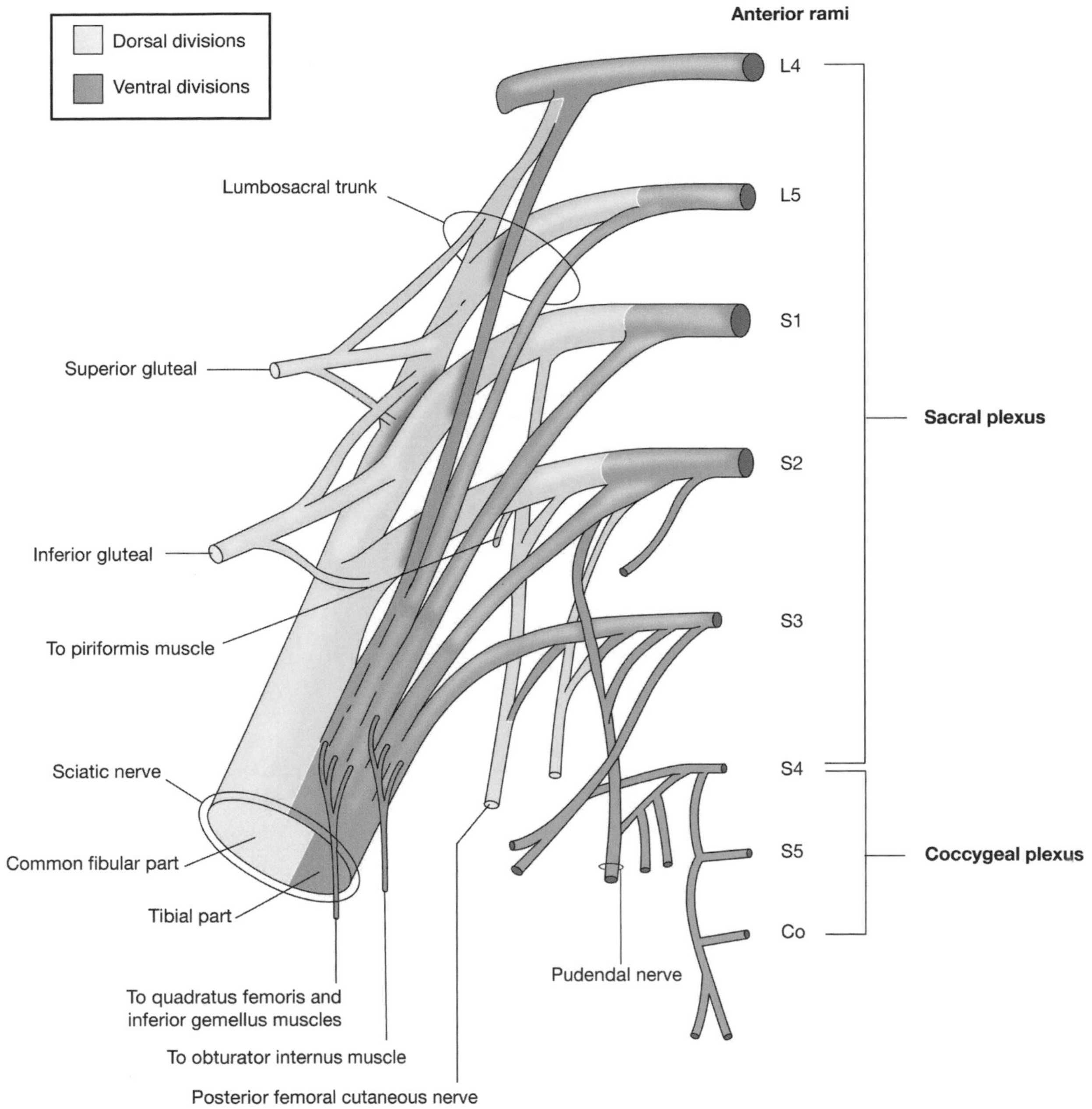

FIGURE 3.24

Sacral and Coccygeal Plexuses

tion pattern of the blood in body, for example, the blood will be rerouted from skin and intestines to skeletal muscles. The sympathetic system suppresses the peristaltic movements of the gastrointestinal tract and constricts its sphincters.

The parasympathetic component stores the energy. This system usually is activated after meal and reduces the heart beat, increases the peristaltic movements of the gastrointestinal tract and endocrine glands secretions, dilates the sphincters of the gastrointestinal tract and urinary system, and also causes sleepiness.

TABLE 3.6: *The Main Branches (Nerves) of the Sacral Plexus and Their Distribution*

NERVE	COURSE			DISTRIBUTION
Superior gluteal	Leaves the pelvis through the greater sciatic foramen to enter the gluteal region			Gluteus medius, minimus, and tensor fascia lata muscles
Inferior gluteal				Gluteus maximus muscle
Nerves to deep gluteal muscles				Deep gluteal muscles
Posterior cutaneous nerve of thigh				Skin of the posterior thigh and part of the posterior leg
Pudendal	Leaves the pelvis through the greater sciatic foramen to enter the gluteal region, then passes to perineum through the lesser sciatic foramen			Muscles of the perineum Skin of the perineum
Sciatic	Leaves the pelvis through the greater sciatic foramen to enter the gluteal region, descends in the posterior thigh, and splits above the popliteal fossa into tibial and common fibular nerves	**Tibial nerve**: descends through the popliteal fossa, posterior leg, behind the medial malleolus, and enters the sole of foot and divides into **medial and lateral plantar nerves**		Hamstring muscles (except the short head of biceps femoris), muscles of the posterior compartment of the leg. Muscles of the sole of the foot are supplied by the medial and lateral plantar nerves. Most of the skin of the posterior leg and lateral border of foot
		Common fibular nerve: descends through the popliteal fossa, winds around the neck of fibula and divides into **deep and superficial fibular nerves.**	**Deep fibular nerve**: descends in anterior leg and enters the dorsum of the foot	Muscles of the anterior compartment of the leg and dorsum of the foot
			Superficial fibular nerve: descends in the lateral leg and superficially enters the dorsum of the foot	Muscles of the lateral compartment of the leg Most of the skin of the dorsum of the foot

Sympathetic Nervous System

The sympathetic part of the autonomic nervous system is composed of centers, ganglia, and afferent and efferent fibers. These fibers connect the centers and ganglia to the target organs (smooth muscles and glands). The preganglionic motor neurons of this system reside in the lateral horn of the spinal cord at the level of T1–L2 (Figure 3.25). The axons of these neurons form the efferent (motor) fibers that travel along with the anterior root of the corresponding spinal nerves. After emerging through the intervertebral foramen these fibers leave the spinal nerve as **white ramus communicans** and enter the sympathetic trunk. The preganglionic fibers may take one of the following four routes (Figure 3.26):

1. They may synapse with the postgaglionic neurons in the sympathetic trunk ganglia at the same level. The axons of the postganglionic neurons form the postganglionic fibers and return to the corresponding spinal nerve as **gray ramus communicans** or directly target the thoracic viscera.

2. They may ascend to higher levels or descend to lower levels along with the sympathetic trunk and synapse with the postganglionic neurons at that level. The postganglionic fibers then enter the spinal nerve as gray ramus communicans at the same level.

3. They may synapse with the postganglionic neurons at the same level and then the postganglionic fibers ascend to higher level or descend to lower level along with the sympathetic trunk to enter the spinal nerves at the corresponding level.

4. Some of these fibers may pass through the sympathetic trunk ganglia without synapsing to form **splanchnic nerves** (**greater, lesser, least, lumbar,** and **sacral**). The splanchnic nerves enter the abdomen and pelvic regions and synapse with the postganglionic neurons in **prevertebral ganglia**. The postganglionic fibers then target the abdominal or pelvic viscera.

The **sympathetic trunk** is formed by ascending and descending fibers and the associated ganglia (**paravertebral ganglia**).

The afferent sympathetic fibers accompany the efferent sympathetic fibers (Figure 3.26). These sensory fibers start from the receptors within the wall of the viscera. The cell bodies of these fibers reside in the dorsal root ganglia of the spinal nerves T1-L2 and their axons enter the dorsal horn of the spinal cord.

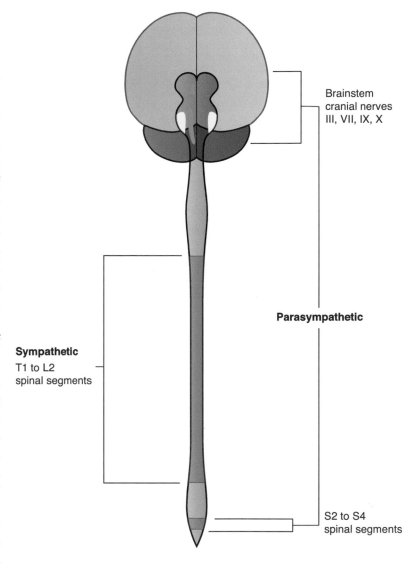

Brainstem cranial nerves III, VII, IX, X

Parasympathetic

Sympathetic
T1 to L2
spinal segments

S2 to S4
spinal segments

FIGURE 3.25

Autonomic Nervous System

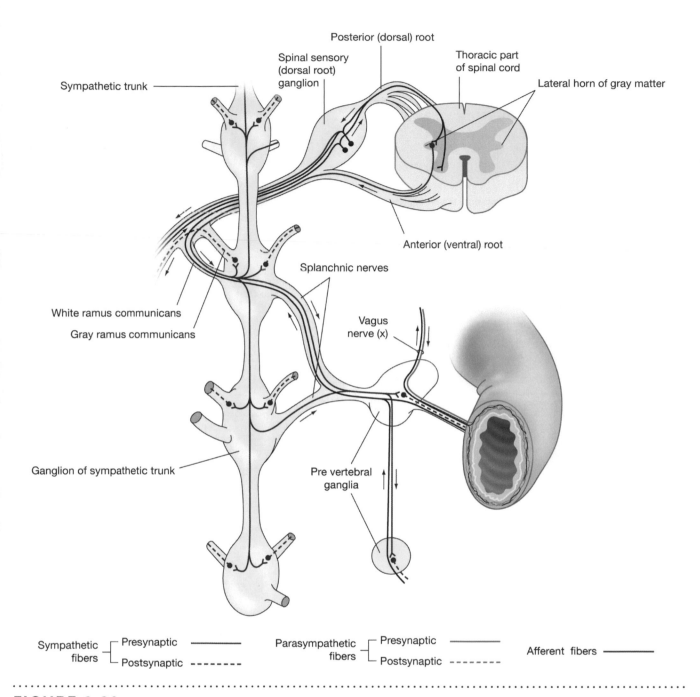

FIGURE 3.26
Sympathetic Nervous System Distribution

· · · · **The Parasympathetic Nervous System**

This part of the autonomic nervous system is also composed of centers, ganglia, and afferent and efferent fibers. The preganglionic motor neurons of this system reside in either the parasympathetic nuclei of the cranial nerves III, VII, IX, and X in the brain stem or in the lateral horn of the spinal cord segments S2–S4 (Figure 3.25).

The postganglionic parasympathetic neurons in the head are located in the ciliary, pterygopalatine, otic, and submandibular ganglia, but in other regions they are found in the ganglia within the wall of the target organs.

The parasympathetic component of cranial nerves functions as follows (Figure 3.27):

a. In CN III constricts the sphincter pupil.
b. In CN VII controls the secretion of the lacrimal, submandibular, and sublingual glands.
c. In CN IX regulates the secretion of the parotid gland.
d. In CN X supplies the thoracic and part of the abdominal viscera.

The preganglionic parasympathetic fibers that arise from the spinal segments S2–S4 (**pelvic splanchnic nerves**) enter the pelvis via sacral nerves and innervate the distal part of the gastrointestinal tract and pelvic viscera.

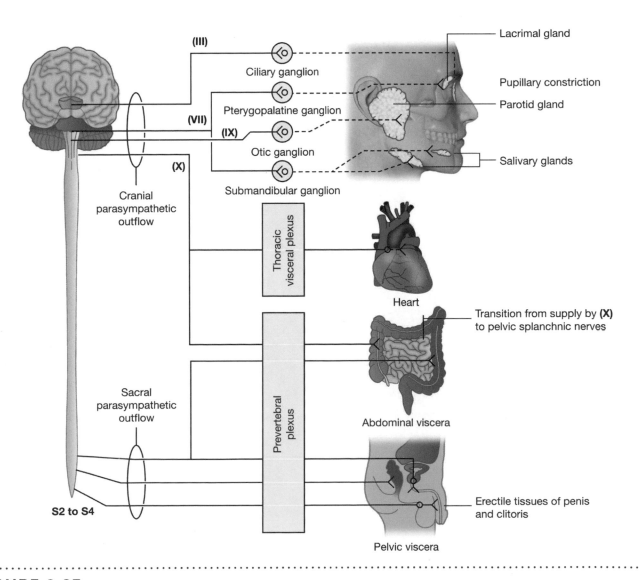

FIGURE 3.27

Parasympathetic Nervous System Distribution

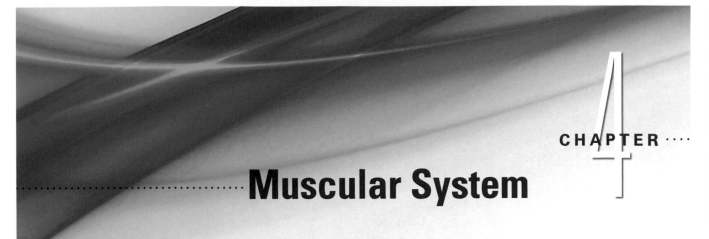

CHAPTER 4

Muscular System

LEARNING OBJECTIVES
Upon completion of this chapter you should be able to:

1. Explain the different types of muscular tissue and nomenclature of the skeletal muscles.
2. Categorize the muscles of head and neck and explain their characteristics.
3. Classify the muscles of the trunk and describe their features.
4. Identify the major muscular groups of the upper limb and define their characteristics.
5. Discuss the major muscular groups of the lower limb and explain their characteristics.
6. Name the transitional areas of the upper and lower limbs and discus their boundaries and contents.

···· Types of Muscle Tissue

There are three different types of muscle tissue in human body.

1. **Smooth muscle tissue** contributes to the wall of the blood vessels and hollow viscera (i.e., stomach, urinary bladder) and causes relatively regular but involuntary movements in these viscera.
2. **Cardiac muscle tissue** is exclusively found in heart and causes the rhythmic involuntary contraction of the heart.
3. **Skeletal muscle tissue** is required for locomotion. Skeletal muscles typically attach to the bones and their contraction causes movements of the bones at the level of the joints. The function of these muscles is regulated by the somatic nervous system. Skeletal muscles possess four major characteristics:

    a. **Origin:** the attachment of the muscle that usually remains stationary during muscle contraction.
    b. **Insertion:** the attachment of the muscle that usually moves during muscle contraction.
    c. **Function (Action):** this is the movement caused by the muscle contraction. When a muscle contracts it generally moves the insertion towards the origin.
    d. **Innervation:** skeletal muscle contraction is governed by the peripheral component of the somatic nervous system.

· · · · Skeletal Muscles Nomenclature

The skeletal muscles are mostly named based on the following criteria:

1. **Shape:** some muscles are named after their shape, for example, deltoid muscle (triangular shape) or rhomboid muscle (diamond shape).
2. **Location:** some muscles are named based on their location in the body, for example, pectoral muscles (in the pectoral region) and intercostals (between the ribs).
3. **Attachment site:** some muscles are named based on their attachment sites, for example, the sternocleidomastoid muscle (attaches to the sternum, clavicle, and mastoid process of the temporal bone).
4. **Number of the heads:** a few muscles have more than one head (origin), for example, biceps (two heads) and triceps (three heads).
5. **Function:** some muscle groups are named based on their function, for example, flexor muscles and extensor muscles.
6. **Direction of the fibers:** in some cases the direction of the muscle fibers is the determinant factor for naming a muscle such as rectus abdominis and transversus abdominis.
7. **Size:** some muscles are named based on their size, for example, vastus lateralis and latissimus dorsi.

It is worth mentioning that in some cases two or more of the above mentioned criteria are used to name a muscle, for example, gluteus maximus.

· · · · Head and Neck Muscles

Head and neck muscles are categorized in several groups based on their location and/or function:

1. **Muscles of Facial Expression**
   The majority of these muscles originate from the skull bones and insert to the skin of the face thus their contraction causes different expressions on the face (Figure 4.1). They are innervated by CN VII (facial nerve) and are classified in three groups based on their location.

   a. **The muscles around the orbital cavity:** the main muscle in this group, **orbicularis oculi**, completely surrounds the orbit and closes the eyelids.

   b. **The muscles around the nasal cavity:** a major muscle in this group is the **nasalis muscle** that bridges over the nose and flares the nostrils.

   c. **The muscles around the oral cavity:** the most important muscle in this group, **orbicularis oris**, completely surrounds the oral fissure and closes and purses the lips.

2. **Muscles of Mastication**
   There are four muscles of mastication on each side that move the mandible as in chewing. They are innervated by the mandibular branch (division) of the trigeminal nerve (CN V).

   a. **Masseter muscle:** it originates from the zygomatic arch and inserts to the mandible (Figure 4.2). It elevates the mandible and clenches the teeth.

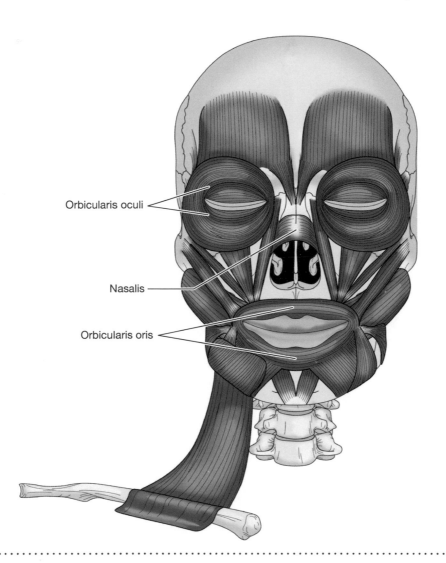

FIGURE 4.1
Muscles of Facial Expression

b. **Temporalis muscle:** it originates from the temporal fossa of the skull and inserts to the coronoid process of the mandible. This muscle elevates the mandible (Figure 4.2).

c. **Medial pterygoid muscle:** it mainly originates from the sphenoid bone and inserts to the mandible (Figure 4.3). It elevates the mandible and moves it side to side.

d. **Lateral pterygoid muscle:** it originates from the sphenoid bone and inserts to the condyle of the mandible and the articular disc of temporomandibular joint (Figure 4.3). It protrudes the mandible and moves it side to side.

3. **Extraocular Muscles**
   The extraocular muscles are seven in number that either move the eyeball in different directions or elevate the upper eyelid (Figure 4.4). They are innervated by cranial nerves III, IV, and VI.

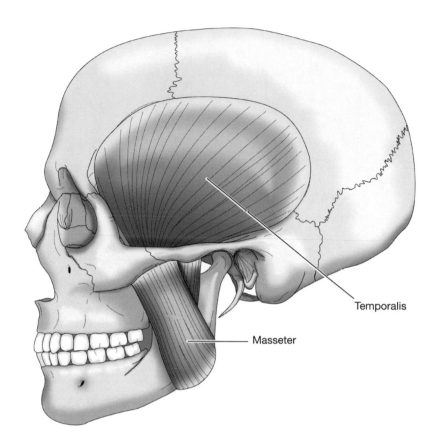

FIGURE 4.2
*Temporalis and Masseter
Muscles*

Temporalis

Masseter

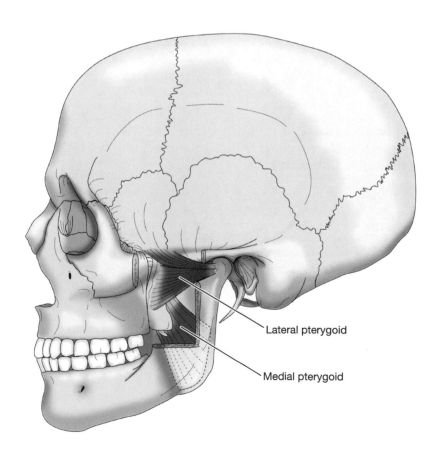

FIGURE 4.3
*Medial and Lateral
Pterygoid Muscles*

Lateral pterygoid

Medial pterygoid

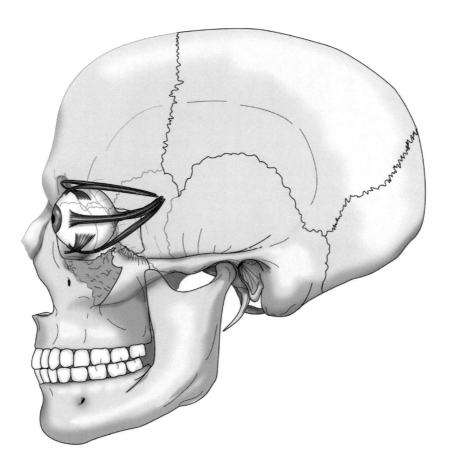

FIGURE 4.4
*Extraocular Muscles
(lateral view)*

4. **Pharyngeal Muscles**
   The pharyngeal muscles are grouped as inner longitudinal and outer circu-lar muscles. The longitudinal muscles shorten the pharynx and elevate the larynx (Figure 4.5A). The circular muscles constrict the pharynx, thus known as **pharyngeal constrictor** muscles. All pharyngeal muscles are innervated by CN X (except stylopharyngeus).

5. **Muscles of the Soft Palate**
   The muscles of the soft palate mainly arise from the cranial base and insert to the soft palate (Figure 4.5B). These muscles may elevate or depress the soft palate or stretch it to the sides. All muscles of the soft palate are inner-vated by CN X (except tensor veli palatini).

6. **Muscles of the Tongue**
   The muscles of tongue are classified as intrinsic and extrinsic muscles. The intrinsic muscles have both their attachments (origin and insertion) inside the tongue, whereas the extrinsic muscles mostly originate from the bones outside the tongue and insert into the tongue (Figure 4.6). All the tongue muscles are innervated by CN XII (except palatoglossus).

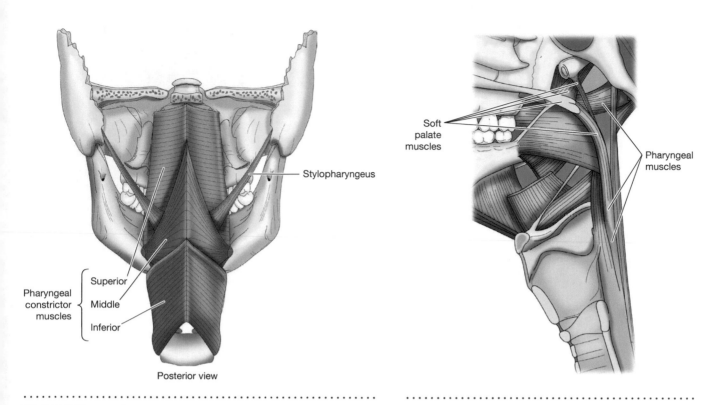

Stylopharyngeus

Pharyngeal
constrictor
muscles
- Superior
- Middle
- Inferior

Posterior view

Soft
palate
muscles

Pharyngeal
muscles

FIGURE 4.5A
Pharyngeal Muscles

FIGURE 4.5B
Muscles of Soft Palate (sagittal section)

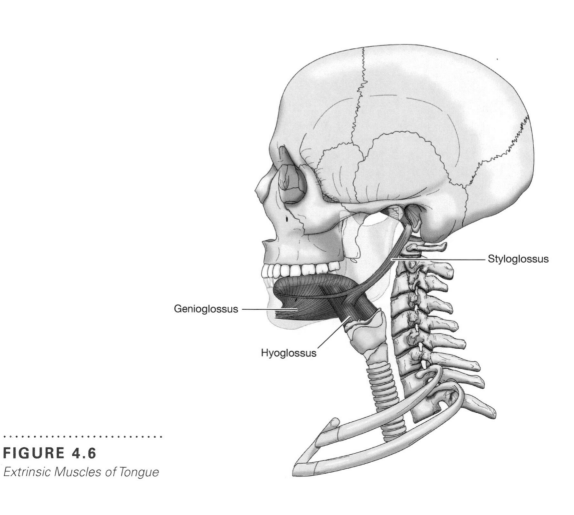

Styloglossus

Genioglossus

Hyoglossus

FIGURE 4.6
Extrinsic Muscles of Tongue

7. Muscles of the Larynx

The muscles of larynx are divided to intrinsic and extrinsic groups. The intrinsic muscles are stretched between the laryngeal cartilages and change the length or tension of the vocal cords during phonation and respiration (Figure 4.7). All the intrinsic laryngeal muscles are innervated by CN X.

The suprahyoid and infrahyoid muscles of the neck can elevate or depress the larynx respectively thus considered as the extrinsic muscles of the larynx. The innervation of the extrinsic muscles of the larynx will be discussed with the muscles of the neck.

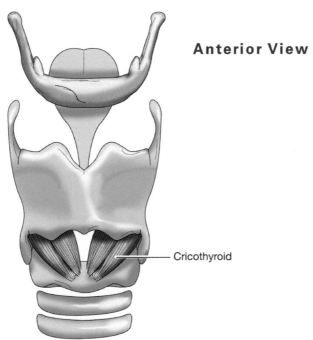

Anterior View

Cricothyroid

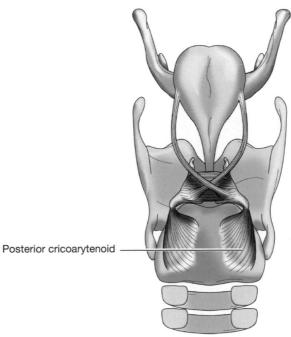

Posterior View

Posterior cricoarytenoid

FIGURE 4.7

Intrinsic Muscles of Larynx

8. **Muscles of the Neck**

The muscles of the neck are categorized in the superficial and deep muscles. The major superficial muscles of the neck include:

a. **Sternocleidomastoid (SCM):** this muscle originates from the sternum and clavicle and inserts to the mastoid process of the temporal bone (Figure 4.8). The sternocleidomastoid muscle extends and laterally flexes the neck and contralaterally rotates the head and is innervated by CN XI.

b. **Infrahyoid muscles:** these muscles mainly originate from sternum and inserts to thyroid cartilage or hyoid bone (Figure 4.9). They depress hyoid bone and larynx. These muscles are predominately innervated by ansa cervicalis.

c. **Suprahyoid muscles:** these muscles originate either from temporal bone or mandible and insert to the hyoid bone (Figures 4.8 and 4.9). They either elevate the hyoid bone and larynx or depress the mandible. These muscles are mainly innervated by CN V and CN VII.

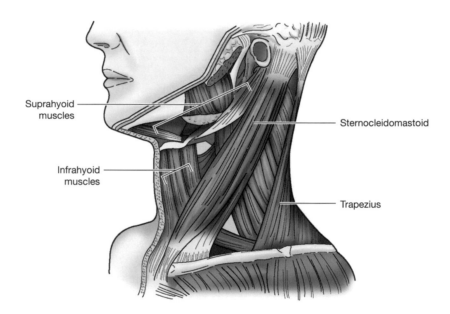

FIGURE 4.8

Muscles of the Neck (superficial group, lateral view)

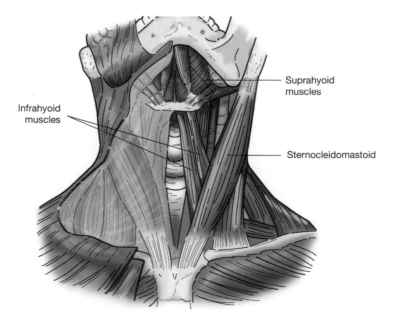

FIGURE 4.9

Muscles of the Neck (superficial group, anterior view)

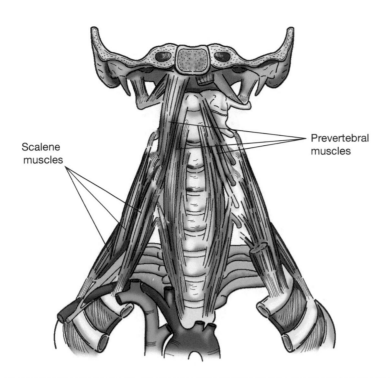

FIGURE 4.10
Muscles of the Neck (deep group, anterior view)

The major deep muscles of the neck include:

a. **Scalene muscles:** these muscles originate from the transverse processes of the cervical vertebrae and insert to the first or second ribs (Figure 4.10). They either elevate the first two ribs or laterally flex the neck. These muscles are innervated by some of the anterior rami of cervical spinal nerves.

b. **Prevertebral muscles:** these muscles originate from upper thoracic or cervical vertebrae and insert to upper cervical vertebrae or occipital bone (Figure 4.10). The prevertebral muscles mainly flex the head and neck and are innervated by some of the anterior rami of the cervical spinal nerves.

· · · · Trunk Muscles

The trunk muscles include the back, thoracic, abdominal, and pelvic muscles.

Muscles of Back

The back muscles are classified in superficial, intermediate, and deep layers.

Superficial Back Muscles include trapezius, latissimus dorsi, levator scapulae, and rhomboids. These muscles connect the upper limbs to the trunk and mostly act on the upper limb (Figure 4.11). See Table 4. 1.

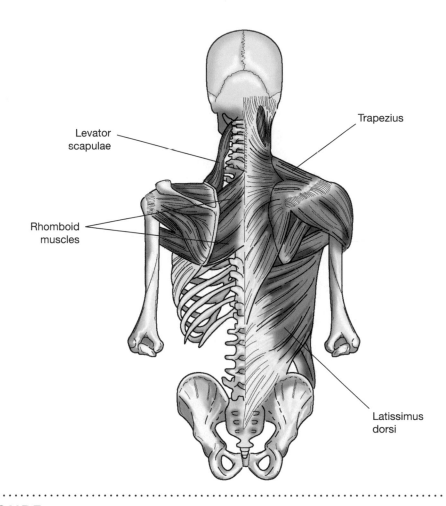

FIGURE 4.11
Muscles of the Back (superficial layer)

TABLE 4.1: *The Superficial Layer of Back Muscles*

MUSCLE	ORIGIN	INSERTION	MAIN ACTION(S)	INNERVATION
Trapezius	Occipital bone, cervical and thoracic vertebrae	Clavicle, acromion, and spine of scapula	Elevation, depression, and retraction (adduction) of the scapula	CN XI
Latissimus dorsi	Lower thoracic and lumbar vertebrae and iliac crest	Intertubercular groove of humerus	Extension, adduction, and medial rotation of shoulder joint	Thoracodorsal nerve
Levator scapulae	Upper cervical vertebrae	Superior angle of scapula	Elevation of scapula	Dorsal scapular nerve
Rhomboids	Upper thoracic vertebrae	Medial border of scapula	Elevation and retraction (adduction) of scapula	

Intermediate Back Muscles include the serratus posterior superior and serratus posterior inferior (Figure 4.12). They are considered as accessory respiratory muscles. See Table 4.2.

Deep Back Muscles are in turn divided to erector spinae and transversospinalis muscles (Figures 4.13 and 4.14). These muscles maintain the erect position of the trunk and extend or rotate the vertebral column (Table 4.3).

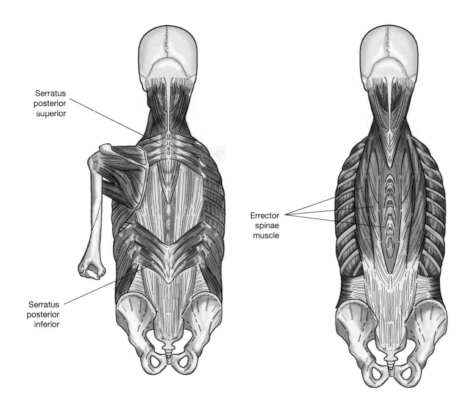

FIGURE 4.12
*Muscles of the Back
(intermediate layer)*

FIGURE 4.13
*Muscles of the Back
(deep layer)*

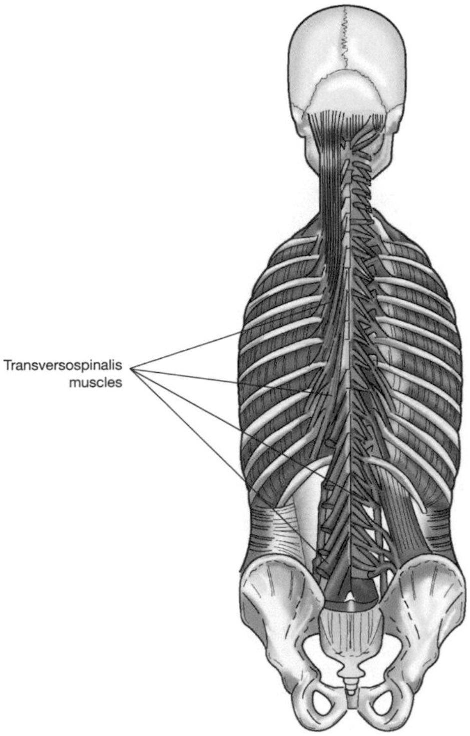

FIGURE 4.14
*Muscles of the Back
(deep layer)*

TABLE 4.2: *The Intermediate Layer of Back Muscles*

MUSCLE	ORIGIN	INSERTION	MAIN ACTION (S)	INNERVATION
Serratus posterior superior	Vertebrae CVII to TIII	Ribs II to V	Elevation of ribs II to V	Second to fifth intercostal nerves
Serratus posterior inferior	Vertebrae TXI to LII	Ribs IX to XII	Depression of ribs IX to XII	Ninth to eleventh intercostal nerves and subcostal nerve

TABLE 4.3: *The Deep Layer of Back Muscles*

MUSCLE	ORIGIN	INSERTION	MAIN ACTION(S)	INNERVATION
Erector spinae	Posterior surface of the sacrum, iliac crest, lumbar vertebrae	Ribs, thoracic and cervical vertebrae, and skull	Extension and lateral flexion of the vertebral column and head	Posterior rami of the corresponding spinal nerves
Transversospinalis	Mainly the transverse processes of the vertebrae	Mainly the spinous processes of the vertebrae	Extension and rotation of the vertebral column	Posterior rami of the corresponding spinal nerves

Muscles of Thorax

The muscles of thorax are grouped as extrinsic and intrinsic muscles. The extrinsic muscles originate from thorax and insert to upper limb. The major muscles in this group include the pectoralis major, pectoralis minor, and serratus anterior muscles (Figures 4.15 and 4.16). See Table 4.4.

The origin and insertion of the intrinsic muscles are mainly in thorax. The major muscles in this group include intercostal muscles (Figure 4.17) and the diaphragm (Figure 4.18). See Table 4.5.

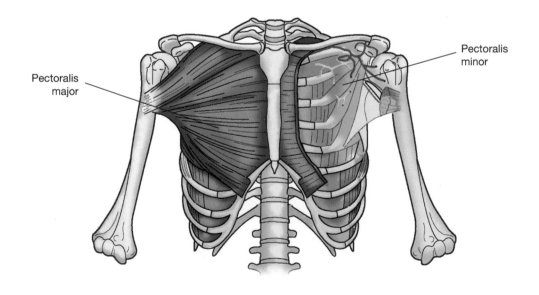

Pectoralis major

Pectoralis minor

FIGURE 4.15

Muscles of Thorax (extrinsic, anterior view)

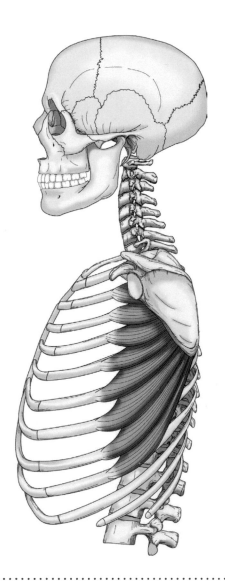

FIGURE 4.16
Serratus Anterior Muscle

TABLE 4.4: *Extrinsic Muscles of Thorax*

MUSCLE	ORIGIN	INSERTION	MAIN ACTION(S)	INNERVATION
Pectoralis major	Clavicle and sternum	Intertubercular groove of humerus	Adduction and medial rotation of shoulder joint	Medial and lateral pectoral nerves
Pectoralis minor	Ribs II to V	Coracoid process of scapula	Protraction (abduction) of scapula	Medial and lateral pectoral nerves
Serratus anterior	Ribs I to IX	Medial border of scapula	Protraction (abduction) of scapula	Long thoracic nerve

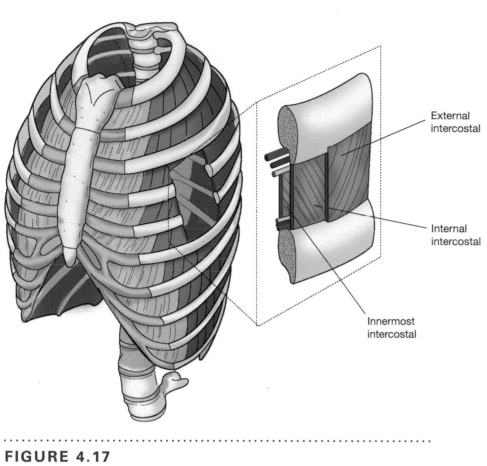

FIGURE 4.17
Thoracic Muscles (intrinsic group)

External intercostal

Internal intercostal

Innermost intercostal

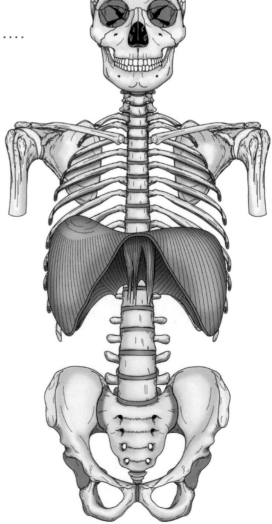

FIGURE 4.18
Diaphragm

TABLE 4.5: *Intrinsic Muscles of Thorax*

MUSCLE	ORIGIN	INSERTION	MAIN ACTION(S)	INNERVATION
External intercostal	Inferior border of the rib above	Superior border of the rib below	Elevation of the rib below	Intercostal nerves
Internal intercostal*	Superior border of the rib below	Inferior border of the rib above	Depression of the rib above	
Innermost intercostal**	Internal surface of the rib below	Internal surface of the rib above		
Diaphragm***	Xiphoid process of sternum, lower six ribs, and the upper three lumbar vertebrae	Central tendon of diaphragm	Increases the volume of (expands) the thoracic cavity	Phrenic nerve

*: The intercostal muscles are mainly involved in respiration by increasing and decreasing the thoracic cage volume during the inhalation and exhalation.

**: The innermost intercostal muscles are found only at the middle half of the intercotal spaces.

***: There are three main openings in diaphragm for the passage of the aorta, esophagus, and inferior vena cava known as **aortic opening**, **esophageal hiatus**, and **inferior vena cava opening**, respectively.

Muscles of Abdomen

The muscles of abdomen are categorized in anterolateral (Figures 4.19 and 4.20) and posterior abdominal wall muscles (Figure 4.21). See Table 4.6.

Note

1. **Aponeurosis** is a sheet-like tendon that attaches some muscles to their insertion.
2. **Inguinal ligament** is the thick inferior free border of the aponeurosis of the external abdominal oblique muscle stretched between the anterior superior iliac spine and pubic bone.
3. **Rectus sheath** is a fibrous sheath formed by the aponeuroses of the external, internal, and transverse abdominal muscles and almost completely invests the rectus abdominis muscle (Figure 4.22).
4. **Linea alba** is a band of dense connective tissue that is formed by the union of the aponeuroses of the anterolateral abdominal muscles in the midline. It extends from xyphoid process to pubic symphysis (Figures 4.19 and 4.22).
5. **Inguinal canal** is a short oblique canal located parallel and a little above the medial half of the inguinal ligament (Figure 4.23). It is formed by and between the external, internal and transverse abdominal muscles. It has two openings known as **deep and superficial inguinal rings**. This canal mainly contains the spermatic cord in male and the round ligament of the uterus in female.

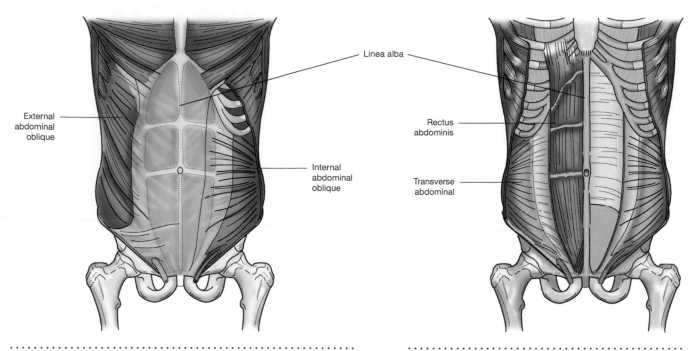

External
abdominal
oblique

Linea alba

Internal
abdominal
oblique

FIGURE 4.19
Muscles of Abdomen (superficial layer)

Linea alba

Rectus
abdominis

Transverse
abdominal

FIGURE 4.20
Muscles of Abdomen (deep layer)

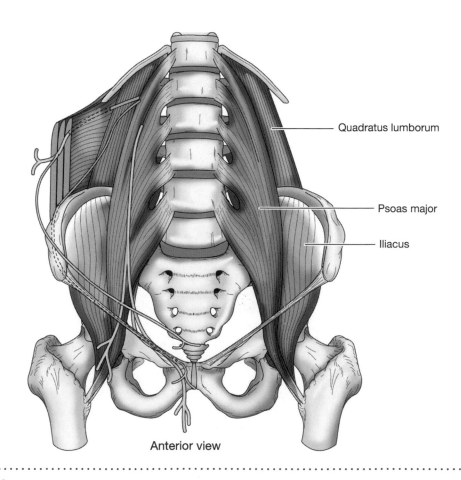

Quadratus lumborum

Psoas major

Iliacus

Anterior view

FIGURE 4.21
Posterior Abdominal Wall Muscles

TABLE 4.6: *Anterolateral Abdominal Wall Muscles*

MUSCLE	ORIGIN	INSERTION	MAIN ACTION(S)	INNERVATION
External abdominal oblique	Lower eight ribs	Iliac crest, pubic bone and linea alba	Compression of the abdominal viscera, flexion, and contralateral rotation of the trunk	Anterior rami T7 to T12
Internal abdominal oblique	Iliac crest and inguinal ligament	Lower four ribs and linea alba	Compression of the abdominal viscera, flexion and ipsilateral rotation of the trunk	Anterior rami T7 to L1
Transverse abdominal	Iliac crest, inguinal ligament, and lower six ribs	linea alba	Compression of the abdominal viscera	
Rectus abdominis	Pubic bone and pubic symphysis	Xiphoid process and costal cartilages V to VII	Compression of the abdominal viscera and flexion of the trunk	Anterior rami T7 to T12

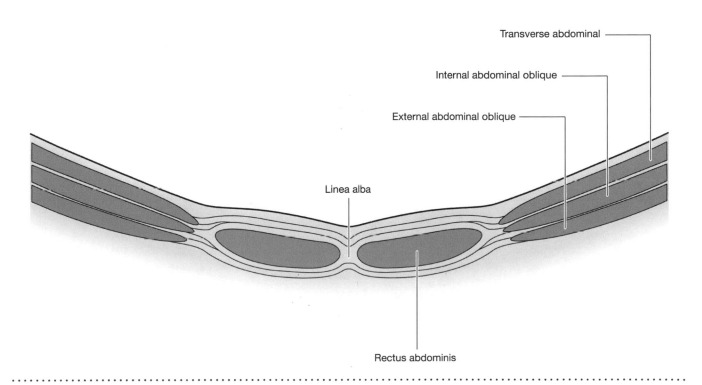

FIGURE 4.22

Rectus Sheath (transverse section of the anterior abdominal wall)

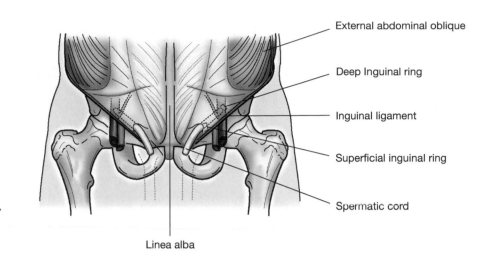

External abdominal oblique

Deep Inguinal ring

Inguinal ligament

Superficial inguinal ring

Spermatic cord

Linea alba

FIGURE 4.23
Inguinal Canal

TABLE 4.7: *The Main Muscles of Posterior Abdominal Wall*

MUSCLE	ORIGIN	INSERTION	MAIN ACTION(S)	INNERVATION
Psoas major*	Lumbar vertebrae and intervening discs	Lesser trochanter of femur	Flexion of hip joint	Anterior rami L1–L3
Iliacus*	Iliac fossa			Femoral nerve
Quadratus lumborum	Vertebra LV and iliac crest	Lumbar vertebrae and rib XII	Fixation of rib XII and lateral flexion of trunk	Anterior rami T12–L4

*: These two muscles join together before attaching to the lesser trochanter of the femur thus referring to as iliopsoas muscle.

Muscles of Pelvis

The muscles of pelvis can be classified as pelvic wall muscles, pelvic diaphragm, and perineal muscles.

The pelvic wall muscles include piriformis and obturator internus muscles. These muscles arise in the pelvic cavity an insert to the femur. They will be discussed with the gluteal muscles.

Pelvic diaphragm consists of **levator ani** and **coccygeus** muscles (Figure 4.24). These two muscles together form a muscular membrane located between the true pelvis and perineum. Levator ani arises from inner surface of the pelvic bone and its anterior fibers merge with the fibers of the opposite side levator ani, whereas the posterior fibers insert to the sacrum and coccyx. Coccygeus muscle originates from ischial spine and inserts to coccyx and sacrum. Pelvic diaphragm supports pelvic viscera and is innervated by branches from the sacral plexus.

Perineal muscles are contained within perineum.

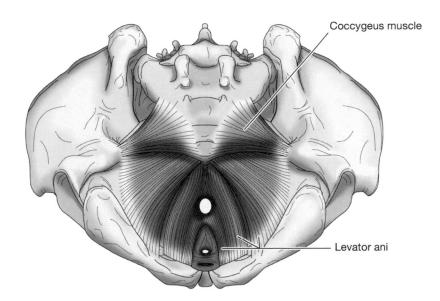

FIGURE 4.24
Pelvic Diaphragm
(inferior view)

The **perineum** is a diamond-shaped area located inferior to the pelvic diaphragm between the thighs and bounded by the inferior pelvic aperture (outlet). This area can be subdivided into an anterior **urogenital triangle** and a posterior **anal triangle**.

The urogenital triangle contains the distal part of urethra, external genitalia, and some of the perineal muscles. The main muscles in this area include **bulbospongiosus** and **ischiocavernosus** that partially cover the root of the external genitalia (Figures 4.25 and 4.26). These muscles assist either in erection (both genders) or draining the last drop of urine (male).

The anal triangle mainly contains the anal canal surrounded by **external anal sphincter**. The perineal muscles are innervated by the **pudendal nerve**.

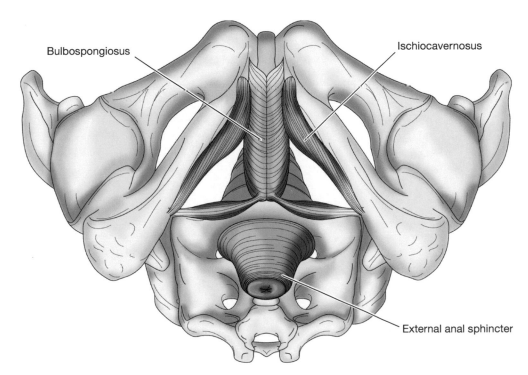

FIGURE 4.25
Male Perineal Muscles
(inferior view)

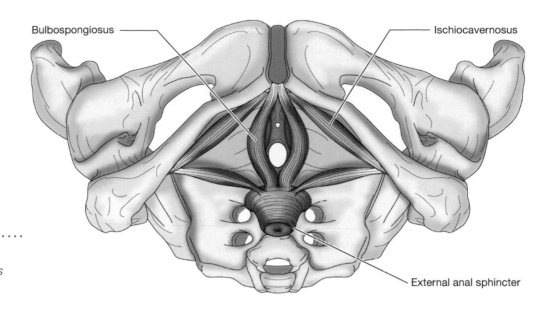

FIGURE 4.26
*Female Perineal Muscles
(inferior view)*

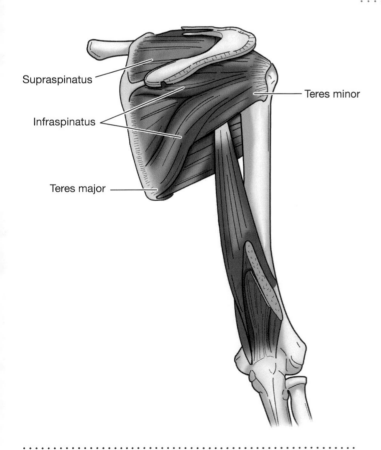

FIGURE 4.27
Muscles of Scapular Region

···· Upper Limb Muscles

The muscles of the upper limb can be classified to two main groups.

1. Muscles attaching the upper limb to the trunk. This group includes pectoralis major, pectoralis minor, serratus anterior, trapezius, latissimus dorsi, levator scapulae, rhomboid major, and rhomboid minor muscles. All these muscles have already been discussed with the trunk musculature.
2. Muscles of the different regions of the upper limb. This group includes the muscles of the scapular (Figures 4.27 and 4.28), deltoid (Figure 4.29), arm, forearm, and hand regions. See Table 4.8.

Note

With the exception of the teres major, the muscles mentioned in Table 4.8 collectively are referred to as **rotator cuff** muscles (Figures 4.27 and 4.28). The tendons of these muscles reinforce the shoulder joint capsule (except on the inferior aspect) and stabilize the joint. See Table 4.9.

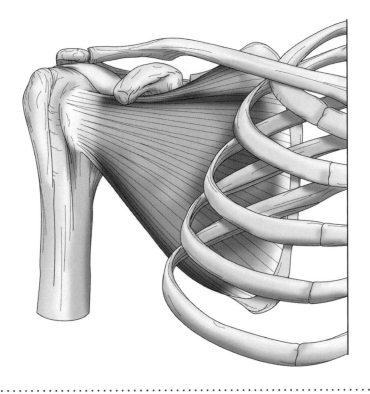

FIGURE 4.28
Subscapularis Muscle

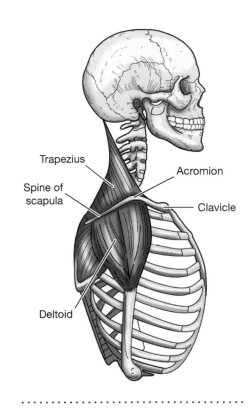

FIGURE 4.29
Deltoid Muscle

TABLE 4.8: *Muscles of Scapular Region*

MUSCLE	ORIGIN	INSERTION	MAIN ACTION(S)	NERVE
Subscapular	Subscapular fossa of scapula	Lesser tubercle of humerus	Medial rotation of shoulder joint	Upper and lower subscapular
Supraspinatus	Supraspinous fossa of scapula	Greater tubercle of humerus	Abduction of shoulder joint	Suprascapular
Infraspinatus	Infraspinous fossa of scapula		**Lateral rotation of shoulder joint**	
Teres minor	Upper lateral border of scapula			Axillary
Teres major	Lower lateral border of scapula	Intertubercular groove of humerus	Medial rotation of shoulder joint	Lower subscapular

TABLE 4.9: *Muscle of Deltoid Region*

MUSCLE	ORIGIN	INSERTION	MAIN ACTION(S)	NERVE
Deltoid	Spine of scapula, acromion, and clavicle	Deltoid tuberosity of humerus	Abduction of shoulder joint	Axillary

Muscles of the Arm

The muscles of arm are grouped in an anterior and a posterior compartment. These compartments are made by humerus and extensions of the deep fascia attaching to the humerus (Figure 4.30). The muscles of the anterior compartment include **biceps brachii, brachialis**, and **coracobrachialis** muscles (Figures 4.31 and 4.32). These muscles mainly flex the shoulder and / or elbow joints and are innervated by musculocutaneous nerve. See Table 4.10.

The posterior compartment only contains **triceps brachii** muscle (Figure 4.33) that extends shoulder and elbow joints and is innervated by radial nerve. See Table 4.11.

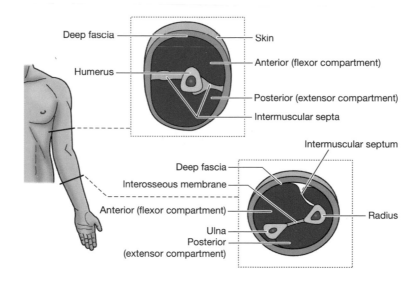

FIGURE 4.30
Arm and Forearm Compartments

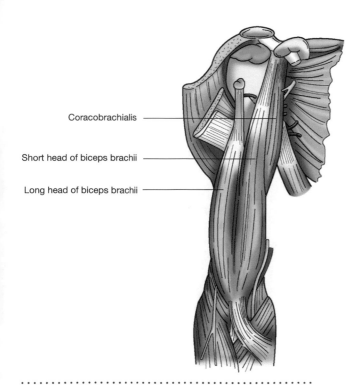

FIGURE 4.31
Muscles of Arm (anterior compartment)

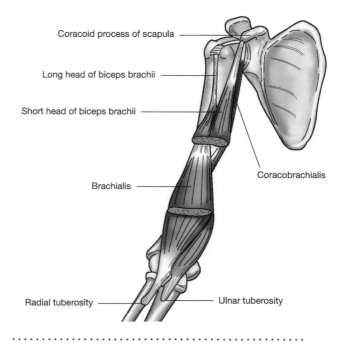

FIGURE 4.32
Muscles of Arm (anterior compartment)

TABLE 4.10: *Muscles of the Anterior Compartment of Arm*

MUSCLE	ORIGIN	INSERTION	MAIN ACTION(S)	NERVE
Biceps brachii	**Long head:** supraglenoid tubercle of scapula **Short head:** coracoid process of scapula	Radial tuberosity of radius	Flexion of elbow joint and supination of forearm	Musculocutaneous
Coracobrachialis	Coracoid process of scapula	Shaft of humerus	Flexion of shoulder joint	
Brachialis	Shaft of humerus	Ulnar tuberosity	Flexion of elbow joint	

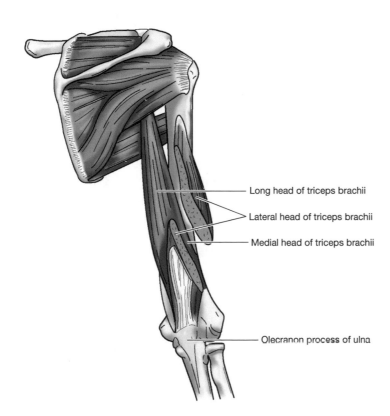

Long head of triceps brachii

Lateral head of triceps brachii

Medial head of triceps brachii

Olecranon process of ulna

FIGURE 4.33

Muscles of Arm (posterior compartment)

TABLE 4.11: *Muscle of the Posterior Compartment of Arm*

MUSCLE	ORIGIN	INSERTION	MAIN ACTION(S)	NERVE
Triceps brachii	**Long head:** infraglenoid tubercle **Lateral and medial heads:** Shaft of humerus	Olecranon process of ulna	Extension of elbow joint	Radial

Muscles of Forearm

The muscles of forearm are grouped into a flexor-pronator (anterior) and an extensor-supinator (posterior) compartment. These compartments are made by radius, ulna, interosseous membrane, and an extension of the deep fascia attaching to the radius (Figure 4.30).

The **muscles of the anterior compartment** (Figure 4.34) are subdivided into superficial (Table 4.12), intermediate (Table 4.13), and deep layers (Table 4.14).

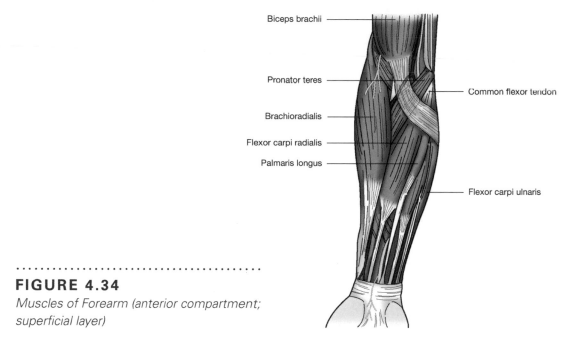

Biceps brachii

Pronator teres

Brachioradialis

Flexor carpi radialis

Palmaris longus

Common flexor tendon

Flexor carpi ulnaris

FIGURE 4.34

Muscles of Forearm (anterior compartment; superficial layer)

TABLE 4.12: *Muscles of the Superficial Layer of Anterior Compartment of Forearm*

MUSCLE	ORIGIN	INSERTION	MAIN ACTION(S)	NERVE
Pronator teres	Medial epicondyle of humerus and coronoid process of ulna	Shaft of radius	Pronation of forearm	Median
Flexor carpi radialis	Medial epicondyle of humerus	Second metacarpal	Flexion and abduction of wrist joint	
Plamaris longus	Medial epicondyle of humerus	Plamar aponeurosis*	Flexion of wrist joint	
Flexor carpi ulnaris	Medial epicondyle of humerus and olecranon process of ulna	Fifth metacarpal	Flexion and adduction of wrist joint	Ulnar

*: The thicker central part of the deep fascia of hand is known as palmar aponeurosis.

TABLE 4.13: *Muscle of the Intermediate Layer of Anterior Compartment of Forearm*

MUSCLE	ORIGIN	INSERTION	MAIN ACTION(S)	NERVE
☀Flexor digitorum superficialis	Medial epicondyle of humerus, coronoid process of ulna, and shaft of radius	Middle phalanges of fingers 2 to 5	Flexion of wrist, metacarpophalangeal and proximal interphalangeal joints	Median

TABLE 4.14: *Muscles of the Deep Layer of Anterior Compartment of Forearm*

MUSCLE	ORIGIN	INSERTION	MAIN ACTION(S)	NERVE
☀Flexor digitorum profundus	Shaft of ulna and interosseous membrane	Distal phalanges of fingers 2 to 5	Flexion of wrist, metacarpophalangeal, and proximal and distal interphalangeal joints	Median and ulnar
Flexor pollicis longus	Shaft of radius and interosseous membrane	Distal phalanx of thumb	Flexion of interphalangeal joint of thumb	Median
Pronator quadratus	Distal one fourth of shaft of ulna	Distal one fourth of shaft of radius	Pronation of forearm	

The majority of these muscles arise from medial epicondyle of humerus (via common flexor tendon), and insert to radius, metacarpals, and phalanges (Figures 4.35, 4.36, and 4.37). These muscles are involved in pronation of the forearm and flexion of the wrist and fingers. They are innervated by median and/or ulnar nerves.

The **muscles of the posterior compartment** of forearm are subdivided into superficial and deep layers (Figures 4.38 and 4.39). The majority of these muscles arise from lateral epicondyle of humerus (via common extensor tendon), and insert to radius, metacarpals, and phalanges via extensor hood. The extensor hood is an expansion of the extensor muscles tendon that covers the dorsal aspect of the proximal phalanges and inserts to the middle and distal phalanges. This hood is also known as **dorsal digital expansion** (Figure 4.40). See Table 4.15.

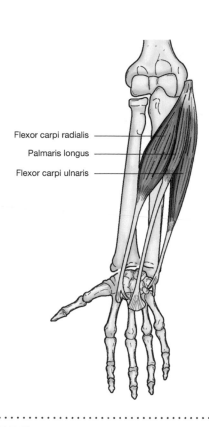

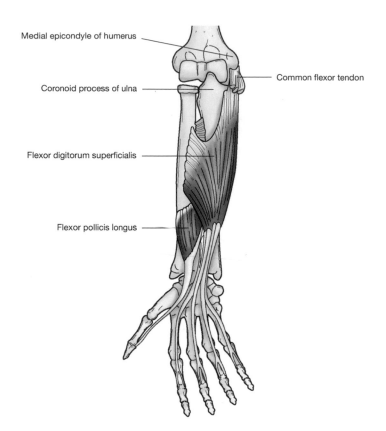

FIGURE 4.35

Muscles of Forearm (anterior compartment; superficial layer)

FIGURE 4.36

Muscles of Forearm (anterior compartment; intermediate and deep layers)

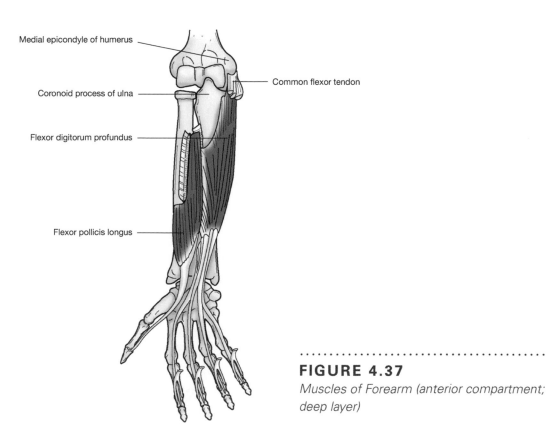

FIGURE 4.37

Muscles of Forearm (anterior compartment; deep layer)

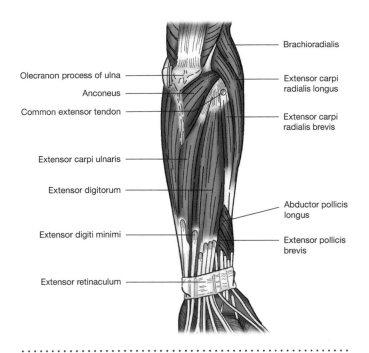

Brachioradialis

Olecranon process of ulna

Anconeus

Common extensor tendon

Extensor carpi radialis longus

Extensor carpi radialis brevis

Extensor carpi ulnaris

Extensor digitorum

Abductor pollicis longus

Extensor digiti minimi

Extensor pollicis brevis

Extensor retinaculum

FIGURE 4.38
Muscles of Forearm (posterior compartment; superficial layer)

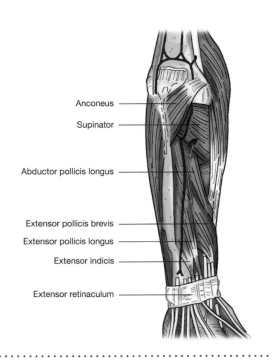

Anconeus

Supinator

Abductor pollicis longus

Extensor pollicis brevis

Extensor pollicis longus

Extensor indicis

Extensor retinaculum

FIGURE 4.39
Muscles of Forearm (posterior compartment; deep layer)

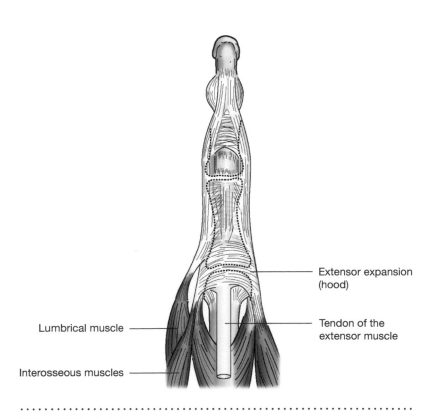

Extensor expansion (hood)

Tendon of the extensor muscle

Lumbrical muscle

Interosseous muscles

FIGURE 4.40
Dorsal Digital Expansion (extensor hood), right middle finger

TABLE 4.15: *Muscles of the Superficial Layer of Posterior Compartment of Forearm*

MUSCLE	ORIGIN	INSERTION	MAIN ACTION(S)	NERVE
Brachioradialis	Lateral supracondylar ridge of humerus	Styloid process of radius	Flexion of the elbow joint	Radial
Extensor carpi radialis longus		Second metacarpal	Extension and abduction of wrist joint	
Extensor carpi radialis brevis		Third metacarpal	Extension and abduction of wrist joint	
Extensor digitorum	Lateral epicondyle of humerus	Middle and distal phalanges of fingers 2 to 5 (via extensor hood)	Extension of wrist joint and extension of metacarpophalangeal and interphalangeal joints of fingers 2 to 5	
Extensor digiti minimi		Middle and distal phalanges of the fifth finger (via extensor hood)	Extension of metacarpophalangeal and interphalangeal joints of the fifth finger	
Extensor carpi ulnaris	Lateral epicondyle of humerus and shaft of ulna	Fifth metacarpal	Extension of the wrist joint	
Anconeus	Lateral epicondyle of humerus	Olecranon process and shaft of ulna	Extension of elbow joint	

The muscles of the posterior compartment of forearm are involved in supination of the forearm and extension of the wrist and fingers. The tendon of these muscles are held in place by the thickening of the deep fascia (**extensor retinaculum**) while passing behind the wrist (Figure 4.38). All muscles of the posterior compartment of forearm are innervated by radial nerve. See Table 4.16.

Hand Muscles

The intrinsic muscles of the hand are classified as thenar, hypothenar, and central groups.

Thenar muscles form the thenar eminence at the base of the thumb and move the thumb as in abduction, flexion and opposition (Figures 4.41 and 4.42). These muscles mostly arise from carpal bones and insert to the first metacarpal or proximal phalanx of thumb. They are mainly innervated by median nerve.

TABLE 4.16: *Muscles of the Deep Layer of Posterior Compartment of Forearm*

MUSCLE	ORIGIN	INSERTION	MAIN ACTION(S)	NERVE
*Supinator	Lateral epicondyle of humerus and shaft of ulna	Shaft of radius	Supination of forearm	Radial
Abductor pollicis longus	Shaft of ulna and radius	First metacarpal	Abduction of the first carpometacarpal joint	
Extensor pollicis brevis	Shaft of radius and interosseous membrane	Proximal phalanx of thumb	Extension of metacarpophalangeal joint of thumb	
Extensor pollicis longus	Shaft of ulna and interosseous membrane	Distal phalanx of thumb	Extension of interphalangeal and metacarpophalangeal joints of thumb	
Extensor indicis	Shaft of ulna	Middle and distal phalanges of the second finger (via extensor hood)	Extension of metacarpophalangeal and interphalangeal joints of the second finger	

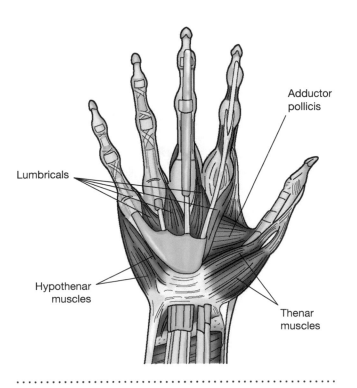

FIGURE 4.41
Hand Muscles (superficial dissection, palmar view)

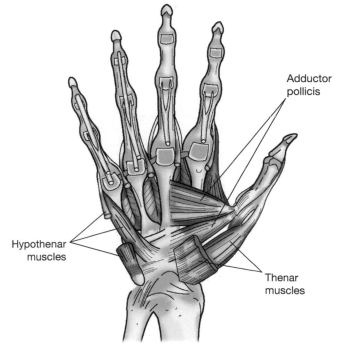

FIGURE 4.42
Hand Muscles (deep dissection, palmar view)

Hypothenar muscles form the hypothenar eminence at the base of the fifth finger and move this finger as in abduction, flexion and opposition (Figures 4.41 and 4.42). These muscles mostly arise from carpal bones and insert to the fifth metacarpal or proximal phalanx of fifth fingers. They are innervated by ulnar nerve.

Central muscles of hand include lumbricals, palmar and dorsal interossei, and adductor pollicis.

The **lumbricals** are four worm-like muscles arising from the tendon of flexor digitorum profundus muscle and inserting to the extensor hood of the four medial fingers (Figure 4.41). They assist in flexion of the metacarpophalangeal joints while extending the interphalangeal joints of the four medial fingers. They are innervated by ulnar or median nerves.

The **interossei** are subdivided into palmar and dorsal groups. They arise from metacarpals and insert to the extensor hood of the medial four fingers. The **palmar interossei** (Figure 4.43) adduct the medial four fingers, whereas the **dorsal interossei** (Figure 4.44) abduct these fingers. It's worth mentioning that the axis of abduction and adduction of medial four fingers passes through the third finger. The interossei muscles are innervated by the ulnar nerve.

Adductor pollicis muscle mainly arises from the second and third metacarpals and inserts to the proximal phalanx of thumb (Figure 4.42). It is innervated by ulnar nerve.

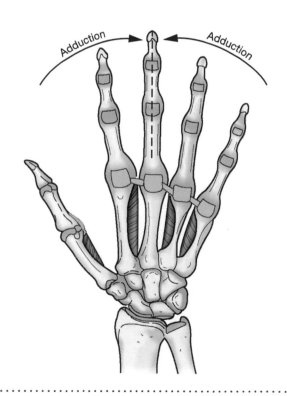

FIGURE 4.43

Palmar Interossei

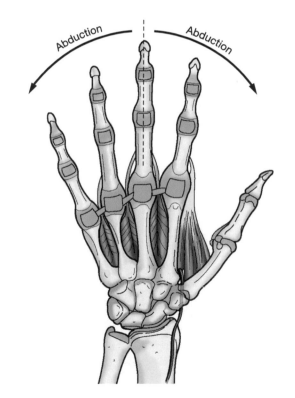

FIGURE 4.44

Dorsal Interossei

Transitional Areas of the Upper Limb

There are three transitional areas located between major parts of the upper limb (Figure 4.45).

1. **Axilla:** this is a pyramidal space (Figure 4.46) situated between the root of the neck and shoulder area that acts as a passage for the blood vessels and nerves of the upper limb (axillary artery and vein and cords of the brachial plexus). It has four walls, a base, and an apex. The anterior, medial, posterior, and lateral walls are mainly formed by the pectoralis major, serratus anterior, subscapularis and coracobrachialis muscles respectively (Figure 4.47). The base of axilla is formed by the skin of the armpit and its apex is located behind the midclavicle.

2. **Cubital fossa:** it is a triangular space mainly bounded by muscles and located in front of the elbow joint (Figure 4.34). The median nerve and brachial artery are the main contents of this fossa.

3. **Carpal tunnel:** it is a fibro-osseous tunnel made by the carpal bones and the thinking of the deep fascia (**flexor retinaculum**) in front of the wrist joint (Figure 4.48). This tunnel contains the tendons of flexor muscles of fingers and median nerve.

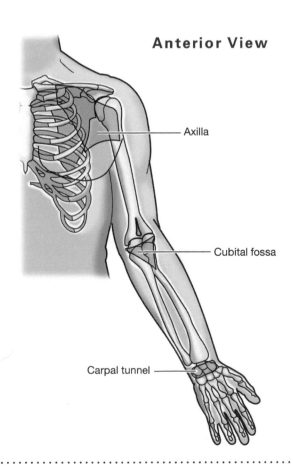

Anterior View

Axilla

Cubital fossa

Carpal tunnel

FIGURE 4.45

Transitional Areas of Upper Limb

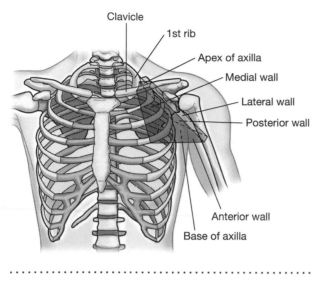

Clavicle
1st rib
Apex of axilla
Medial wall
Lateral wall
Posterior wall
Anterior wall
Base of axilla

FIGURE 4.46
Axilla

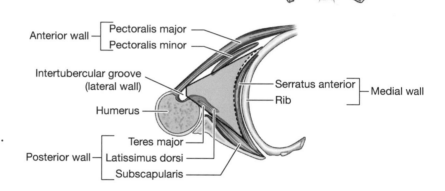

Anterior wall — Pectoralis major
Pectoralis minor
Intertubercular groove (lateral wall)
Serratus anterior — Medial wall
Rib
Humerus
Teres major
Posterior wall — Latissimus dorsi
Subscapularis

FIGURE 4.47
Axilla (horizontal section)

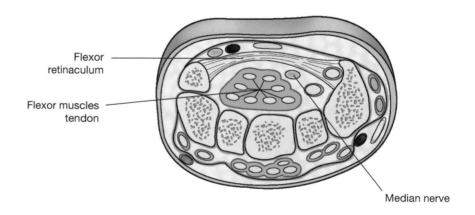

Flexor retinaculum
Flexor muscles tendon
Median nerve

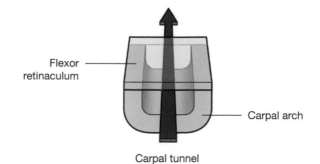

Flexor retinaculum
Carpal arch
Carpal tunnel

FIGURE 4.48
Carpal Tunnel

···· Lower Limb Muscles

The lower limb is divided into gluteal, thigh, leg, and foot regions. The muscles of these regions are grouped in different compartments or layers. The muscles of each region have similar actions and are innervated by the same nerve(s).

Muscles of the Gluteal Region

The muscles of the gluteal region are classified as the superficial and deep groups (Figures 4.49 and 4.50). The muscles of the superficial group are mainly extensor and abductor of the hip joint (Table 4.17), whereas the muscles of the deep group are predominantly lateral rotator of the hip joint (Table 4.18). The muscles of this region are innervated by branches of the sacral plexus.

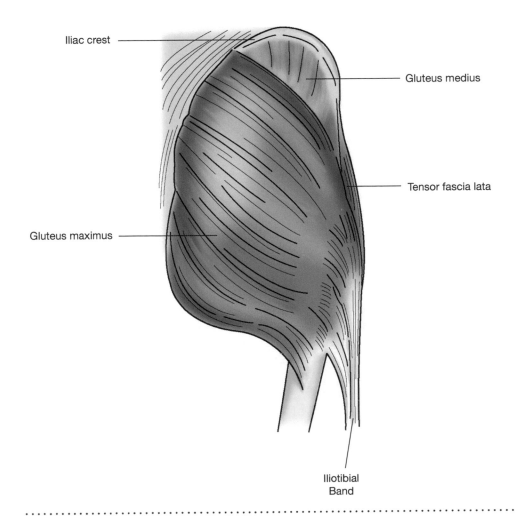

Iliac crest

Gluteus medius

Tensor fascia lata

Gluteus maximus

Iliotibial Band

FIGURE 4.49

Muscles of the Gluteal Region (superficial dissection)

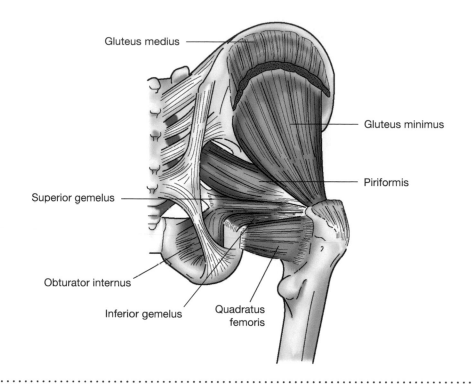

FIGURE 4.50
Muscles of the Gluteal Region (deep dissection)

TABLE 4.17: *Muscles of the Superficial Group of the Gluteal Region*

MUSCLE	ORIGIN	INSERTION	MAIN ACTION(S)	NERVE
Gluteus maximus	Posterior surface of sacrum and ilium	Gluteal tuberosity and iliotibial tract*	Extension of hip joint	Inferior gluteal
Gluteus medius	External surface of ilium	Greater trochanter of femur	Abduction of hip joint	Superior gluteal
Gluteus minimus				
Tensor fascia lata	Iliac crest	Iliotibial tract	Abduction and medial rotation of hip joint	

*: Iliotibial tract is the thinking of the deep fascia of the thigh (fascia lata) on the lateral side of this region. It attaches to the lateral tibial condyle.

TABLE 4.18: *The Main Muscles of the Deep Group of the Gluteal Region*

MUSCLE	ORIGIN	INSERTION	MAIN ACTION(S)	NERVE
Piriformis	Anterior surface of sacrum	Greater trochanter of femur	Lateral rotation of hip joint	Sacral plexus
Obturator internus	Internal surface of obturator membrane			
Quadratus femoris	Ischial tuberosity	Quadrate tubercle on intertrochanteric crest of femur		

Muscles of the Thigh

The muscles of thigh are grouped in anterior, medial, and posterior compartments. These compartments are made by femur and extensions of the deep fascia of the thigh attaching to the femur (Figure 4.51).

The muscles of the anterior compartment (Figures 4.52 and 4.53) are mainly extensor of the knee joint and are innervated by the femoral nerve (Table 4.19). The medial compartment muscles (Figures 4.53 and 4.54) are primarily adductor of the hip joint and are mostly innervated by the obturator nerve (Table 4.20). The muscles of the posterior compartment (Figures 4.55 and 4.56) are predominantly flexor of the knee joint and are innervated by the sciatic nerve (Table 4.21).

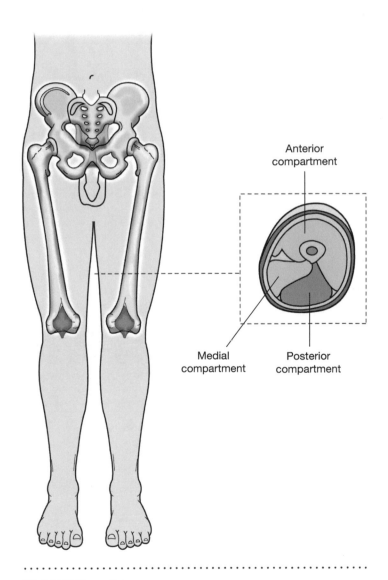

Anterior compartment

Medial compartment

Posterior compartment

FIGURE 4.51
Compartments of Thigh

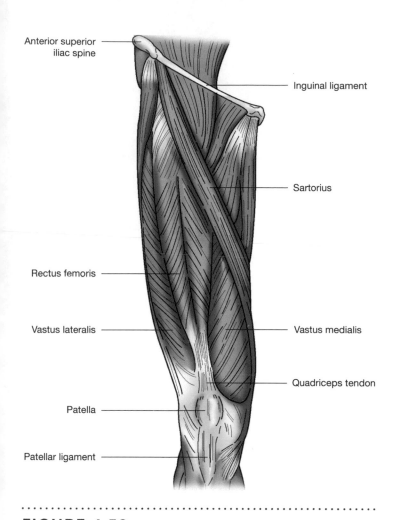

FIGURE 4.52

*Muscles of the Anterior Compartment of Thigh
(superficial dissection)*

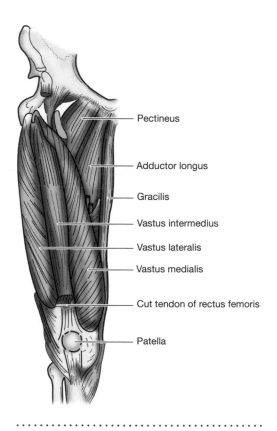

FIGURE 4.53

*Muscles of the Anterior Compartment of
Thigh (deep dissection)*

TABLE 4.19: *The Main Muscles of the Anterior Compartment of the Thigh*

MUSCLE		ORIGIN	INSERTION	MAIN ACTION(S)	NERVE
Sartorius		Anterior superior iliac spine	Upper medial surface of tibia	Flexion of hip and knee joints	Femoral
Quadriceps	Rectus femoris	Anterior inferior iliac spine	Patella via quadriceps tendon*	Extension of knee joint	
	Vastus lateralis	Shaft of femur			
	Vastus				
	Vastus medialis				

*: Quadriceps tendon after embracing the patella continues as patellar ligament that attaches to the tibial tuberosity (Figure 4.50).

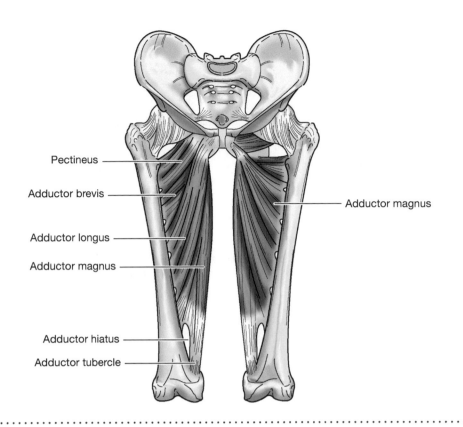

Pectineus

Adductor brevis

Adductor longus

Adductor magnus

Adductor magnus

Adductor hiatus

Adductor tubercle

FIGURE 4.54

Muscles of the Medial Compartment of Thigh

TABLE 4.20: *Muscles of the Medial Compartment of the Thigh*

MUSCLE	ORIGIN	INSERTION	MAIN ACTION(S)	NERVE
Pectineus	Pubic bone	Proximal of posterior surface of femoral shaft	Adduction of hip joint	Femoral/obturator
Gracilis		Upper medial surface of tibia		
Adductor longus		Linea aspera of femur		Obturator
Adductor brevis				
✳**Adductor magnus**	Ischiopubic ramus and ischial tuberosity	Linea aspera and adductor tubercle of femur*	Adduction and extension of hip joint	Obturator and sciatic
Obturator externus	External surface of obturator membrane	Greater trochanter of femur	Lateral rotation of hip joint	Obturator

*: There is an opening between two insertions of the adductor magnus muscle that is known as adductor hiatus (Figure 4.54).

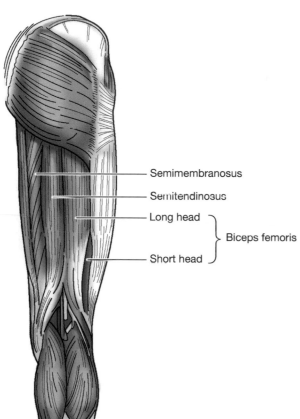

FIGURE 4.55

Muscles of Gluteal Region and Posterior Compartment of Right Thigh (superficial dissection)

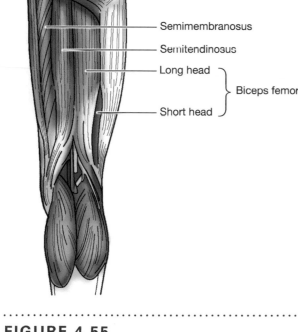

FIGURE 4.56

Muscles of Gluteal Region and Posterior Compartment of Right Thigh (deep dissection)

TABLE 4.21: *Muscles of the Posterior Compartment of the Thigh*

MUSCLE	ORIGIN	INSERTION	MAIN ACTION(S)	NERVE
Biceps femoris	Long head: Ischial tuberosity Short head: linea aspera of femur	Head of fibula	Flexion of the knee joint	Sciatic
Semitendinosus	Ischial tuberosity	Upper medial surface of tibia		
Semimembranosus		Medial tibial condyle		

Muscles of the Leg

The muscles of leg are grouped in anterior, posterior, and lateral compartments. These compartments are made by tibia, fibula, interosseous membrane and extensions of the deep fascia attaching to fibula (Figure 4.57).

The muscles of the anterior compartment (Figure 4.58) are mainly dorsi flexor of the ankle joint and extensor of toes and are innervated by the deep fibular nerve. (See Table 4.22.)

The posterior compartment muscles are in turn subdivided into superficial and deep groups (Figures 4.59 and 4.60). The superficial group muscles are primarily plantar flexor of the ankle joint, whereas the deep group muscles are mostly flexor of toes (Table 4.23). Both groups of the posterior compartment of leg are innervated by the tibial nerve (Table 4.24).

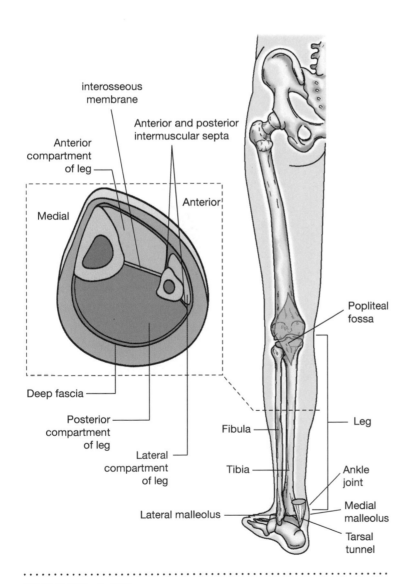

FIGURE 4.57
Compartments of Leg

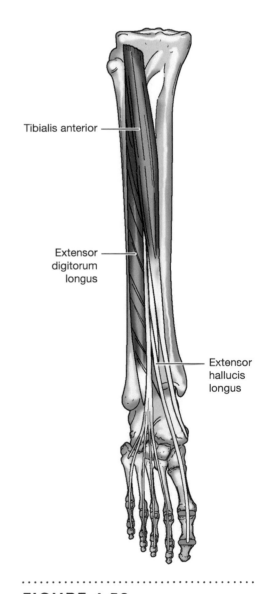

FIGURE 4.58
Muscles of the Anterior Compartment of Right Leg

TABLE 4.22: *The Main Muscles of the Anterior Compartment of the Leg*

MUSCLE	ORIGIN	INSERTION	MAIN ACTION(S)	NERVE
Tibialis anterior	Shaft of tibia and interosseous membrane	Medial cuneiform and base of the first metatarsal	Dorsi flexion of ankle joint and inversion of foot	Deep fibular
Extensor hallucis longus	Shaft of fibula and interosseous membrane	Distal phalanx of big toe	Dorsi flexion of ankle joint, extension of interphalangeal joint of big toe and first metatarsophalangeal joint	
Extensor digitorum longus	Shaft of fibula and lateral tibial condyle	Middle & distal phalanges of toes 2 to 5	Dorsi flexion of ankle joint, extension of metatarsophalangeal, and interphalangeal joints of toes 2 to 5	

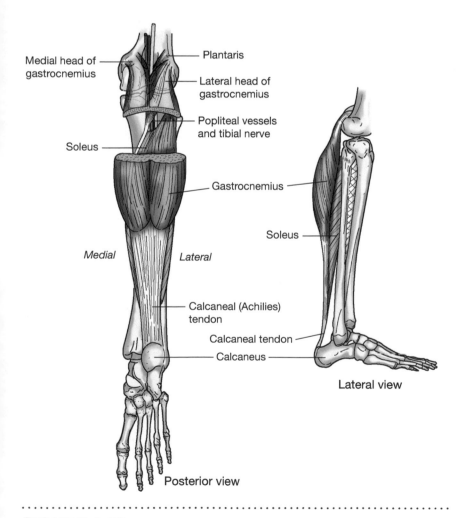

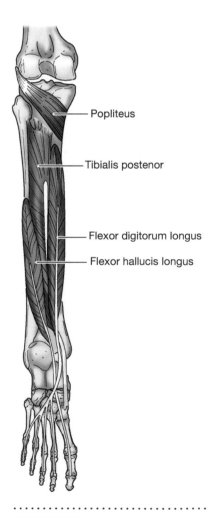

FIGURE 4.59

Muscles of the Posterior Compartment of Right Leg (superficial)

FIGURE 4.60

Muscles of the Posterior Compartment of Left Leg (deep)

TABLE 4.23: *The Main Muscles of the Superficial Group of the Posterior Compartment of the Leg*

MUSCLE	ORIGIN	INSERTION	MAIN ACTION(S)	NERVE
✳ **Gastrocnemius**	Medial and lateral femoral condyles	Calcaneus via calcaneal (Achilles tendon)	Plantar flexion of ankle joint	Tibial
Soleus	Head and shaft of fibula and soleal line of tibia			

TABLE 4.24: *The Muscles of the Deep Group of the Posterior Compartment of the Leg*

MUSCLE	ORIGIN	INSERTION	MAIN ACTION(S)	NERVE
Flexor digitorum longus	Shaft of tibia	Distal phalanges of toes 2 to 5	Plantar flexion of ankle, flexion of metatarsophalangeal, proximal, and distal interphalangeal joints of toes 2 to 5	
Flexor hallucis longus	Shaft of fibula and interosseous membrane	Distal phalanx of the big toe	Plantar flexion of ankle, flexion of metatarsophalangeal, and interphalangeal joints of the big toe	Tibial
✳ **Tibialis posterior**	Shaft of tibia, fibula, and interosseous membrane	Mainly to navicular and medial cuneiform	Plantar flexion of ankle joint and inversion of foot	
Popliteus	Lateral condyle of the femur	Upper posterior surface of tibia	Medial rotation of knee joint	

The muscles of the lateral compartment (Figure 4.61) are predominantly evertor of the foot and are innervated by the superficial fibular nerve. See Table 4.25.

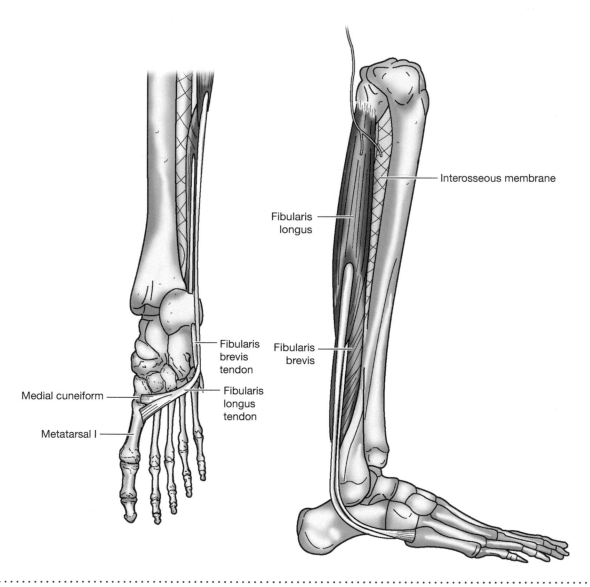

FIGURE 4.61
Muscles of the Lateral Compartment of Right Leg

TABLE 4.25: *The Muscles of the Lateral Compartment of the Leg*

MUSCLE	ORIGIN	INSERTION	MAIN ACTION(S)	NERVE
Fibularis longus	Shaft of fibula	Medial cuneiform and first metatarsal	Eversion of foot	Superficial fibular
Fibularis brevis		Fifth metatarsal		

Muscles of the Foot

The intrinsic muscles of the foot are located either on the dorsal or plantar aspect of the foot.

The only muscle of the dorsum of the foot; **extensor digitorum brevis**, arises from calcaneus and inserts to the tendons of the extensor digitorum longus muscle (Figure 4.62). This muscle assists in extension of the toes and is innervated by the deep fibular nerve. The most medial part of this muscle gives rise to a tendon that attaches to the proximal phalanx of the big toe known as **extensor hallucis brevis**.

The muscles of the plantar aspect of the foot are arranged in four layers that are numbered from superficial to deep. The muscles of the first layer (Figure 4.63) abduct the first and fifth toes and flex the lateral four toes. The muscles of the second layer (Figure 4.64) mainly flex the lateral four toes. The third layer muscles (Figure 4.65) flex the first and fifth toes and adduct the first toe. The muscles of the fourth layer (Figures 4.66 and 4.67) adduct or abduct the toes. It's worth mentioning that the axis of abduction and adduction of lateral four toes passes through the second toe. All muscles of the plantar aspect of the foot are involved in maintaining the arches of the foot and are innervated by the by medial or lateral plantar nerves.

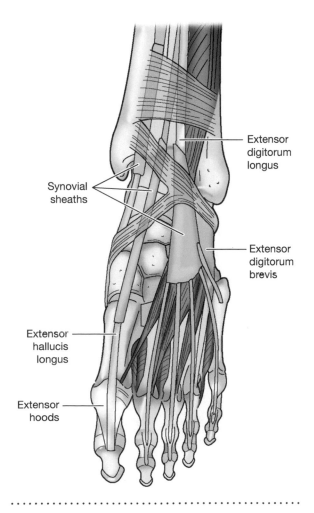

FIGURE 4.62

Muscles of the Dorsum of Foot

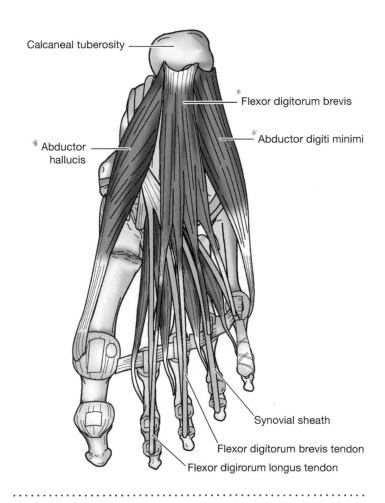

FIGURE 4.63

Muscles of the Plantar Aspect of Foot (first layer)

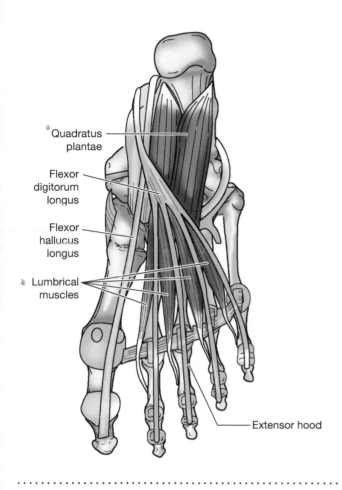

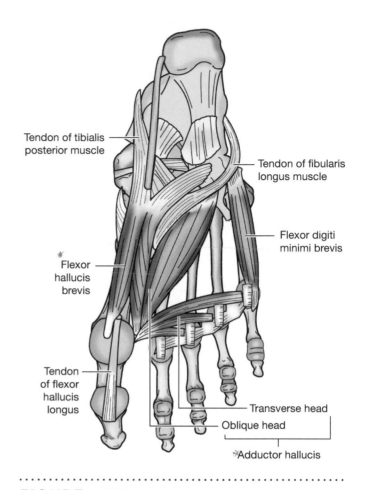

FIGURE 4.64

Muscles of the Plantar Aspect of Foot (second layer)

FIGURE 4.65

Muscles of the Plantar Aspect of Foot (third layer)

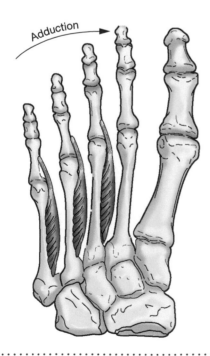

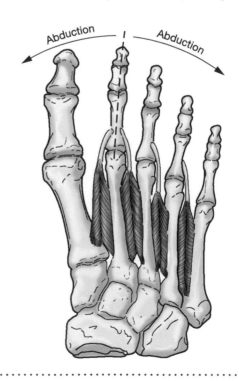

FIGURE 4.66

Right Plantar Interossei

FIGURE 4.67

Right Dorsal Interossei

Transitional Areas of the Lower Limb

There are three transitional areas (Figure 4.68) located in lower limb that act as a passage for major blood vessels and nerves.

1. **Femoral triangle:** it is formed between and by some of the muscles of the anterior and medial compartments of thigh (Figure 4.52). Femoral vein, artery, and nerve are the main contents of this triangle. The apex of the femoral triangle is continuous with a muscular canal mainly formed by the adductor muscles hence termed as **adductor canal**. The distal end of the adductor canal opens to the popliteal fossa via the adductor hiatus.

2. **Popliteal fossa:** this is a diamond-shaped area located behind the knee joint (Figure 4.55). It is bounded by the muscles of the posterior compartment of the thigh superiorly and gastrocnemius muscle inferiorly. It houses the popliteal artery & vein and tibial & common fibular nerves.

3. **Tarsal tunnel:** it is a fibro-osseous tunnel made by the medial malleolus and the thinking of the deep fascia (**flexor retinaculum**) medial to the ankle (Figure 4.69). This tunnel contains the tendons of the deep muscles of the posterior compartment of the leg, tibial nerve, and posterior tibial artery and vein.

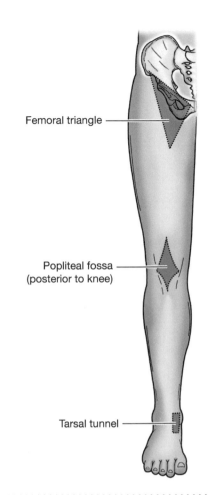

FIGURE 4.68
Transitional Area of Lower Limb

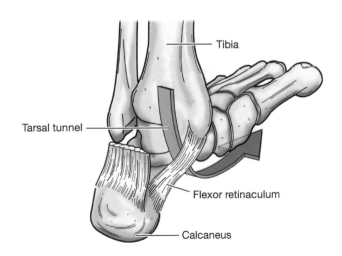

FIGURE 4.69
Left Tarsal Tunnel

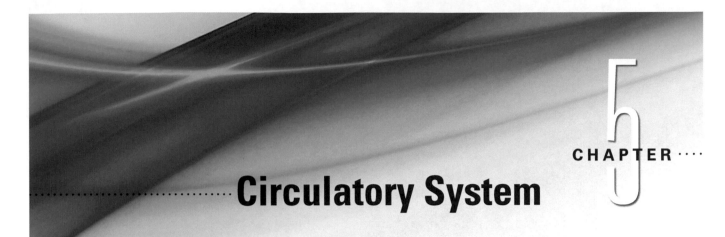

Circulatory System

LEARNING OBJECTIVES

Upon completion of this chapter you should be able to:

1. Explain the boundaries, subdivision, and contents of the mediastina.
2. Discuss the external and internal features of the heart.
3. Describe the heart coverings.
4. Define the conducting system of the heart.
5. Explain the blood supply and venous drainage of the heart.
6. Discuss the arterial supply of the different regions of the body.
7. Explain the venous drainage of the different regions of the body.

The circulatory system distributes the oxygen and nutrients to all human body cells and picks up the waste materials produced by the cells to be eliminated by other systems such as the respiratory and urinary systems. The circulatory system includes the heart and blood vessels.

Mediastinum

The mediastinum is a space bounded anteriorly by sternum and costal cartilages, laterally by the lungs, and posteriorly by the bodies of the thoracic vertebrae (Figure 5.1). It contains the heart, its large vessels, and other anatomical structures such as the esophagus, trachea, and thoracic aorta. The mediastinum is divided into a superior and an inferior part by a transverse imaginary plane passing through the sternal angle anteriorly and the intervertebral disc between vertebrae TIV and TV posteriorly. The inferior mediastinum is subdivided into three parts. The **middle mediastinum** is mainly occupied by the heart and pericardium. The **anterior mediastinum** is located between the sternum and pericardium, whereas the **posterior mediastinum** is placed between the pericardium and bodies of vertebrae TV to TXII.

The superior mediastinum contains the arch of the aorta and its branches, right and left brachiocephalic veins, the inferior part of the superior vena cava, end of the azygus vein, right and left phrenic nerves, right and left vagus nerves, trachea, esophagus, thymus gland, and thoracic duct (Figure 5.2).

The anterior mediastinum mainly contains the thymus gland.

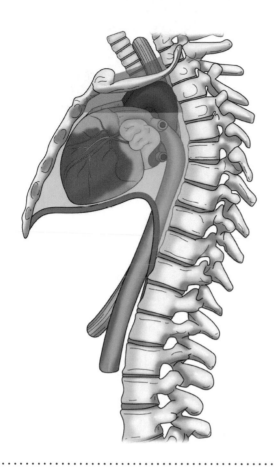

FIGURE 5.1

Subdivisions of Mediastinum (lateral view)

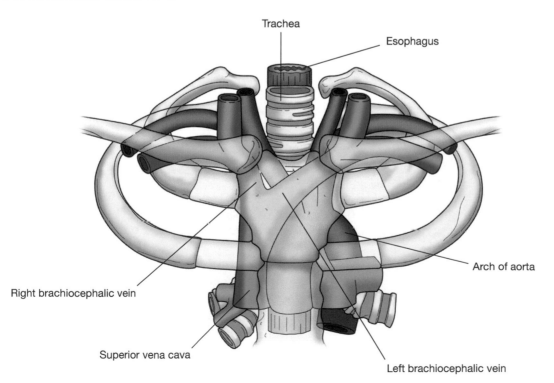

FIGURE 5.2

Superior Mediastinum

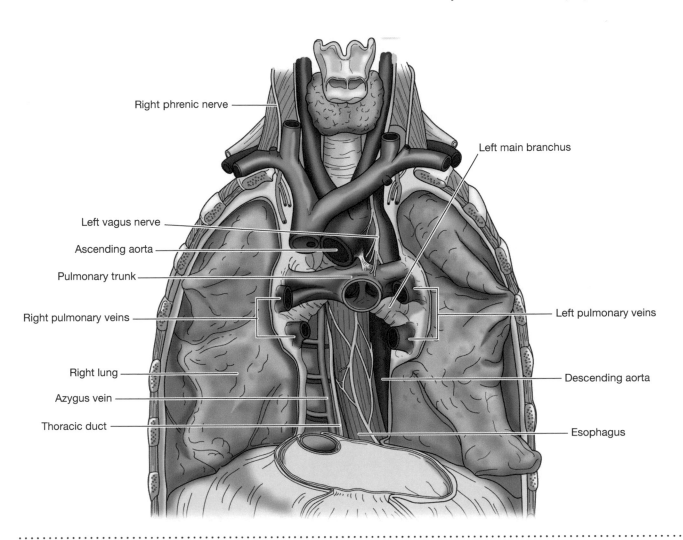

Right phrenic nerve

Left main branchus

Left vagus nerve

Ascending aorta

Pulmonary trunk

Right pulmonary veins

Left pulmonary veins

Right lung

Descending aorta

Azygus vein

Thoracic duct

Esophagus

FIGURE 5.3
Middle and Posterior Mediastinums

The middle mediastinum houses the heart, the pericardium, and the main vessels of the heart (the ascending aorta, pulmonary trunk, and pulmonary veins), right and left phrenic nerves, and main bronchi (Figure 5.3).

The posterior mediastinum holds the descending aorta, azygus and hemiazygus veins, right and left vagus nerves, the thoracic duct, esophagus, sympathetic chain (trunk), and the splanchnic nerves (Figure 5.3).

· · · · Heart

The heart is a muscular conical pump located in the middle mediastinum. It is almost the same size as an individual's fist. The right atrium receives deoxygenated blood from the entire body and passes it to the right ventricle (Figure 5.4). The right ventricle pumps the blood to the lungs (**pulmonary circulation**). The left atrium receives oxygenated blood from the lungs and passes it to the left ventricle. The left ventricle pumps the blood throughout the body (**systemic circulation**).

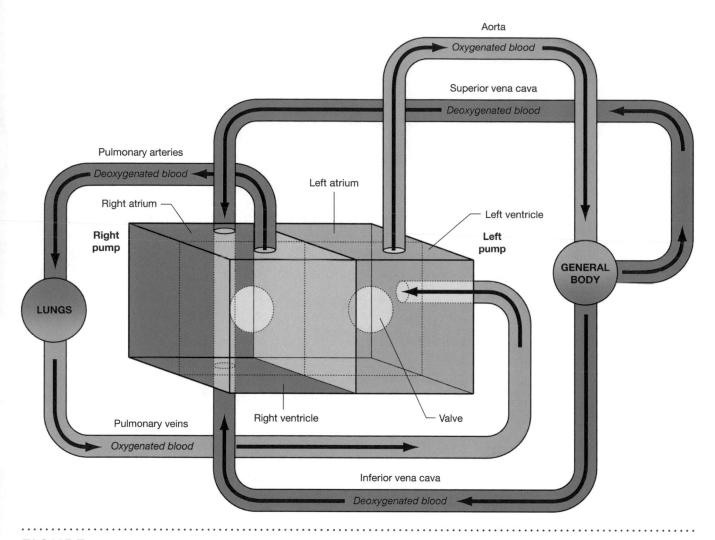

FIGURE 5.4
Pulmonary and Systemic Circulations

Surface Anatomy of the Heart

The heart image on the chest wall is demarcated by a quadrangle: the four corners of which are as follows (Figure 5.5):

- Left second intercostal space, 1 inch away from the midline.
- Right third costal cartilage, 1 inch away from the midline.
- Right sixth costal cartilage, 1 inch away from the midline.
- Left fifth intercostal space, 3 to 4 inches away from the midline.

External Features of the Heart

The external view of the heart presents the following features:

1. **Heart sulci:** there are four sulci on the heart (Figures 5.6 and 5.7).

   a. The **coronary sulcus** encircles the heart and separates the atria from the ventricles.

   b. The **interventricular sulci** are located between the ventricles on the anterior and inferior surfaces.

   c. The **interatrial sulcus** separates the atria on the outside.

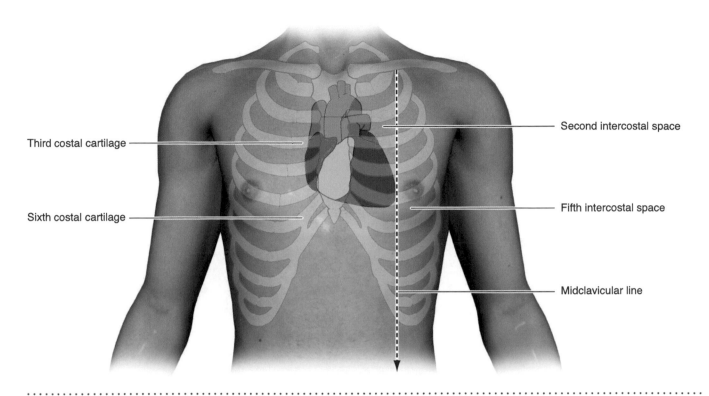

FIGURE 5.5
Surface Anatomy of the Heart

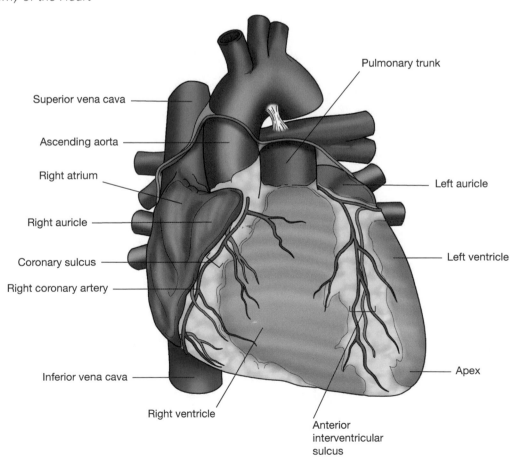

FIGURE 5.6
Anterior Surface of the Heart

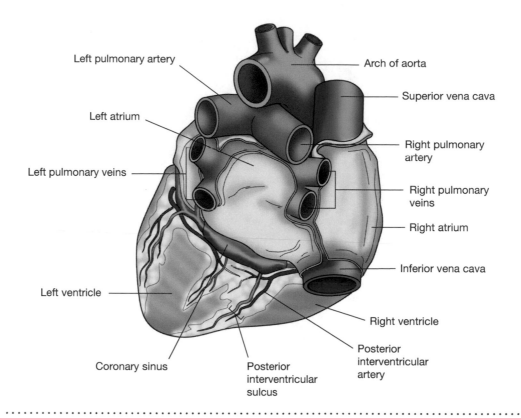

FIGURE 5.7

Diaphragmatic Surface and Base of the Heart

2. **Heart surfaces:** the heart has four surfaces (Figures 5.6 and 5.7).

   a. The **anterior (sternocostal) surface** is related to the sternum and the second to sixth costal cartilages.

   b. The **inferior (diaphragmatic) surface** is leaning on the diaphragm. The posterior interventricular sulcus is located on this surface.

   c. The **left pulmonary surface** is related to the left lung.

   d. The **right pulmonary surface** is related to the right lung.

3. **Heart borders:** the heart has three borders (Figures 5.6 and 5.7):

   a. The **superior border** is formed by the left atrium.

   b. The **right border** is formed by the right atrium.

   c. The **inferior border** separates the anterior surface from the inferior surface.

4. **Heart base:** the heart base faces posteriorly and is mainly formed by the left atrium. The interatrial sulcus is located on the base of the heart (Figure 5.7).

5. **Heart apex:** it is formed by the left ventricle and is directed anteriorly, inferiorly, and to the left (Figure 5.6).

Heart Chambers

The heart has four chambers:

1. **Right Atrium**

   The right atrium receives the superior and inferior vena cavae and coronary sinus. There is conical muscular appendage known as auricle attached to the right atrium. The **pectinate muscle** that lines the anterior part of the right atrium extends into the **right auricle** (Figure 5.8).

   On the interatrial septum there is an impression known as **fossa ovalis**. This fossa is the remnant of the embryonic foramen ovalis that used to connect the right and left atria together.

   The right atrium is connected to the right ventricle via the right atrioventricular opening. This opening is guarded by the **right atrioventricular (tricuspid) valve**.

2. **Right Ventricle**

   The walls of the right ventricle are thicker than that of the right atrium and carry some muscular ridges known as **trabeculae carneae** (Figure 5.9). A group of these muscles known as **papillary muscles** arise from the walls of this ventricle and insert to the leaflets of the tricuspid valve via tendon-like structures known as **chorda tendinae**. The pulmonary artery arises from the superior part of the right ventricle. At the beginning of this artery there is a semilunar valve known as **pulmonary valve** that prevents the blood from flowing back to the right ventricle. The right ventricle is separated from the left ventricle by interventricular septum.

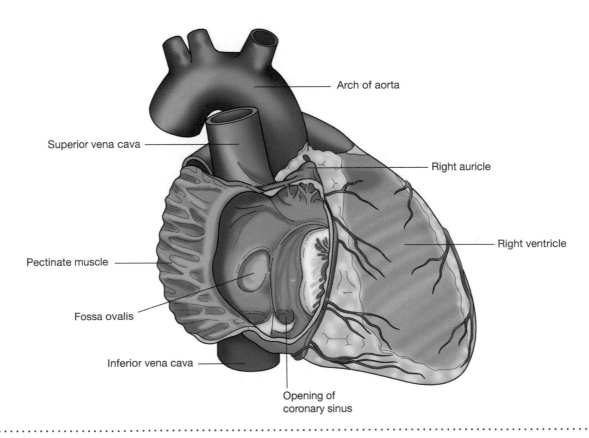

FIGURE 5.8

Right Atrium

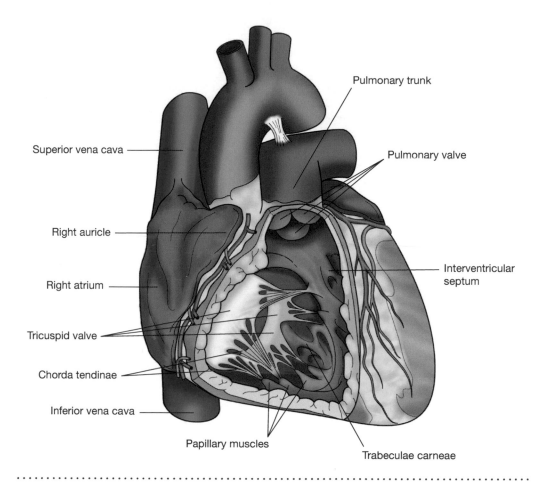

Superior vena cava

Right auricle

Right atrium

Tricuspid valve

Chorda tendinae

Inferior vena cava

Papillary muscles

Pulmonary trunk

Pulmonary valve

Interventricular septum

Trabeculae carneae

FIGURE 5.9
Right Ventricle

3. **Left Atrium**
   The left atrium receives the pulmonary veins. The pectinate muscle of the left atrium is only found in the **left auricle** (Figure 5.10). The left atrium is connected to the left ventricle via the left atrioventricular opening. This opening is guarded by the **left atrioventricular (bicuspid or mitral) valve**.

4. **Left Ventricle**
   The walls of the left ventricle are the thickest among all heart chambers (Figure 5.11). Trabeculae carneae, papillary muscles, and chorda tendinae are similar to that of the right ventricle. The aorta arises from the superior part of the left ventricle. At the beginning of the aorta there is a semilunar valve known as the **aortic valve** that prevents the blood from flowing back to the left ventricle.

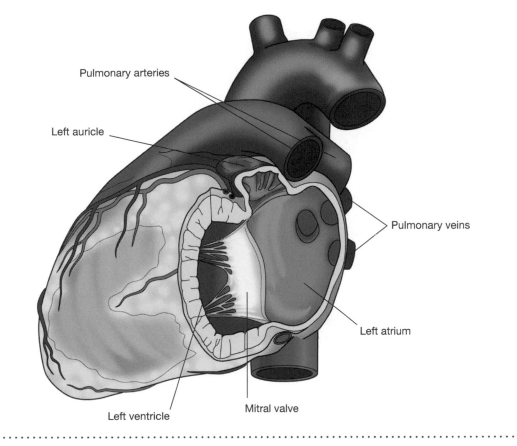

Pulmonary arteries

Left auricle

Pulmonary veins

Left atrium

Left ventricle

Mitral valve

FIGURE 5.10

Left Atrium

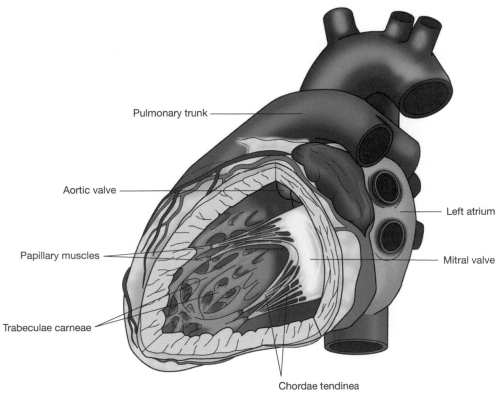

Pulmonary trunk

Aortic valve

Left atrium

Papillary muscles

Mitral valve

Trabeculae carneae

Chordae tendinea

FIGURE 5.11

Left Ventricle

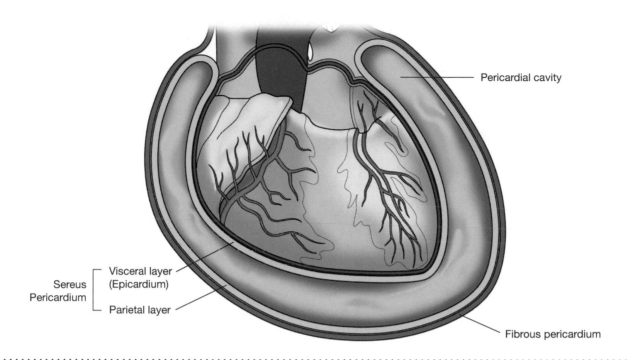

Sereus Pericardium
- Visceral layer (Epicardium)
- Parietal layer

Pericardial cavity

Fibrous pericardium

FIGURE 5.12
Pericardium

Pericardium

The heart is surrounded by the pericardial sac. The pericardial sac is composed of two layers: an outer fibrous layer (fibrous pericardium) and an inner serous layer (serous pericardium) (Figure 5.12).

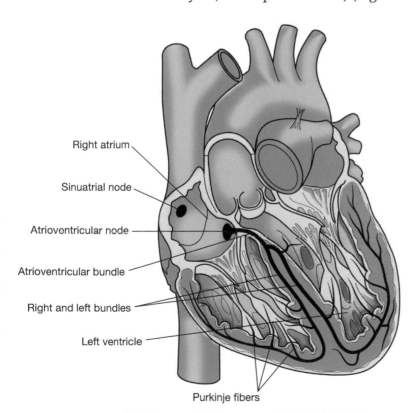

Right atrium

Sinuatrial node

Atrioventricular node

Atrioventricular bundle

Right and left bundles

Left ventricle

Purkinje fibers

FIGURE 5.13
Conducting System of the Heart

a. **Fibrous pericardium** surrounds the heart and attaches to the central tendon of diaphragm inferiorly and to the great vessels of the heart superiorly.

b. **Serous pericardium** is made of two layers. The **parietal layer** lines the inner surface of the fibrous pericardium. The **visceral layer (epicardium)** attaches to the surface of the heart. The **pericardial cavity** is a narrow space between the parietal and visceral layers of the serous pericardium and is filled with a small amount of serous fluid. This fluid facilitates the heart movements.

Conducting System of the Heart

The conducting system of the heart is made by modified cardiac muscle fibers and includes the following components (Figure 5.13):

1. **Sinuatrial node:** it is located on the right atrium wall close to SVC (superior vena cava) opening. This node is known as the **pacemaker node**.
2. **Atrioventricular node:** this node is located on the right side of the interatrial septum close to the opening of the coronary sinus.
3. **Atrioventricular bundle (bundle of His):** it starts from the atrioventricular node and after entering the interventricular septum divides into the right and left branches and gives rise to the Purkinje fibers. The **Purkinje fibers** distribute into the right and left ventricular walls.

The impulse starts from the sinuatrial node that causes the contraction of the atrial walls and then reaches to the atrioventricular node. The impulse is passed to the ventricular walls via the atrioventricular bundle and Purkinje fibers that lead to the ventricular contraction.

The heart beat is regulated by branches from autonomic nervous systems (Figure 5.14). The sympathetic branches arise from the cervical and thoracic sympathetic ganglia and the parasympathetic branches derive from vagus nerves. These branches unite under the aortic arch and form the **cardiac plexus**. The sympathetic component of the plexus increases the heart rate, whereas the parasympathetic component decreases the heart rate.

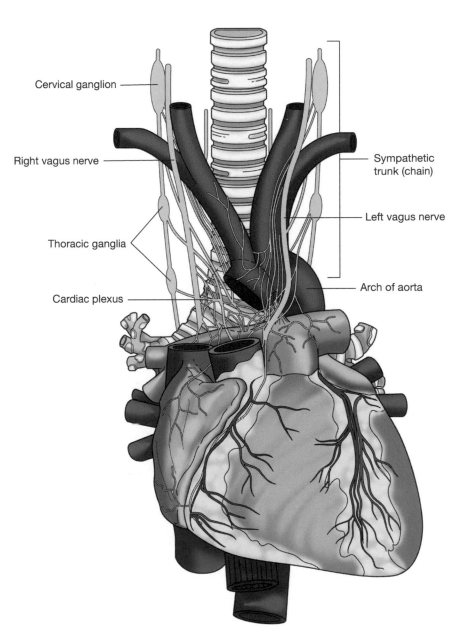

Cervical ganglion

Right vagus nerve

Thoracic ganglia

Cardiac plexus

Sympathetic trunk (chain)

Left vagus nerve

Arch of aorta

FIGURE 5.14
Cardiac Plexus

Arterial Supply of the Heart

The heart is supplied by the right and left coronary arteries (Figure 5. 15).

The **right coronary artery** arises from the ascending aorta, runs in the right side of the coronary sulcus, and supplies the right atrium and ventricle. The terminal branch of the right coronary artery is known as the **posterior interventricular artery**, which runs in the posterior interventricular sulcus and contributes to the blood supply of both ventricles.

The **left coronary artery** arises from the ascending aorta and shortly after divides to **anterior interventricular** and **circumflex branches**. The anterior interventricular artery runs in the anterior interventricular sulcus and contributes to the blood supply of both ventricles. The circumflex artery follows the coronary sulcus to the left side of the heart and mainly supplies the left ventricle.

Venous Drainage of the Heart

The venous blood of the heart is drained by three major cardiac veins (Figure 5.16). The **great cardiac vein** is located in the anterior interventricular sulcus, the **middle cardiac vein** runs in the posterior interventricular sulcus, and the **small cardiac**

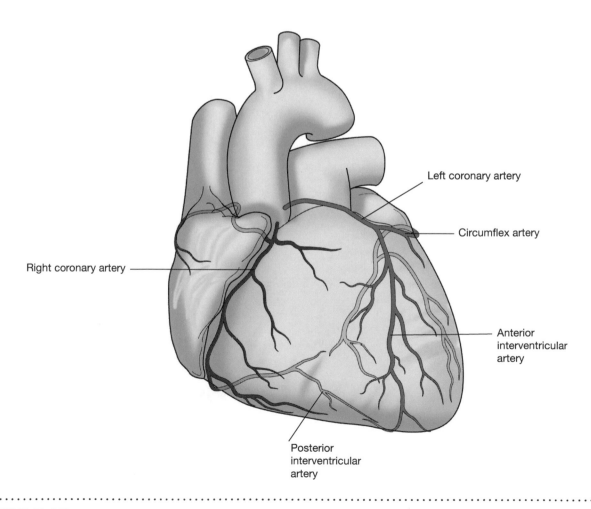

FIGURE 5.15

Arterial Supply of the Heart

Anterior View

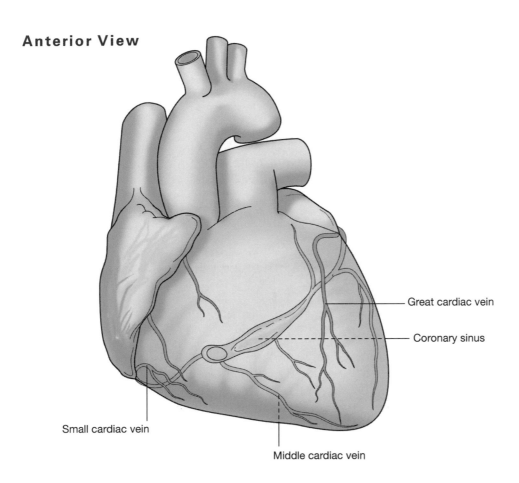

Great cardiac vein

Coronary sinus

Small cardiac vein

Middle cardiac vein

Posterior View

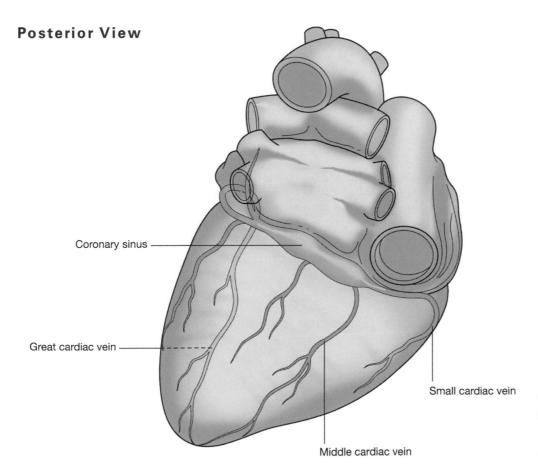

Coronary sinus

Great cardiac vein

Small cardiac vein

Middle cardiac vein

FIGURE 5.16

Venous Drainage of the Heart

vein follows the right side of the coronary sulcus. These veins drain into the **coronary sinus** located in the coronary sulcus on the inferior surface of the heart that in turn drains to the right atrium.

···· Arterial Supply of the Body

The vessel that carries the blood away from the heart is called an **artery**. The major arteries of the body are listed as follows:

Pulmonary Trunk

The pulmonary trunk carries deoxygenated blood to the lungs. It arises from the right ventricle and divides into the **right and left pulmonary arteries** under the arch of aorta (Figure 5.9 and 5.10).

Aorta

The aorta carries oxygenated blood throughout the body (Figure 5.17). It arises from the left ventricle as the **ascending aorta** and arches to the left to continue as the **descending aorta**. It descends on the left side of the vertebral column in the posterior mediastinum (**thoracic aorta**) and passes through the diaphragm to enter the abdominal cavity (**abdominal aorta**). The abdominal aorta terminates at the level of vertebra LIV by dividing into the **right and left common iliac arteries**.

Branches of the ascending aorta: The only branches arising from ascending aorta are the left and right coronary arteries.

Branches of the arch of aorta: Three branches arise from the arch of aorta. Beginning on the right these branches include the brachiocephalic trunk, left common carotid artery, and left subclavian artery.

1. **Brachiocephalic trunk:** it is the first branch of the arch of aorta that divides into the **right common carotid artery** and **right subclavian artery** (Figure 5.17). The right common carotid and right subclavian arteries have the same course and branches as of the left common carotid and left subclavian arteries.
2. **Left common carotid artery:** it is the second branch of the arch of aorta that ascends on the left side of the neck and divides into the **external and internal carotid arteries** at the level of the superior border of thyroid cartilage (Figure 5.18). The common carotid arteries supply the head and neck regions.
3. **Left subclavian artery:** this is the third branch of the arch of aorta that passes under the left clavicle toward the left upper limb and continues as the axillary artery after passing over the first rib (Figure 5.17).

External carotid artery: It supplies the neck and that part of the head, which is outside of the cranial cavity. Its main branches include the following (Figure 5.19):

1. The **superior thyroid artery** supplies the thyroid gland and larynx.
2. The **lingual artery** supplies the tongue.
3. The **facial artery** supplies the face.

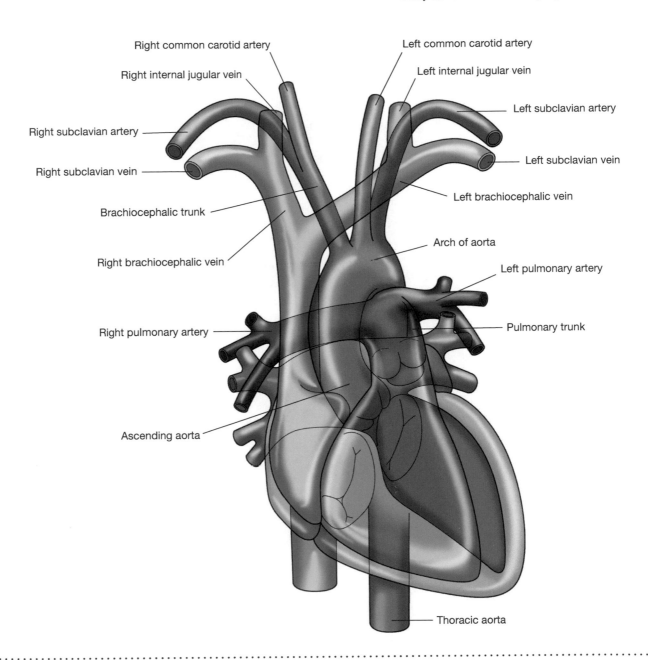

FIGURE 5.17
Major Vessels of the Heart

4. The **superficial temporal artery** is one of the terminal branches of the external carotid artery passing anterior to the external ear and supplies the scalp (soft tissue covering the cranium) on the sides of the cranium.

5. The **maxillary artery** is one of the terminal branches of the external carotid artery. It supplies the deep part of the face including the nasal and oral cavities and pharynx.

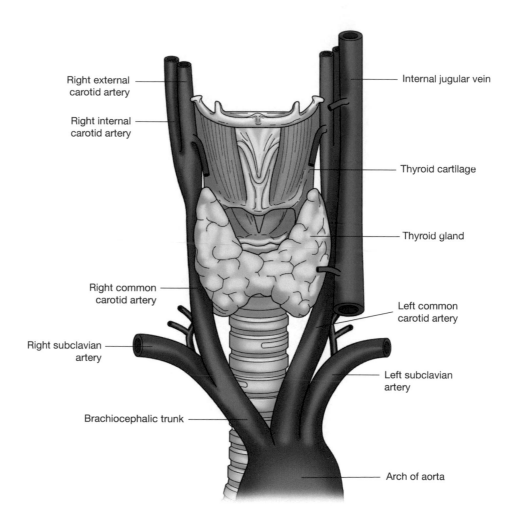

FIGURE 5.18
Common Carotid Arteries

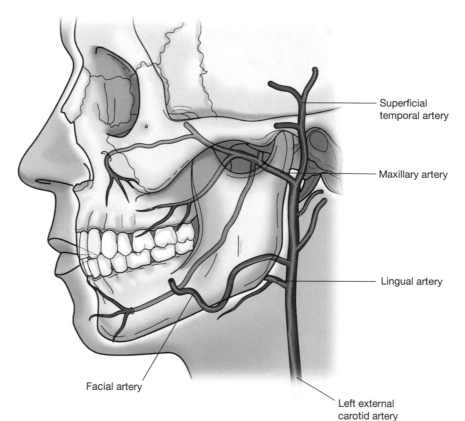

FIGURE 5.19
External Carotid Artery

Internal carotid artery: This artery does not have any branches in the neck (Figure 5.20A and 5.20B). It enters the cranial cavity and forms an arterial circle known as **Circle of Willis** in contribution with vertebral artery. Its main branches inside the skull include the following:

1. The **ophthalamic artery**: supplies the contents of the orbital cavity.
2. The **middle cerebral artery**: supplies most of the lateral surface of the cerebral hemispheres.
3. The **anterior cerebral artery**: supplies major parts of the medial surface of the cerebral hemispheres.

Subclavian artery: The main branches of this artery include the following:

1. The **vertebral artery**: this artery passes through the transverse foramina of the cervical vertebrae (except CVII), and enters the skull via foramen

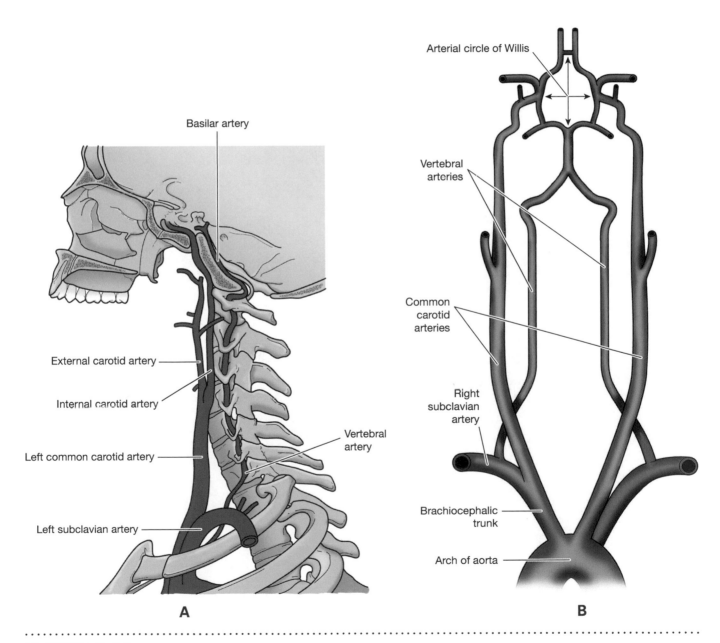

FIGURE 5.20

(A) Internal Carotid Artery (B) Arterial Cricle of Willis

magnum (Figure 5.20A and Figure 5.20B). The vertebral artery supplies the spinal cord and medulla oblongata (anterior and posterior spinal arteries), and cerebellum. The right and left vertebral arteries join to form the **basilar artery**. The basilar artery after supplying pons and cerebellum ends by dividing into **posterior cerebral arteries** that in turn mainly supply the inferior surface of the cerebral hemispheres.

2. The **internal thoracic artery**: this artery descends behind the costal cartilages on either side of the sternum (Figure 5. 21). At the level of each intercostal space it gives rise to **anterior intercostal arteries**, which will join with the **posterior intercostal arteries** (branches of thoracic aorta). The anterior intercostal arteries contribute in blood supply of the intercostal muscles, breast gland, and muscles of the anterior chest wall.

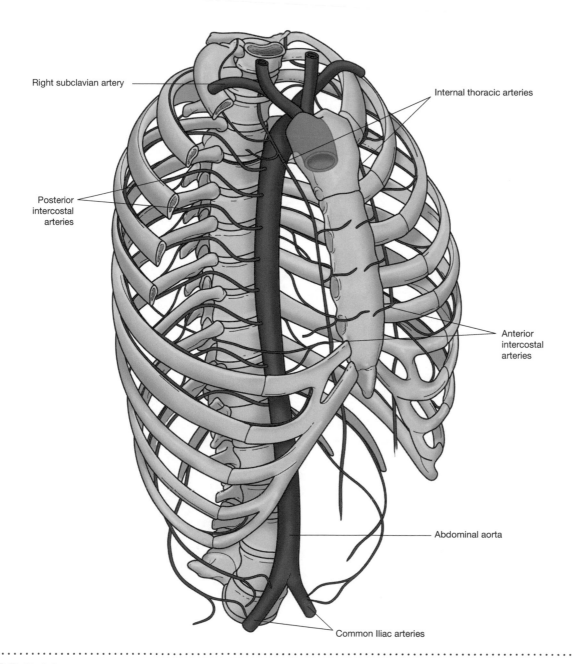

FIGURE 5.21

Arterial Supply of the Thoracic Wall

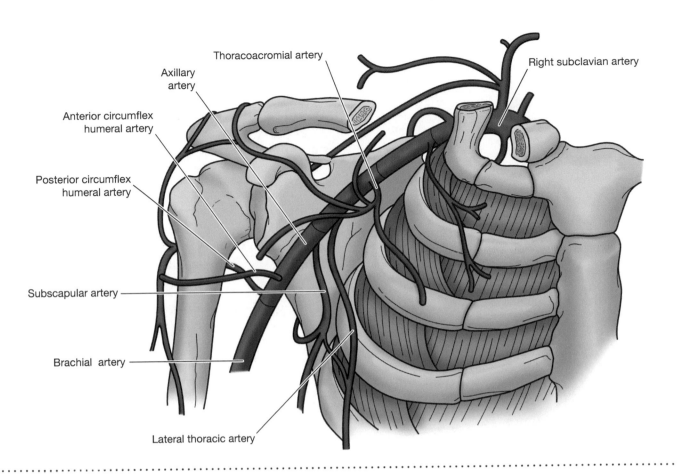

FIGURE 5.22
Axillary Artery

Axillary artery: It is the continuation of the subclavian artery contained within the axilla (Figure 5.22). This artery extends between the first rib and the lower margin of the teres major muscle. The main branches of the axillary artery include:

1. The **thoracoacromial artery**: it mainly supplies the anterior wall of the axilla.
2. The **lateral thoracic artery**: it supplies the medial wall of the axilla.
3. The **subscapular artery**: this artery supplies the scapular region.
4. The **anterior and posterior circumflex humeral arteries**: they wind around the surgical neck of the humerus to supply the muscles of this area.

Brachial artery: It is the continuation of the axillary artery and extends from the lower margin of the teres major muscle to the cubital fossa (Figure 5.23). The brachial artery supplies the anterior compartment of the arm, and its main branch, **deep brachial artery**, supplies the posterior compartment of the arm. This artery splits into radial and ulnar arteries after the cubital fossa.

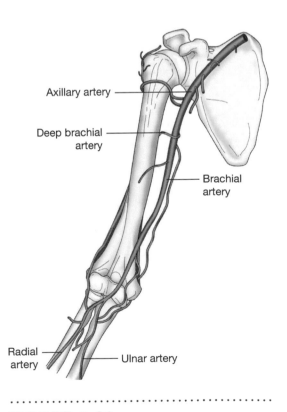

FIGURE 5.23
Brachial Artery

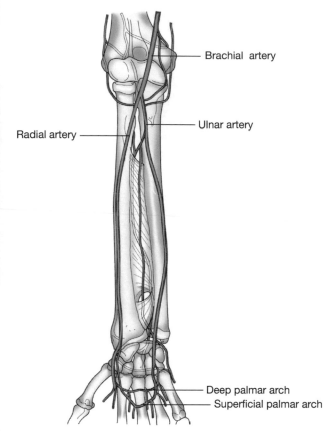

Radial artery: It descends on the lateral side of the forearm, winds lateral to the wrist and after passing through the first dorsal interosseous muscle, enters the palmar aspect of the hand and contributes in formation of the deep palmar arch (Figure 5.24).

Ulnar artery: This artery continues on the medial side of the forearm toward the wrist and after entering the palmar aspect of the hand contributes in the formation of the superficial palmar arch (Figure 5.24).

Palmar arches: There are two arterial palmar arches. The **superficial palmar arch** is mainly formed by the ulnar artery, whereas the **deep palmar arch** is predominantly formed by the radial artery. Branches of these arches supply the hand (Figure 5.25).

FIGURE 5.24
Radial and Ulnar Arteries

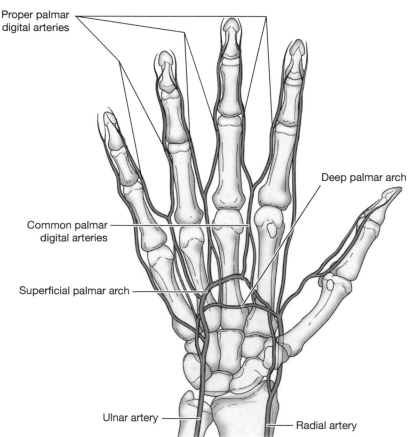

FIGURE 5.25
Superficial and Deep Palmar Arches

Descending Aorta

The descending aorta is divided into thoracic aorta and abdominal aorta.

Branches of the thoracic aorta: The thoracic aorta is the continuation of the arch of aorta that descends in the posterior mediastinum and passes through diaphragm at the level of vertebra TXII. The branches of thoracic aorta are divided into the parietal and visceral groups (Figure 5.26).

1. **Parietal braches** are the arteries that contribute in the blood supply of the thoracic walls such as **posterior intercostal arteries**. The posterior intercostal arteries travel within the intercostal spaces and join to the anterior intercostal arteries to contribute in the blood supply of the content of the intercostal spaces.
2. **Visceral branches** supply the thoracic viscera such as **esophageal arteries** that supply the esophagus in the posterior mediastinum.

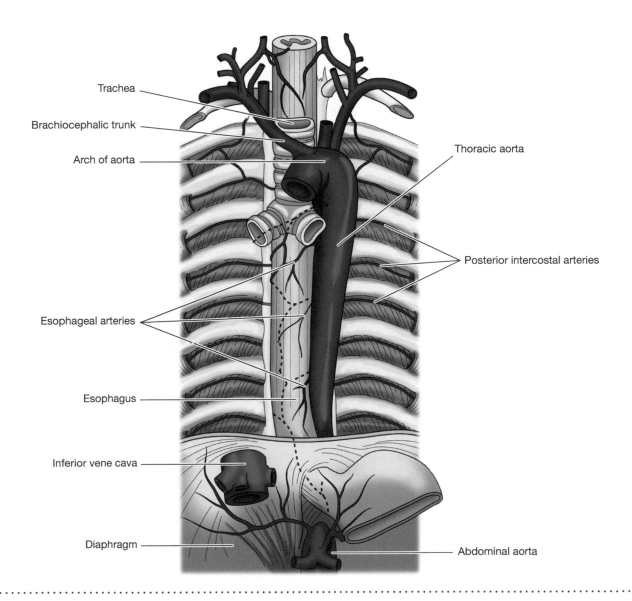

FIGURE 5.26

Thoracic Aorta

Branches of the abdominal aorta: The abdominal aorta is stretched between vertebra TXII and LIV where it splits into the left and right common iliac arteries (Figure 5.27A and Figure 5.27B). Branches of the abdominal aorta are grouped as the following:

1. The **parietal branches** supply the diaphragm and posterior abdominal wall. The four **lumbar arteries** supply the posterior abdominal musculature and lumbar vertebrae (Figure 5.27A).
2. The **visceral branches** supply the abdominal viscera. The main visceral branches include the following (Figure 5.27A and Figure 5.27B):
    a. The **celiac artery**: this artery divides into **left gastric, common hepatic, and splenic** branches. These branches supply the stomach, liver, spleen, parts of the pancreas, and upper half of the duodenum.
    b. The **superior mesenteric artery**: it supplies the lower half of the duodenum, parts of the pancreas, jejunum, ileum, cecum, appendix, ascending colon, and the right two-thirds of the transverse colon.
    c. The **inferior mesenteric artery**: this artery supplies the left one-third of the transverse colon, descending colon, sigmoid colon, rectum, and superior two-thirds of the anal canal.
    d. The **renal arteries**: they supply the kidneys, adrenal glands, and superior part of the ureters.

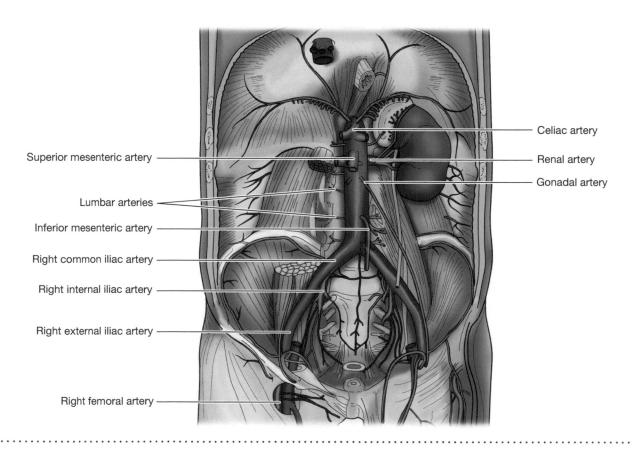

FIGURE 5.27A
Abdominal Aorta

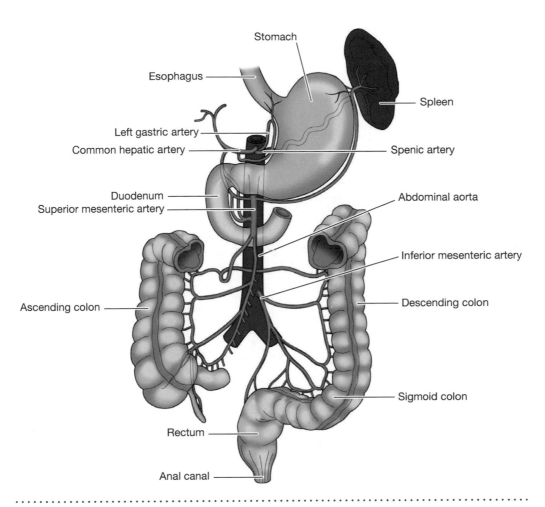

FIGURE 5.27B
Visceral Branches of the Abdominal Aorta

    e. The **gonadal arteries**: they are known as ovarian arteries in female and **testicular arteries** in male and supply ovaries and testicles respectively.

Common Iliac Arteries

The left and right common iliac arteries are the terminal branches of the abdominal aorta that start at the level of vertebra LIV and split into **internal** and **external iliac arteries** at the level of sacroiliac joints (Figure 5.27A).

Branches of the internal iliac artery: Branches of the internal iliac artery are grouped as follows (Figure 5.28):

    1. The **parietal branches** include the following:

        a. The **superior and inferior gluteal arteries** that supply the gluteal region of the lower limb.

        b. The **obturator artery** contributes to the blood supply of the adductor (medial) compartment of the thigh.

        c. The **internal pudendal artery** supplies the contents of the anal and urogenital triangles of the perineum.

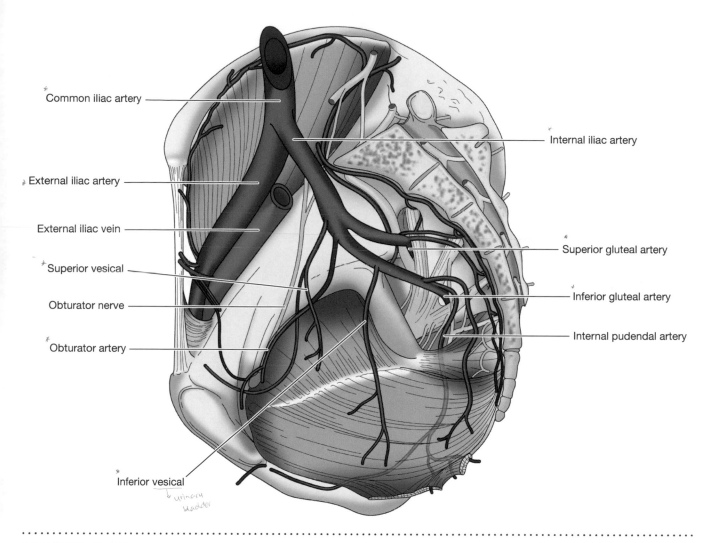

Common iliac artery

External iliac artery

External iliac vein

Superior vesical

Obturator nerve

Obturator artery

Inferior vesical

Urinary bladder

Internal iliac artery

Superior gluteal artery

Inferior gluteal artery

Internal pudendal artery

FIGURE 5.28

Right Internal Iliac Artery

2. The visceral branches supply the pelvic viscera including urinary bladder, rectum, and internal genital organs in female (uterus and vagina) and male (prostate, seminal vesicle, and vas deference).

External iliac artery: This artery starts at the level of sacroiliac joint and passes deep to the inguinal ligament and continues as the femoral artery (Figure 5.27A). The external iliac artery contributes in the blood supply of the anterior abdominal wall and the false pelvis musculature.

Femoral artery: This artery starts at the midpoint of the inguinal ligament, descends in the femoral triangle and adductor canal, and continues as the popliteal artery after passing through the adductor hiatus (Figure 5. 29A and Figure 5.29B). The femoral artery supplies the anterior and medial compartments of the thigh, and its main branch, **deep femoral artery**, supplies the posterior compartment of the thigh.

midinguinal Point

ant and post comp

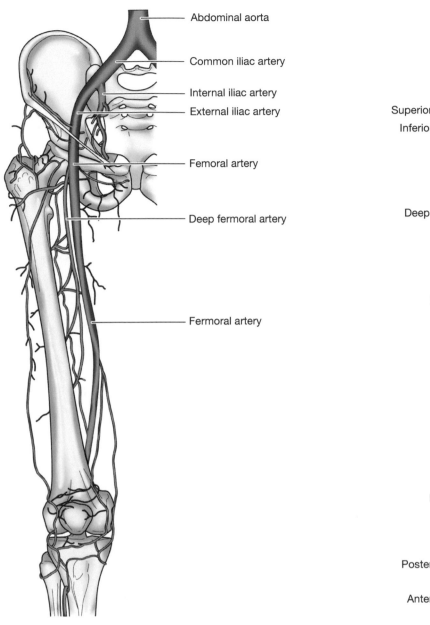

FIGURE 5.29A
Femoral Artery (anterior view)

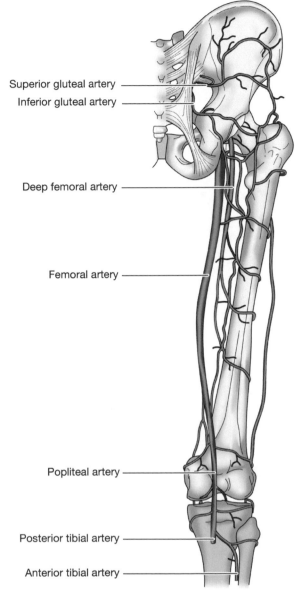

FIGURE 5.29B
Femoral Artery (posterior view)

Popliteal artery: It starts at the adductor hiatus and divides into the anterior and posterior tibial arteries after passing through the popliteal fossa (Figures 5.29A, 5.29B, and 5.30). The popliteal artery supplies the knee joint and the soft tissue around it.

Anterior tibial artery: It passes through the interosseous membrane between the tibia and fibula and enters the anterior compartment of the leg (Figure 5.31). This artery supplies the muscles of the anterior compartment and continues as the dorsal artery of foot (dorsalis pedis artery) after passing the ankle joint.

Dorsalis pedis artery: It supplies the dorsum of the foot and passes through the first dorsal interosseous muscle to enter the sole of the foot and contributes in the formation of the plantar arch (Figure 5.31).

Posterior tibial artery: It is the continuation of the popliteal artery and supplies the posterior and lateral compartments of the leg (Figure 5.30). This artery passes behind the medial malleolus and divides into the medial and lateral plantar arteries after entering the plantar aspect of the foot.

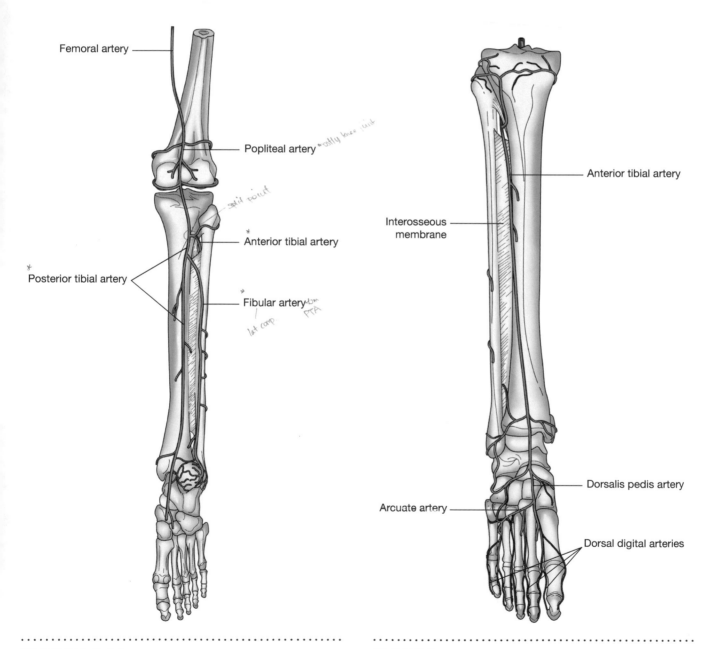

FIGURE 5.30
Popliteal and Posterior Tibial Arteries

FIGURE 5.31
Anterior Tibial Artery

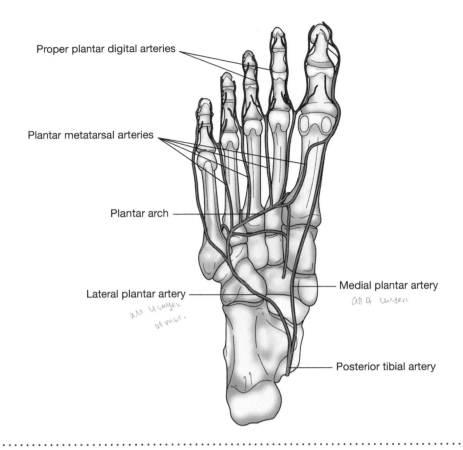

FIGURE 5.32
Plantar Arteries

Plantar arteries: The **medial and lateral plantar arteries** supply the muscles of the sole of the foot and foot joints (Figure 5.32). The lateral plantar artery joins the terminal branch of the dorsalis pedis artery to form the plantar arch. The branches of this arch contribute the blood supply of the toes.

Venous Drainage of the Body

The vessel that carries the blood toward the heart is called **vein**. The veins are classified as superficial and deep veins. The **superficial veins** are contained within the superficial fascia that eventually drain into the deep veins. The **deep veins** follow the course of the arteries.

Venous Drainage of the Head and Neck

The superficial veins of the brain are collected by the dural sinuses (Figure 5.33A and Figure 5.33B). The **dural sinuses** are venous structures located between two layers of the dura mater. The major dural sinuses are names based on their shape or direction and include:

a. The **cavernous sinuses** are located in the middle cranial fossa on either side of the midline and receive the venous blood of the orbital cavity contents.

b. The **superior and inferior sagittal sinuses** are contained within the superior and inferior margins of the falx cerebri respectively.

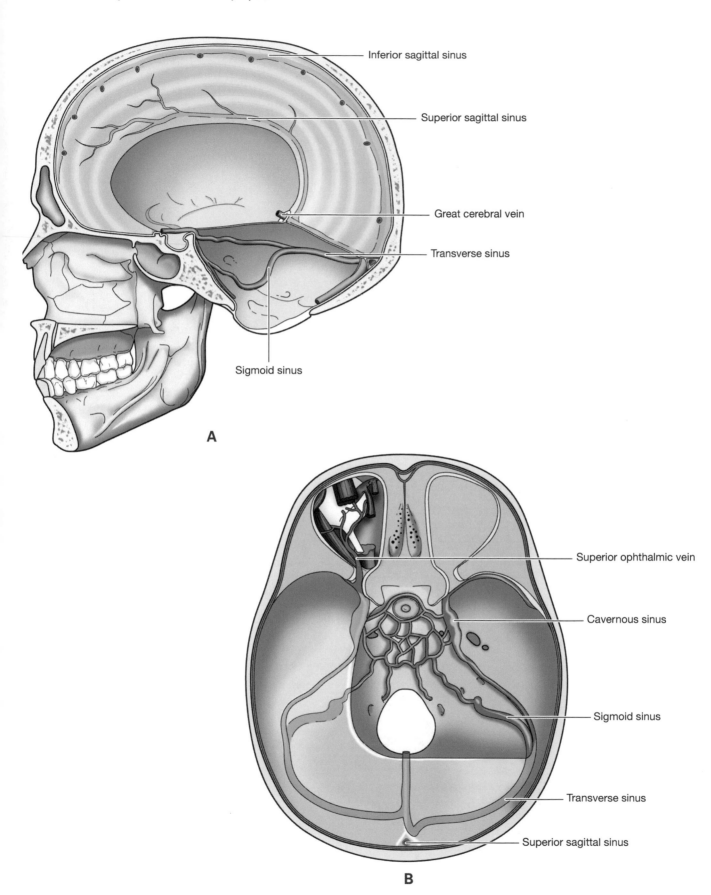

A

B

FIGURE 5.33

Dural Sinuses: (A) sagittal section; (B) transverse section

   c. The **transverse sinuses** are housed in the posterior margin of the tentorium
      cerebelli and receive the superior and inferior sagittal sinuses.
   d. The **sigmoid sinuses** are located in the bony groove on the interior surface
      of the mastoid process of the temporal bones. This sinus receives all the dural
      sinuses (directly or indirectly) and empties into the internal jugular vein.

The deep veins of the brain are mostly received by **great cerebral vein** that in
turn drains into the dural sinuses.

The **internal jugular vein** starts at the level of jugular foramen as the continuation of the sigmoid sinus and travels with the internal and common carotid
arteries and joins the subclavian vein behind the sternoclavicular joint to form
the brachiocephalic vein (Figure 5.34). It mainly receives the venous blood of the
deep parts of the head and neck.

The **anterior and external jugular veins** as the superficial veins of the neck
receive the venous blood of the posterior part of the scalp, superficial parts of the
face and neck, and eventually drain in to the subclavian vein (Figure 5.34).

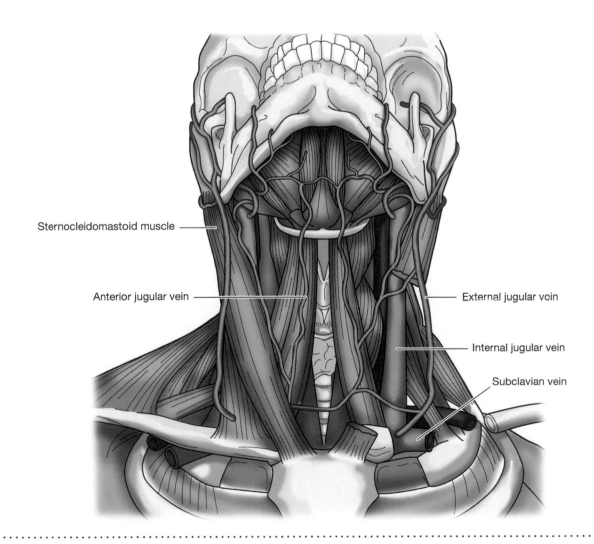

Sternocleidomastoid muscle

Anterior jugular vein

External jugular voin

Internal jugular vein

Subclavian vein

FIGURE 5.34
Venous Drainage of Neck

Venous Drainage of the Upper Limb

The venous blood of the upper limb is collected by deep and superficial veins. The deep veins are synonymous with the arteries and empty to the **axillary vein** (Figure 5.35). The axillary vein continues as the subclavian vein after the lateral border of rib I. The subclavian vein joins the internal jugular vein to form the brachiocephalic vein.

The tributaries of the axillary and subclavian veins are the same as the branches of the synonymous arteries. In addition, the axillary vein receives the cephalic vein and the subclavian vein receives the external and internal jugular veins.

The superficial veins of the upper limb known as **cephalic** and **basilic** veins travel on the lateral and medial side of the forearm respectively (Figure 5.35). These veins arise from dorsal venous plexus on the dorsum of the hand and usually are connected with each other by the **median cubital vein** at the level of cubital fossa. The basilic vein penetrates the deep fascia at the distal arm, ascends on the medial side of the arm and continues as the axillary vein. The cephalic vein ascends on the lateral arm and drains into the axillary vein.

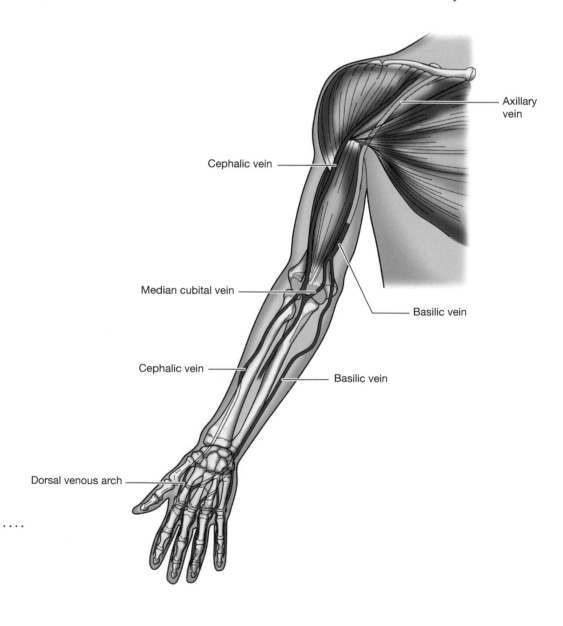

FIGURE 5.35

Superficial Veins of Upper Limb

Venous Drainage of the Thorax

The **pulmonary veins** are a pair of veins on each side that receive oxygenated blood from the lung and drain to the left atrium (Figures 5.3 and 5.7).

The **superior vena cava** is formed by the union of the left and right brachiocephalic veins behind the first costal cartilage on the right side and drains into the right atrium (Figure 5.36). It drains the venous blood of the head, neck, upper limbs, and thorax (except the heart).

The venous blood of the thoracic wall is collected by the anterior and posterior intercostal veins (Figure 5.37). The anterior intercostal veins drain to the ipsilateral brachiocephalic vein. The posterior intercostal veins on the right side drain into the **Azygus** vein, whereas on the left side they drain into the hemiazygus and accessory hemiazygus veins.

The hemiazygus and accessory hemiazygus veins drain into azygus vein that in turn empties into the superior vena cava.

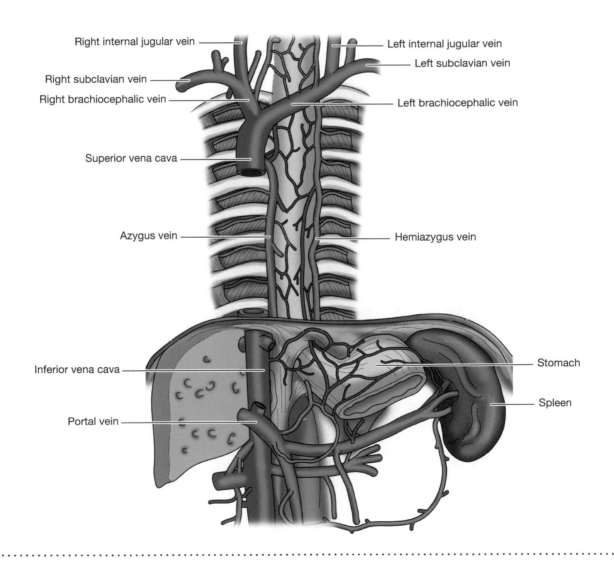

FIGURE 5.36
Superior Vena Cava

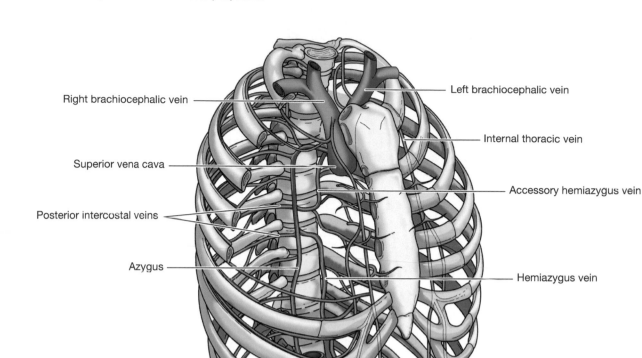

Right brachiocephalic vein

Superior vena cava

Posterior intercostal veins

Azygus

Inferior vena cava

Left brachiocephalic vein

Internal thoracic vein

Accessory hemiazygus vein

Hemiazygus vein

FIGURE 5.37
Venous Drainage of Thoracic Wall

Venous Drainage of the Abdomen

The **inferior vena cava** is formed by the union of the **left** and **right common iliac** veins at the level of vertebra LV (Figure 5.38). It ascends on the right side of the abdominal aorta, passes through the diaphragm at the level of vertebra TVIII, and enters the right atrium. The inferior vena cava receives the venous blood of the lower limbs, pelvis, and abdomen (except the abdominal part of the GI tract, pancreas, and spleen).

The venous blood of the abdominal part of the GI tract, pancreas, and spleen is collected by the superior mesenteric, inferior mesenteric, and splenic veins (Figure 5.39).

The splenic vein receives the inferior mesenteric vein and unites with the superior mesenteric vein to form the **portal vein** that in turn empties into the liver. The hepatic veins drain the venous blood of the liver into the inferior vena cava.

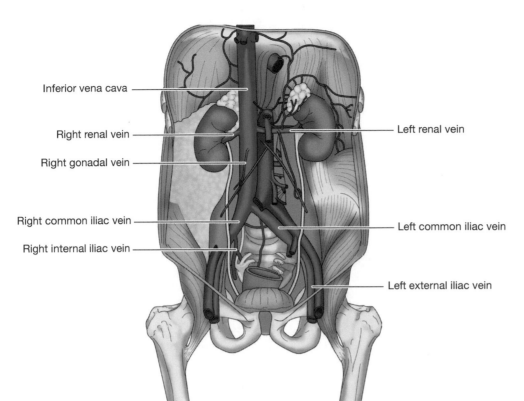

FIGURE 5.38
Venous Drainage of Abdomen

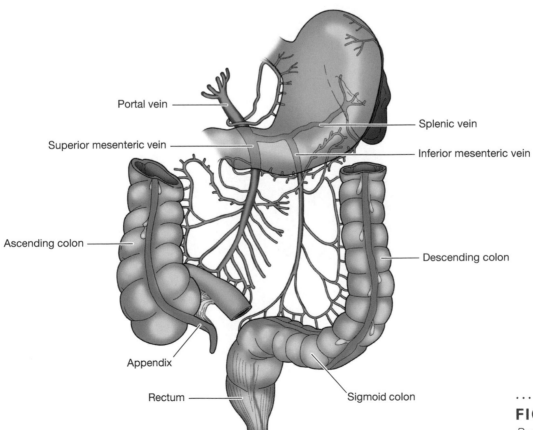

FIGURE 5.39
Portal Vein

Venous Drainage of the Pelvis

The **internal iliac vein** receives the venous blood of the pelvis through the tributaries that follow the synonymous arterial branches (Figure 5.40).

The **external iliac vein** is the continuation of the femoral vein and joins the internal iliac vein to form the common iliac vein (Figure 5.38). It receives the venous blood of the lower anterior abdominal wall and false pelvis walls.

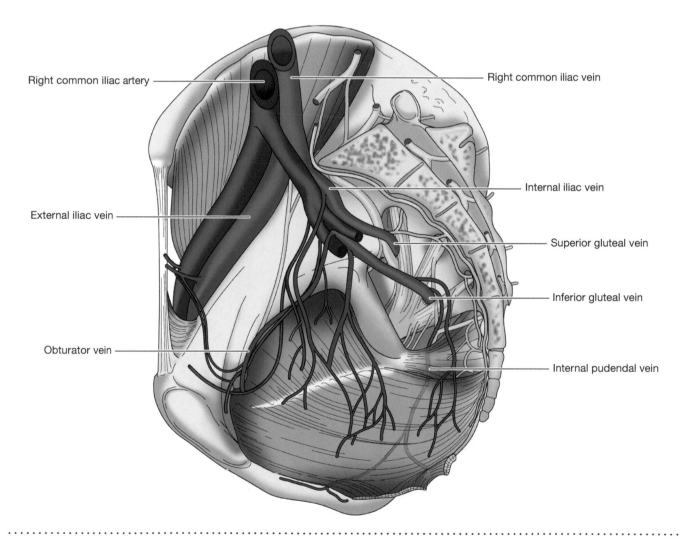

FIGURE 5.40

Venous Drainage of Pelvis (right sagittal section)

Venous Drainage of the Lower Limb

The venous blood of the lower limb is collected by deep and superficial veins (Figure 5.41). The deep veins are synonymous with the arteries and empty to the **femoral vein** (except the gluteal region veins that are drained into the internal iliac vein). The femoral vein receives the great saphenous vein below the inguinal ligament and continues as the external iliac vein after passing deep to the inguinal ligament.

The superficial veins of the lower limb known as **great** and **small saphenous** veins travel on the medial and posterior side of the leg respectively (Figure 5.41). These veins arise from dorsal venous plexus on the dorsum of the foot. The small saphenous vein penetrates the deep fascia of the popliteal fossa and drains into the popliteal vein. The great saphenous vein ascends on the medial thigh and drains into the femoral vein.

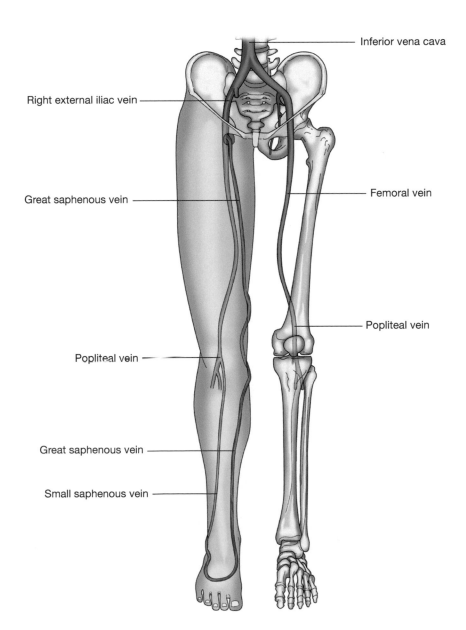

Inferior vena cava

Right external iliac vein

Great saphenous vein

Femoral vein

Popliteal vein

Popliteal vein

Great saphenous vein

Small saphenous vein

FIGURE 5.41

Venus Drainage of Lower Limb

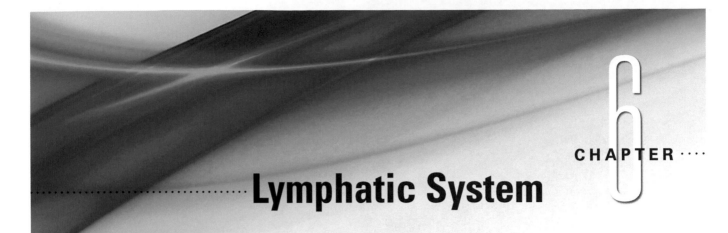

Lymphatic System

LEARNING OBJECTIVES

Upon completion of this chapter you should be able to:

1. Explain the formation of the lymph.
2. Name the lymphatic organs and explain their main functions.
3. Describe the lymphatic drainage of the body.

The lymphatic system is composed of lymphatic vessels and lymphatic organs including lymph nodes, tonsils, thymus, and spleen (Figure 6.1).

The main functions of this system include:

1. Drainage of the interstitial fluid (15% of total volume of capillary exudates that is not picked up by capillaries).
2. Transportation of the lipid and lipid-soluble vitamins from gastrointestinal tract to vascular system.
3. Filtration of the lymph and blood.
4. Immunological defense.

Lymph is a transparent, colorless, or slightly yellow, watery fluid. It closely resembles the blood plasma, but is more dilute (Figure 6.2). Lymphatic vessels collect the remnant of the interstitial fluid and cell debris from different tissues (except nervous tissue). It also receives lipid droplets from the gastrointestinal tract and lymphocytes from blood.

···· Lymphatic Vessels

The lymphatic vessels carry the lymph and pass it through the lymph nodes to be filtered (Figure 6.2). The lymphatic vessels are present in all human organs except the central nervous system, eyeball, inner ear, and cartilages. These vessels join together to form larger ducts or trunks. Those in turn drain into the venous system at the junction of the subclavian and internal jugular veins.

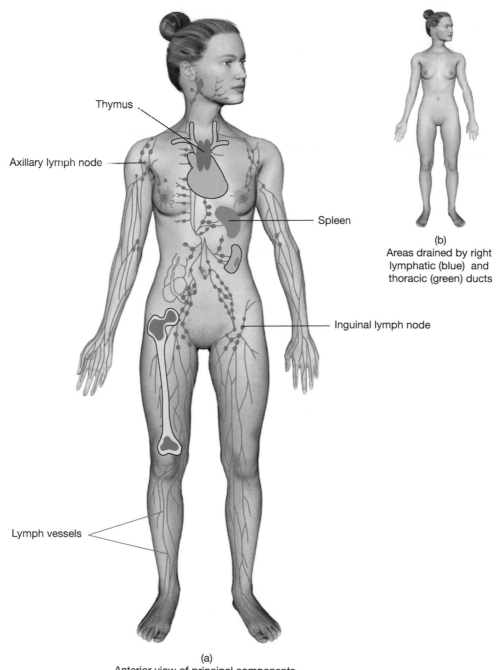

Thymus

Axillary lymph node

Spleen

Inguinal lymph node

Lymph vessels

(a)
Anterior view of principal components
of lymphatic system

(b)
Areas drained by right
lymphatic (blue) and
thoracic (green) ducts

FIGURE 6.1

Lymphatic System Components

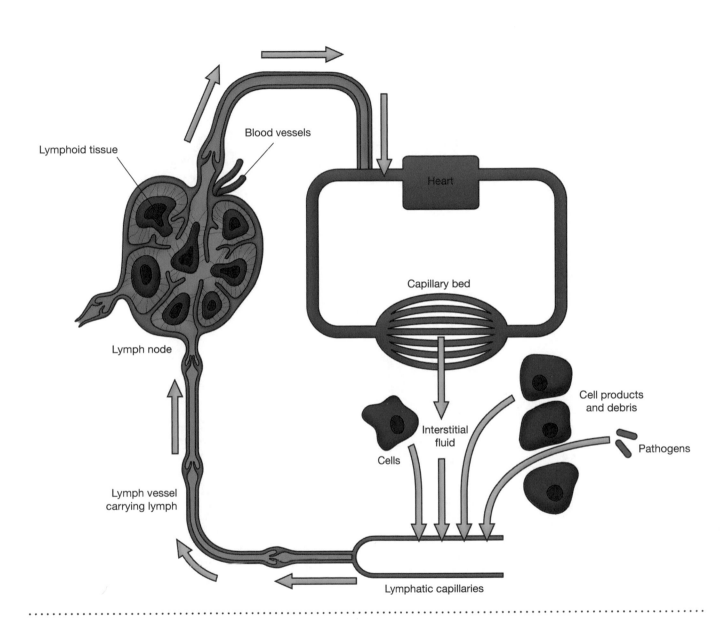

FIGURE 6.2
Lymph Circulation

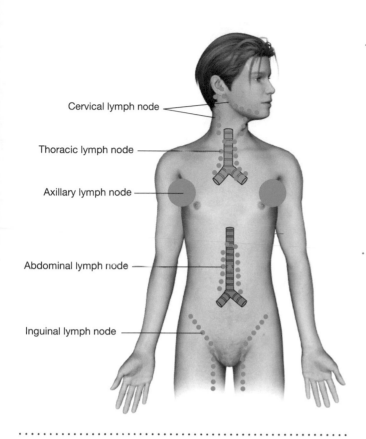

Cervical lymph node

Thoracic lymph node

Axillary lymph node

Abdominal lymph node

Inguinal lymph node

FIGURE 6.3
Lymph Nodes

Lymph Nodes

The lymph nodes are bean-shaped structures found usually in groups and accompany deep and superficial vessels (Figure 6.3). They are particularly numerous in axilla, neck, popliteal fossa, inguinal region, and abdominal and thoracic cavities. The lymph nodes are the site of the lymph filtration and B lymphocytes proliferation.

Thymus

The thymus is a pinkish gland that weights about 10 to 15 grams at birth and reaches to a maximum of 30 to 40 grams at puberty (Figure 6.1). It will be replaced by connective tissue after puberty. This gland is formed by two lobes and is located in the anterior and superior mediastina. The thymus is the main site of the T lymphocytes maturation.

Spleen

The spleen is the largest of the lymphatic organs located in the abdominal cavity in the left hypochondriac region and has two surfaces (medial and lateral), two borders (superior and inferior), and two poles (anterior and posterior) (Figure 6.4).

The lateral or **diaphragmatic surface** is smooth and is guarded by the ribs IX, X, and XI. The medial or **visceral surface** is mainly related to stomach and left kidney and carries the **hilum**. The splenic vessels and autonomic nerves pass through the hilum.

The main function of the spleen is to filter the old and damaged red blood cells from the blood.

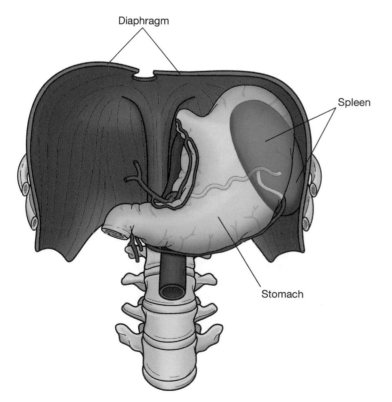

Diaphragm

Spleen

Stomach

FIGURE 6.4
Spleen

···· Tonsils

The tonsils are aggregates of more or less encapsulated lymphoid tissue situated at the entrances to the pharynx (Figure 6.5). Their function is to produce antibodies against antigens.

The tonsils are located at the roof of the nasopharynx (pharyngeal tonsil), either side of the oropharynx (palatine tonsils), and on the posterior one-third of the tongue (lingual tonsils).

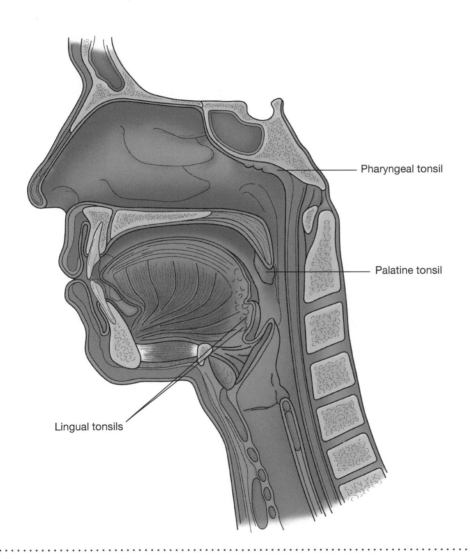

Pharyngeal tonsil

Palatine tonsil

Lingual tonsils

FIGURE 6.5
Tonsils (sagittal section of the head and neck)

···· The Lymphatic Drainage of the Body

Lower Limb Lymphatic Drainage

The lymph of the lower limb is collected by the superficial and deep lymphatic vessels that accompany the corresponding veins. The lymph of these vessels drains into the **inguinal lymph nodes**, which in turn empty to the pelvic and abdominal lymph nodes (Figure 6.6). The lymph of the abdomen eventually drains into the cisterna chyli. The inguinal lymph nodes also receive the lymph of the lower quadrants of the anterior abdominal wall and perineum.

The **cisterna chyli** is a lymphatic sac located in front of the vertebrae LI and LII (Figure 6.7). The thoracic duct originates from the cisterna chyli, passes through the diaphragm, ascends in the posterior mediastinum, and drains into the junction of the left internal jugular and left subclavian veins. The thoracic duct receives the lymph of the lower limbs, pelvic cavity, abdominal cavity, the left side of the thoracic cavity, the left side of the head and neck, and the left upper limb.

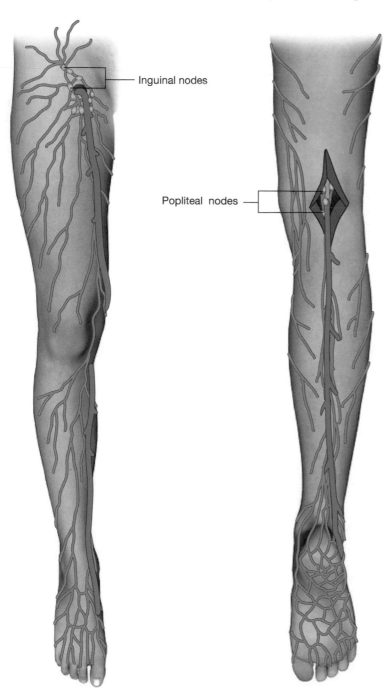

Inguinal nodes

Popliteal nodes

Anterior View   **Posterior View**

FIGURE 6.6

Lower Limb Lymphatic Drainage

Pelvis and Abdomen Lymphatic Drainage

The lymph of the pelvic viscerae drains into the lymph nodes accompanying the internal, external, and common iliac arteries, which in turn are drained into the **para-aortic lymph nodes** (Figure 6.7). These lymph nodes receive the lymph of the posterior abdominal wall, kidneys, and gonads.

The lymph of the gastrointestinal tract, liver, pancreas, and spleen drains into the **pre-aortic lymph nodes**.

Both the para-aortic and pre-aortic lymph nodes are eventually drained into the cisterna chyli.

Thorax Lymphatic Drainage

The lymph of thorax initially drains into the parasternal, diaphragmatic, inter-costal, and midastinal lymph nodes (Figure 6.7). The lymph of these nodes emp-ties into the thoracic duct on the left side and right lymphatic duct on the right side. The **right lymphatic duct** is formed by the union of the right subclavian and right jugular trunks and eventually empties to the junction of the right sub-clavian and right internal jugular veins.

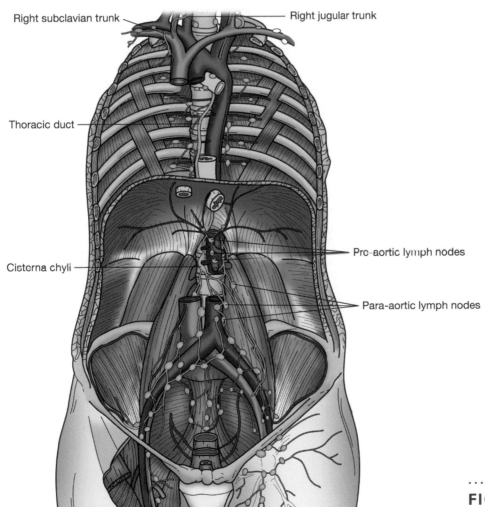

Right subclavian trunk

Right jugular trunk

Thoracic duct

Cisterna chyli

Pre-aortic lymph nodes

Para-aortic lymph nodes

FIGURE 6.7

Trunk Lymphatic Drainage

Head and Neck Lymphatic Drainage

The lymph of the head and neck drains into the superficial and deep lymph nodes (Figure 6.8). These lymph nodes are associated with the superficial and deep veins respectively. The head and neck lymph nodes eventually drain into the left thoracic duct on the left side and into the right lymphatic duct on the right side.

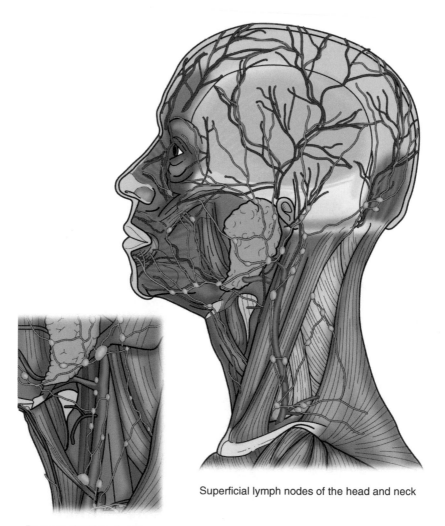

Superficial lymph nodes of the head and neck

Deep cervical lymph nodes

FIGURE 6.8

Head and Neck Lymphatic Drainage

Upper Limb Lymphatic Drainage

The lymph of the upper limb drains into the superficial and deep lymph nodes. These lymph nodes are associated with the superficial and deep veins respectively and eventually drain into the **axillary lymph nodes** (Figure 6.9). The axillary lymph nodes drain into the subclavian duct that in turn empties into the right lymphatic duct on the right side and the thoracic duct on the left side.

The axillary lymph nodes also receive the superficial lymph nodes of the thoracic wall and the upper quadrants of the anterior abdominal wall.

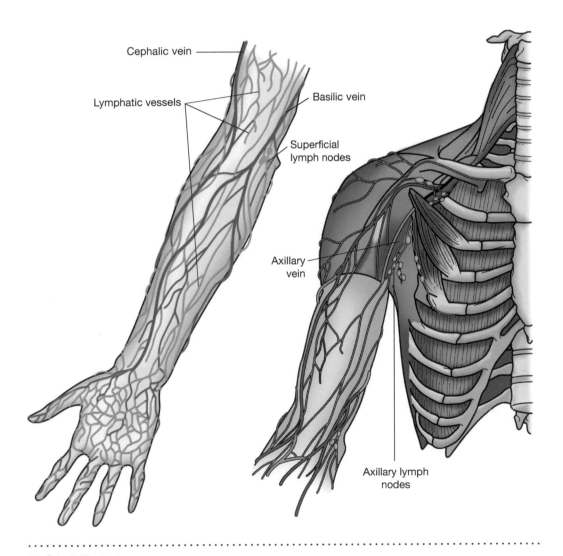

FIGURE 6.9

Upper Limb Lymphatic Drainage

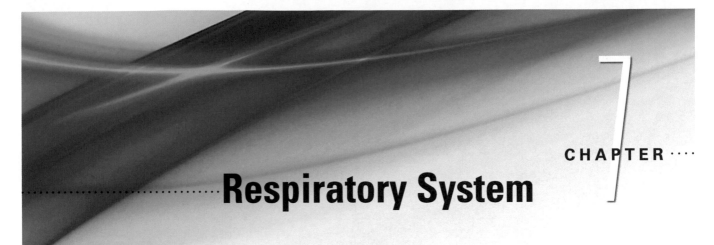

Respiratory System

LEARNING OBJECTIVES

Upon completion of this chapter you should be able to:

1. Name the respiratory system divisions and discuss their functions.
2. Describe the nose.
3. Name the subdivisions of the pharynx and explain their features.
4. Name the laryngeal cartilages and define its internal characteristics.
5. Explain the trachea and its divisions.
6. Discus the lung features and pleura.

The two systems that cooperate to supply O_2 and eliminate CO_2 are the respiratory and cardiovascular systems. The respiratory system provides for gas exchange, whereas the cardiovascular system distributes the respiratory gases.

The respiratory system consists of three parts (Figure 7.1):

1. The **upper airways** include nose and pharynx.
2. The **lower airways** consist of a long list of passages below the pharynx (larynx, trachea, bronchi, and bronchioles).
3. The **lungs**

The main function of the airways is to conduct the inhaled air into the lungs. They also moisten, filtrate, and regulate the temperature of the air.

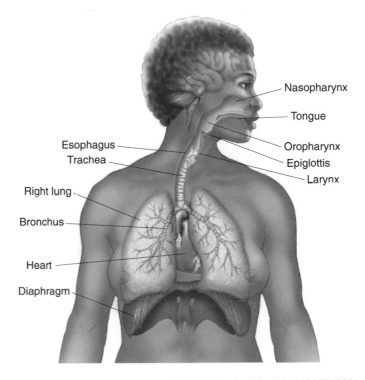

FIGURE 7.1

Respiratory System Components

···· # Nose

The nose is the uppermost part of the respiratory system and is subdivided into the external nose and nasal cavities.

The **external nose** is the anterior extension of the nasal cavities and is formed by bones (such as nasal bone and maxilla) and cartilages (Figure 7.2). It is covered by skin and skeletal muscles. The openings of the external nose to the exterior are known as **nostrils** (external nares), the diameter of which is changed by the contraction of the covering muscles. The area above each nostril, **vestibule**, is lined with the skin that carries short coarse hairs.

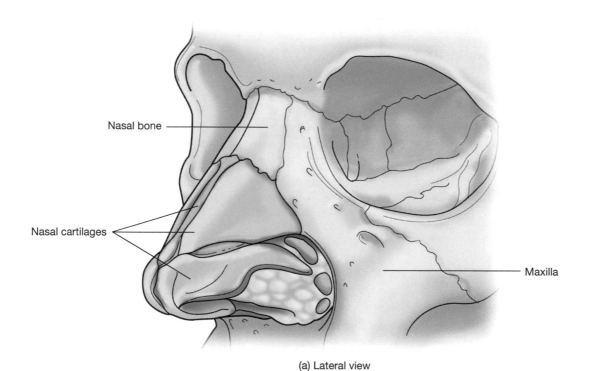

Nasal bone

Nasal cartilages

Maxilla

(a) Lateral view

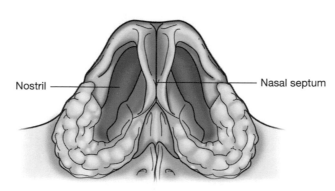

Nostril

Nasal septum

(b) Inferior view

FIGURE 7.2
External Nose

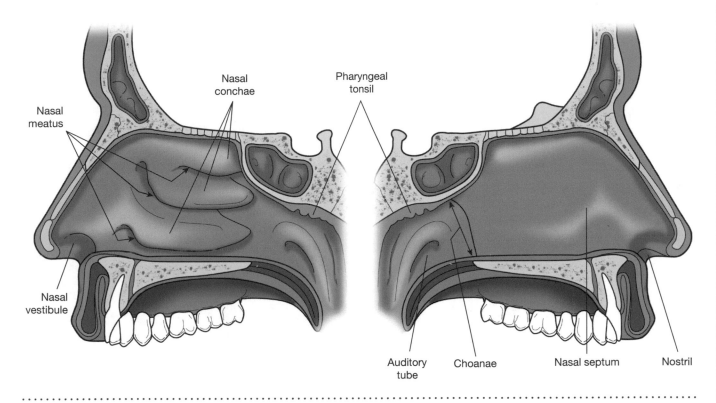

FIGURE 7.3
External Cavity

Nasal cavities are two osseo-cartilaginous spaces separated by nasal septum (Figure 7.3). These spaces start at the vestibule and join to the nasopharynx via the **choanae** (internal nares). Each nasal cavity has a floor, a roof, and a medial and a lateral wall. The roof has some openings for the olfactory nerves. The floor separates the nasal cavity from the oral cavity. The medial wall is smooth and formed by the nasal septum whereas the lateral wall carries three curved bony shelves known as **nasal chonchae**. The spaces bellow the conchae (**meatuses**) receive the paranasal sinuses and nasolacrimal duct.

· · · · Paranasal Sinuses

The paranasal sinuses are several empty spaces contained within the bones of the skull surrounding the nasal cavities (frontal, maxilla, ethmoid, and sphenoid bones). These sinuses are lined with the respiratory mucous membrane and open on the lateral wall of the nasal cavities (Figure 7.4). They lighten the skull, resonate the voice, and enhance the efficiency of the respiratory mucous membrane in filtration, humidification, and thermoregulation of the inhaled air.

(A) Lateral View

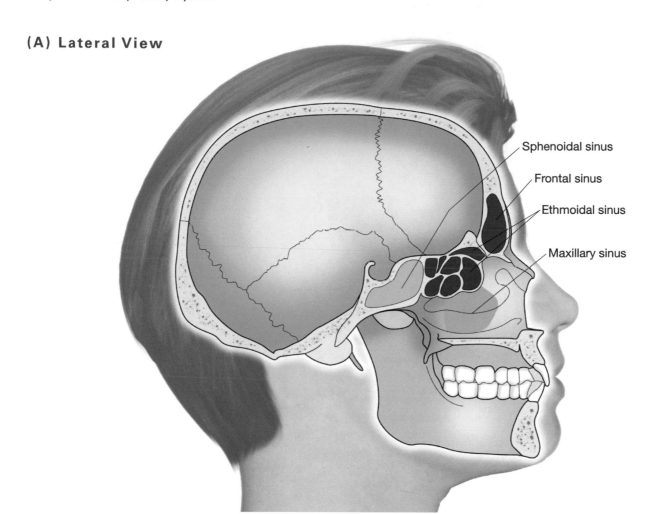

Sphenoidal sinus

Frontal sinus

Ethmoidal sinus

Maxillary sinus

(B) Interior View

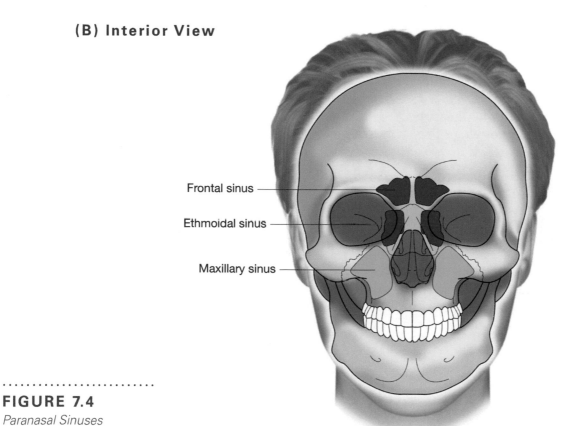

Frontal sinus

Ethmoidal sinus

Maxillary sinus

FIGURE 7.4
Paranasal Sinuses

· · · · **Pharynx**

The pharynx is a 12 to 15 cm muscular tube that starts from the base of the skull and ends at the esophagus (Figure 7.5). It is related to the cervical vertebrae posteriorly and the nasal cavities, oral cavity, and larynx anteriorly thus is subdivided into three parts as follows:

Nasopharynx is located behind the nasal cavities and above the soft palate (Figures 7.3 and 7.5). On its roof there is an aggregation of the lymphoid tissue known as the **pharyngeal tonsil**. The **auditory (Eustachian) tube** opens on the lateral wall of the nasopharynx and connects it to the middle ear.

Oropharynx is located behind the oral cavity and extends from the soft palate to the level of epiglottis (Figure 7.5). The **palatine tonsils** are located on the lateral walls of the oropharynx between the palatoglossal and palatopharyngeal folds.

Laryngopharynx is behind the larynx and extends from the epiglottis to the beginning of the esophagus (Figure 7.5).

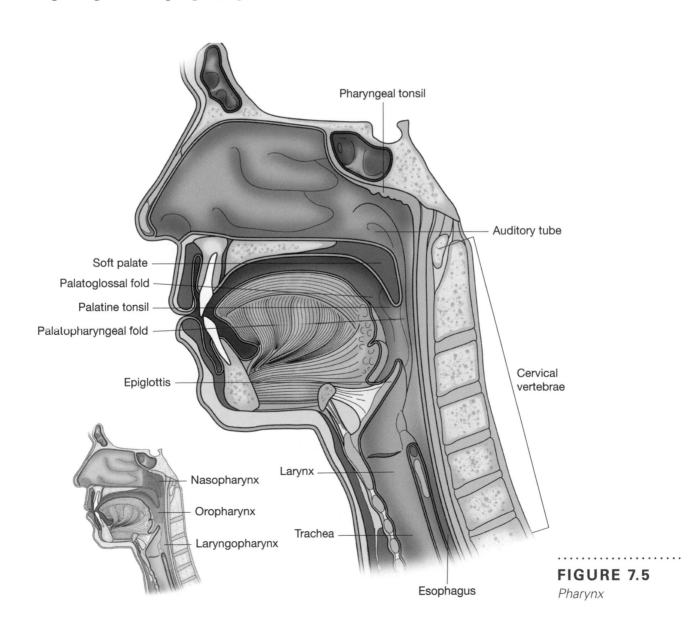

FIGURE 7.5

Pharynx

· · · · Larynx

The larynx is located in front of vertebrae CIV to CVI and opens to the laryngopharynx superiorly and trachea inferiorly (Figure 7.6). It is the organ of phonation and has a cartilaginous skeleton. The cartilages of the larynx are joined by membranes and ligaments. The main laryngeal cartilages include the thyroid, cricoid, epiglottis, and arytenoids.

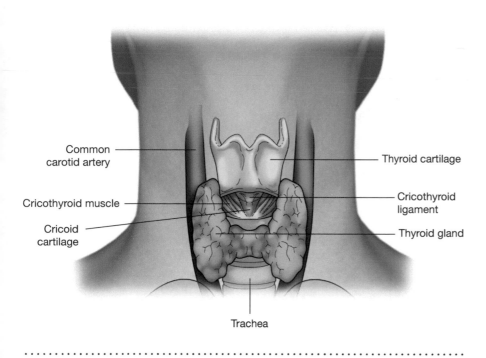

Common carotid artery

Cricothyroid muscle

Cricoid cartilage

Trachea

Thyroid cartilage

Cricothyroid ligament

Thyroid gland

FIGURE 7.6

Larynx

Thyroid cartilage is the largest laryngeal cartilage formed by two laminae that are fused anteriorly to form the **laryngeal eminence (Adam's apple)** in front of the neck but widely open posteriorly (Figure 7.7A, B, and C). The posterior border of each lamina projects superiorly and inferiorly to form the **superior and inferior horns**, respectively. The superior horns are joined to the hyoid bone by a ligament and the inferior horns articulate with the cricoid cartilage. The thyrohyoid membrane connects the superior border of the thyroid cartilage to the hyoid bone and the cricothyroid membrane joins its inferior border to the cricoid cartilage.

The **cricoid cartilage** is the most inferior cartilage of the larynx that resembles a signet ring with its lamina (wide plate) facing posteriorly (Figure 7.7A, B, and C). The cricoid cartilage lamina articulates with the arytenoid cartilages superiorly. The inferior border of the cartilage connects to the first cartilage ring of the trachea by a fibrous membrane.

The **epiglottis cartilage** is a leaflet-shaped cartilage the handle of which is attached to the interior side of the laryngeal eminence and its wide part located behind the tongue and acts as a lid to close the entrance of the larynx during swallowing (Figure 7.7A, B, and C).

The **arytenoid cartilages** are two pyramidal cartilages the bases of which articulate with the cricoid cartilage inferiorly (Figure 7.7B and C). There are two processes at the base of each arytenoid cartilage. One of the processes serves as the attachment site for the vocal ligament and the other one is the point of attachment for some of the intrinsic muscles of larynx.

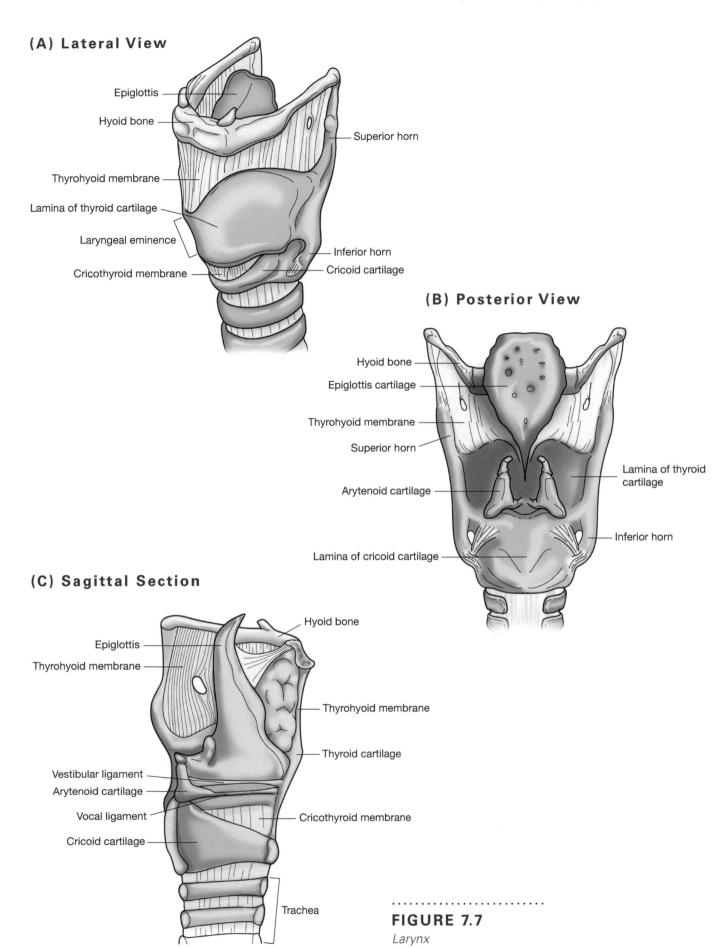

(A) Lateral View

Epiglottis

Hyoid bone

Superior horn

Thyrohyoid membrane

Lamina of thyroid cartilage

Laryngeal eminence

Inferior horn

Cricoid cartilage

Cricothyroid membrane

(B) Posterior View

Hyoid bone

Epiglottis cartilage

Thyrohyoid membrane

Superior horn

Arytenoid cartilage

Lamina of thyroid cartilage

Inferior horn

Lamina of cricoid cartilage

(C) Sagittal Section

Hyoid bone

Epiglottis

Thyrohyoid membrane

Thyrohyoid membrane

Thyroid cartilage

Vestibular ligament

Arytenoid cartilage

Vocal ligament

Cricothyroid membrane

Cricoid cartilage

Trachea

FIGURE 7.7
Larynx

The Interior of the Larynx

Inside the larynx on each side there are two ligaments stretched between the thyroid and arytenoid cartilages (Figure 7.8). The **vestibular ligaments** are located superiorly and do not vibrate during phonation, whereas the **vocal ligaments** are located inferiorly and vibrate during phonation. These ligaments are covered by the interior mucous membrane of larynx to form the **vestibular (false vocal) folds** and the **vocal (true vocal) folds** respectively. The interior of the larynx is subdivided into three regions by the vestibular and vocal folds. The area superior to the vestibular folds is known as **vestibule** and the area inferior to the vocal folds is called **infraglottic space**. The middle region located between the vestibular and vocal folds on each side is called **ventricle**. The gap between the right and left vocal folds is referred to as **rima glottidis**.

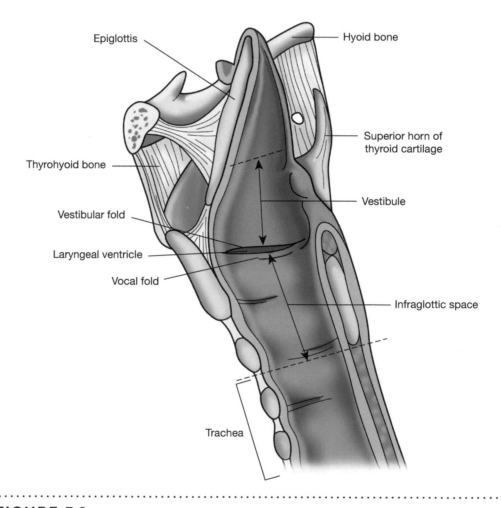

Epiglottis

Hyoid bone

Superior horn of thyroid cartilage

Thyrohyoid bone

Vestibule

Vestibular fold

Laryngeal ventricle

Vocal fold

Infraglottic space

Trachea

FIGURE 7.8

Larynx (internal view)

···· Trachea

The trachea is a fibro-cartilaginous tube that starts from the lower margin of the cricoid cartilage at the level of vertebra CVI, passes the superior mediastinum, and ends at the level of TIV–TV intervertebral disc by dividing into left and right main bronchi (Figure 7.9). It is about 12 cm long and is composed of about twenty incomplete C-shaped cartilage rings, that their posterior ends are attached together by smooth muscle.

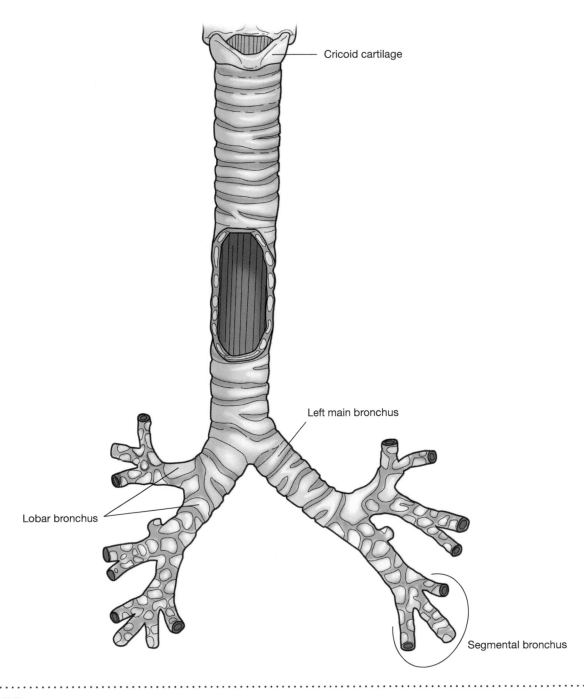

Cricoid cartilage

Left main bronchus

Lobar bronchus

Segmental bronchus

FIGURE 7.9

Trachea

The right main bronchus is shorter, wider, and more vertically positioned compared to the left main bronchus. Trachea is related to esophagus posteriorly, and the thyroid gland (in the neck) and manubrium of the sternum anteriorly.

···· Lungs

The two lungs are located on either side of the mediastinum and are separated by heart and its large vessels and posterior mediastinal structures. Each lung is a half-cone-shaped organ suspended within the pleural cavity by its root attaching to the mediastinum (Figure 7.10A and B).

Each lung has an apex, three surfaces (inferior, lateral and medial), and three borders (anterior, posterior, and inferior).

- The **apex** is round and extends 2.5 cm above the clavicle.
- The **inferior (diaphragmatic) surface** or **base** of the lung is concave and sits on the diaphragm.
- The **lateral (sternocostal) surface** is convex and related to ribs, intercostal muscles, and the sternum (Figure 7.10A). The **medial (mediastinal) surface** is concave and is related to the middle and posterior mediastinal structures (Figure 7.10B). On this surface the **hilum** is located through which the main bronchi, vessels, and nerves enter or leave the lung to form the root of the lung.
- The **anterior border** is sharp, and on the left lung, carries the **cardiac notch**. That part of the left lung below the cardiac notch is known as **lingula**. The **posterior border** is round and is related to the vertebral column. The **inferior border** is sharp and separates the medial and lateral surfaces from the base of the lung (Figure 7.10A and B).

The **right lung** is slightly larger and wider than the left lung and is divided into **three lobes** (superior, middle, and inferior) by **oblique** and **horizontal fissures** (Figure 7.10A and B). The **left lung** is divided into **two lobes** (superior and inferior) by an **oblique fissure**. The lingula of the left lung is the equivalent of the middle lobe on the right lung (Figure 7.10A and B).

After passing through the hilum, the main bronchi divide into lobar and then segmental bronchi. The segmental bronchi continue to divide and produce several generations of divisions, and eventually give rise to bronchioles. The divisions of the main bronchi are referred to as a **bronchial tree** (Figure 7.9).

···· Pleura

The lungs are surrounded by the pleural sacs that are composed of two serous layers: an inner visceral and an outer parietal layer (Figure 7.11). The **visceral pleura** is intimately attached to the surface of the lungs and extends into the fissures of the lungs. It reflects on itself at the hilum to continue as the **parietal pleura** to line the inner surfaces of the ribs, sternum, and mediastinum.

(A) Lateral View

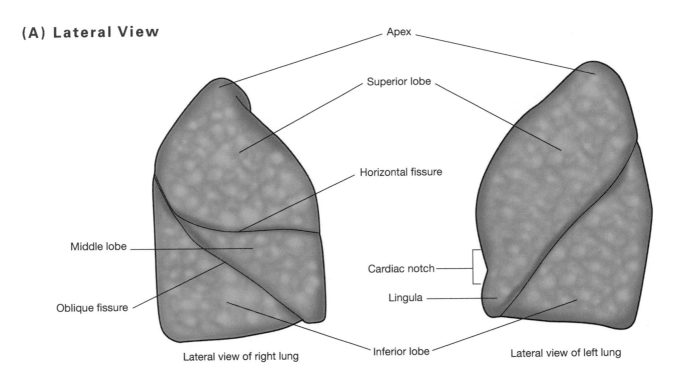

(B) Medial View

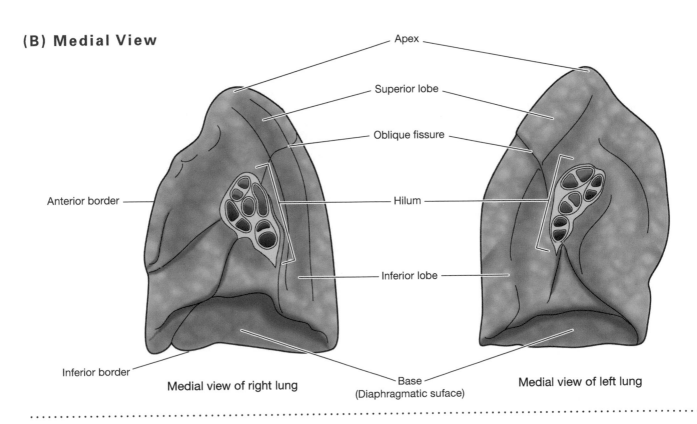

FIGURE 7.10
Lungs

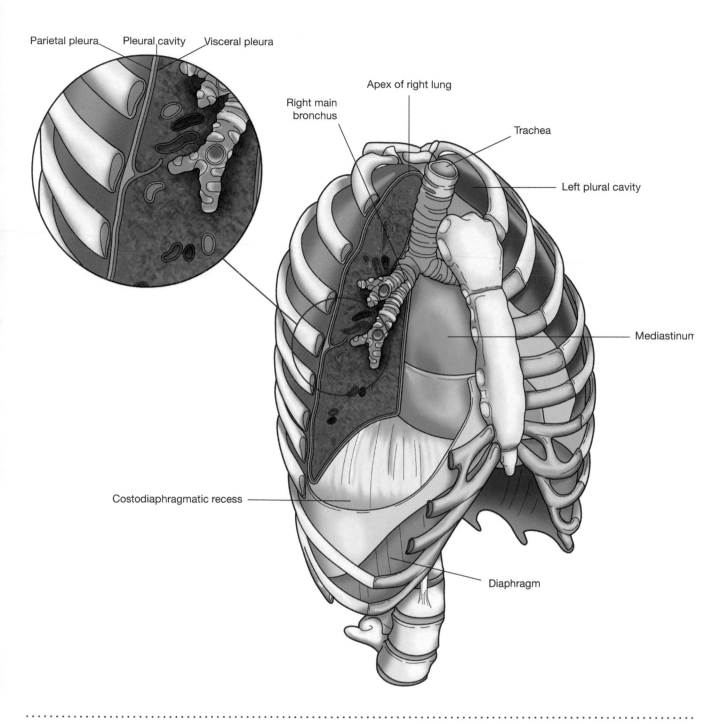

FIGURE 7.11
Pleura and Pleura Cavity

Between the two layers of the pleura, the **pleural cavity** contains a few drops of pleural fluid that lubricate the surfaces and facilitates the movements of the lungs. At the point the parietal pleura changes direction from the lateral (sternocostal) wall to the inferior (diaphragmatic) wall, the two layers of the parietal pleura oppose each other and form a narrow space known as **costodiaphragmatic recess** (Figure 7.11). This space is the lowest point of the pleural cavity.

CHAPTER 8

Digestive System

LEARNING OBJECTIVES

Upon completion of this chapter you should be able to:

1. Explain the oral cavity and its subdivisions.
2. Describe the anatomical features of a tooth.
3. Discuss the structure of the tongue.
4. Describe the esophagus.
5. Explain the peritoneum and its reflections.
6. Describe the anatomical features of the stomach and small and large intestines and explain their subdivisions.
7. Discuss the associated glands of the digestive system.

The digestive system includes those organs that contribute in ingestion and digestion of the food, absorption of nutrients, and elimination of indigestible materials. This system provides nutrients for the cells to be used as a source of energy or for growth and repair.

The digestive system is divided into the alimentary canal and associated organs (Figure 8.1). The **alimentary canal** is a muscular tube approximately 9 meters long that starts from the oral cavity and ends in the anus. The main segments of this canal include the oral cavity, pharynx, esophagus, stomach, small and large intestines, and anal canal. The **associated organs** assist in ingestion and digestion of the food and include teeth, tongue, salivary glands, liver, gall bladder, and pancreas.

···· Oral Cavity

The oral cavity is a space bounded by the lips anteriorly, by the oropharyngeal isthmus posteriorly, by the palate superiorly, by a muscular diaphragm and tongue inferiorly, and by the cheeks laterally (Figure 8.2A). This space is divided into the vestibule and oral cavity proper (Figures 8.2A and B). The **vestibule** is a horseshoe-shaped space bounded by the lips (anteriorly), cheeks (laterally), and dental arches (posteriorly and medially). The **oral cavity proper** is bounded by the palates (superiorly), the muscular diaphragm and tongue (inferiorly), and dental arches (anteriorly and laterally).

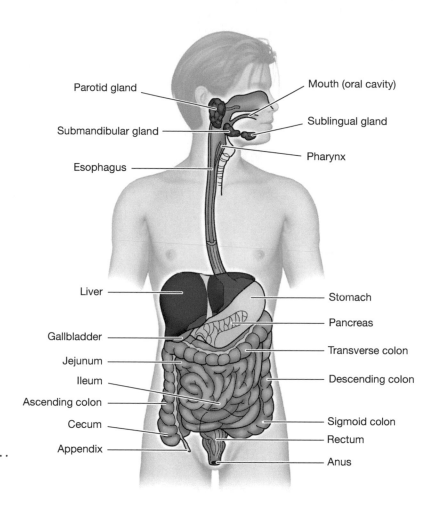

FIGURE 8.1
Digestive System

Parotid gland
Submandibular gland
Esophagus
Liver
Gallbladder
Jejunum
Ileum
Ascending colon
Cecum
Appendix

Mouth (oral cavity)
Sublingual gland
Pharynx
Stomach
Pancreas
Transverse colon
Descending colon
Sigmoid colon
Rectum
Anus

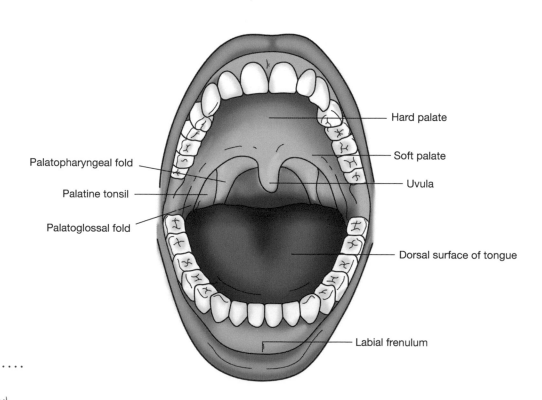

FIGURE 8.2A
Oral Cavity (anterior view)

Palatopharyngeal fold
Palatine tonsil
Palatoglossal fold

Hard palate
Soft palate
Uvula
Dorsal surface of tongue
Labial frenulum

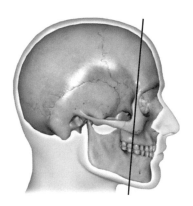

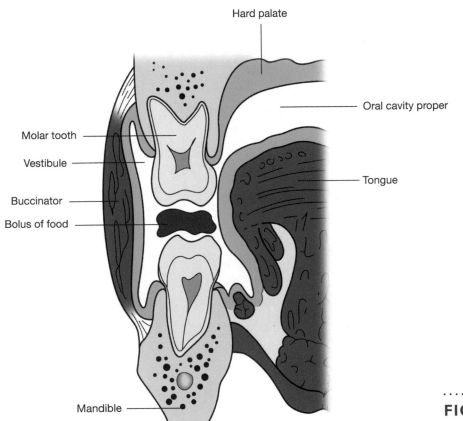

Hard palate

Oral cavity proper

Molar tooth

Vestibule

Tongue

Buccinator

Bolus of food

Mandible

FIGURE 8.2B
Oral Cavity (coronal section)

The **lips** are two muscular folds covered by skin from outside and mucus membrane on inside (Figure 8.2A). The orbicularis oris muscle forms the core of the lips. Each lip is connected to the gum by a mucosal fold known as the **frenulum**.

The **cheeks** are mainly formed by the buccinator muscles covered by the mucus membrane from inside and skin on the outside (Figure 8.2B).

The **palate** includes hard and soft palates. The **hard palate** forms the anterior two-thirds of the roof of the oral cavity and the floor of the nasal cavities (Figures 8.2A and 8.3). It has a bony skeleton covered by mucus membrane. The **soft palate** forms the posterior one-third of the roof and separates the oral cavity proper from the nasopharynx. It has a fibromuscular core covered by mucus membrane. The **uvula**, a conical soft tissue projection, hangs from the posterior border of the soft palate.

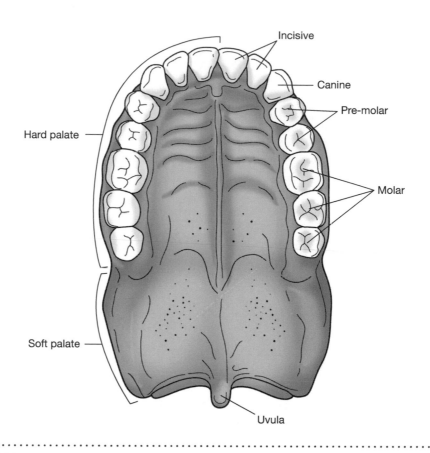

FIGURE 8.3
Hard and Soft Palates

The **oropharyngeal isthmus** is a passage connecting the oral cavity proper to the oropharynx (Figure 8.2A). It is formed by two mucosal folds named as **palato-glossal fold**s.

· · · · Teeth

Each tooth consists of three parts (Figure 8.4):

1. The **crown** is the part of tooth that projects from gingiva and is visible in the oral cavity.
2. The **root** is the part of tooth contained within the alveolar processes of the mandible and maxilla. The root is attached to the bony socket by **periodontal ligament**.
3. The **neck** is the narrow part of the tooth connecting the crown and the root.

The teeth are classified based on the shape of the crown. There are four incisors, two canines, four premolars, and six molars in each jaw.

Most of the tooth is composed of the **dentine** covered by the enamel in the crown and cementum in the root. The **pulp cavity** containing the tooth nerves and blood vessels is housed within the dentine. The extension of the pulp cavity into the roots is called the **root canal**.

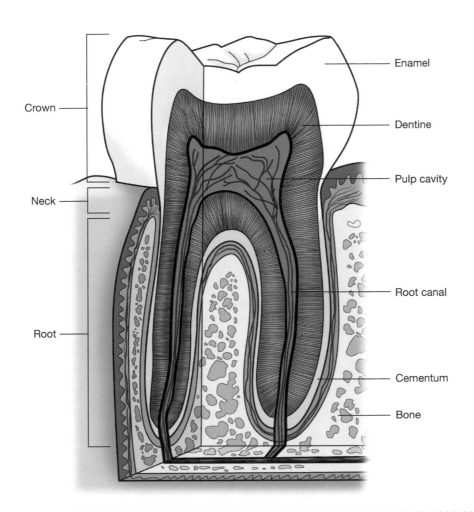

FIGURE 8.4
Tooth (longitudinal section)

· · · · Tongue

The tongue is a muscular organ involved in swallowing, speech, tasting, and chewing. The posterior one-third of the tongue is attached to the floor of the oral cavity and faces the oropharynx known as the **root** or **pharyngeal part** of the tongue (Figures 8.5 and 8.6). The anterior two-thirds of the tongue freely moves in the oral cavity and is known as the **body** or **oral part** of the tongue. A V-shaped groove, **terminal sulcus**, on the superior surface of the tongue separates the anterior and posterior parts of the tongue. On the anterior two-thirds of the superior surface there are some mucosal elevations, **lingual papillae**, that are named based on their shape and include **filiform papillae** (thread-like), **fungiform papillae** (mushroom-like), **folliate papillae** (leaf-like), and **vallate papillae** (Figure 8.6).

The **lingual tonsils** are aggregations of lymphoid tissue on the posterior third of the tongue (Figure 8.6).

The **lingual frenulum** is a muscosal fold that attaches the inferior surface of tongue to the floor of the oral cavity (Figure 8.7).

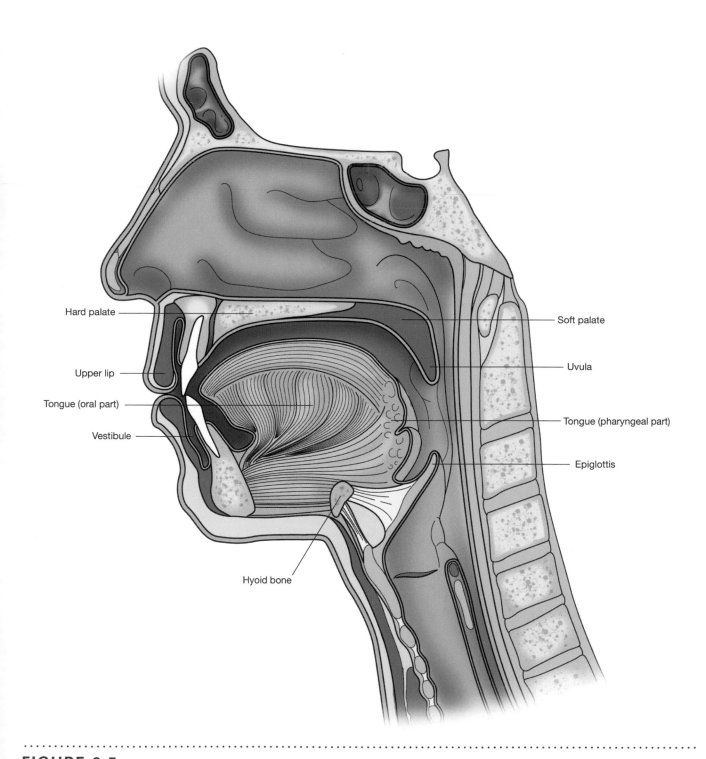

FIGURE 8.5

Oral Cavity (sagittal section)

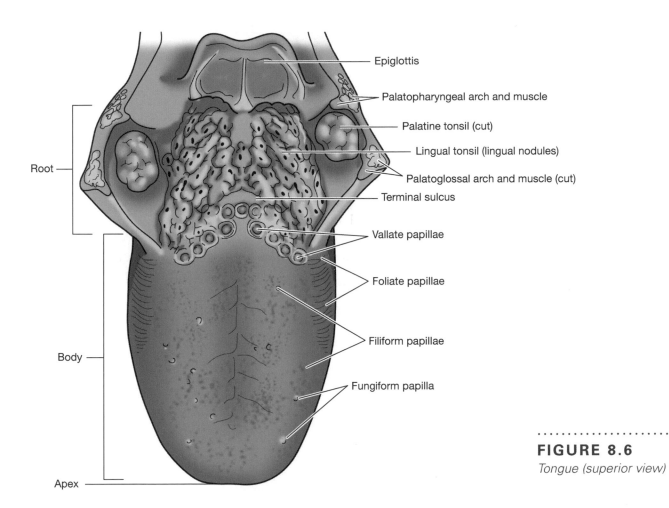

- Epiglottis
- Palatopharyngeal arch and muscle
- Palatine tonsil (cut)
- Lingual tonsil (lingual nodules)
- Palatoglossal arch and muscle (cut)
- Terminal sulcus
- Vallate papillae
- Foliate papillae
- Filiform papillae
- Fungiform papilla

Root

Body

Apex

FIGURE 8.6
Tongue (superior view)

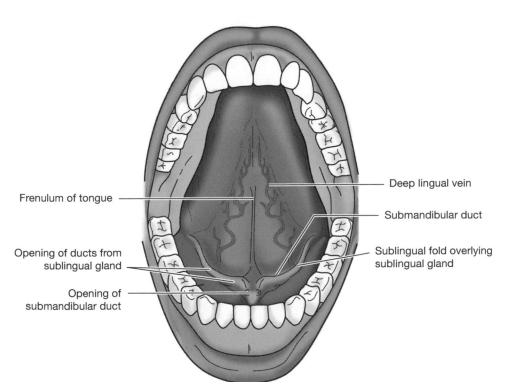

- Frenulum of tongue
- Opening of ducts from sublingual gland
- Opening of submandibular duct
- Deep lingual vein
- Submandibular duct
- Sublingual fold overlying sublingual gland

FIGURE 8.7
Tongue (inferior view)

· · · · **Pharynx**

The pharynx is a muscular tube that connects the nasal cavities to the larynx and the oral cavity to the esophagus. It is described with the respiratory system in Chapter 7.

· · · · **Esophagus**

The esophagus is a 25-cm muscular tube that starts from the laryngopharynx (at the level of vertebra CVI) and ends to the stomach (at the level of vertebra TXI). It passes the neck, superior and posterior mediastina, and the diaphragm to enter the abdomen. It is located in front of the vertebral column on its entire length, and is anteriorly related to the trachea, left atrium of the heart, and diaphragm (Figure 8.8).

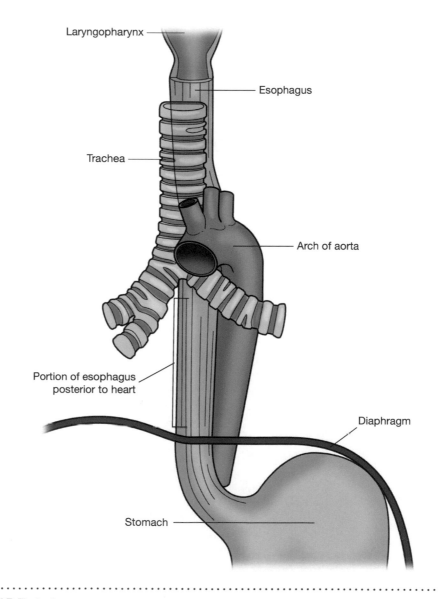

FIGURE 8.8
Esophagus

· · · · **Peritoneum**

The abdominal part of the digestive system is covered by peritoneum (Figure 8.9). The peritoneum is a serous membrane that covers the interior surfaces of the abdominal and pelvic cavities (**parietal peritoneum**) as well as the surface of most of the abdominal and pelvic viscerae (**visceral peritoneum**). The **intra-peritoneal organs** are completely covered by the visceral peritoneum, whereas the **retroperitoneal organs** are located between the parietal peritoneum and the posterior abdominal wall.

The **peritoneal cavity** is a slim space between the parietal and visceral layers of peritoneum that contains a few milliliters of serous fluid to lubricate the surfaces of the abdominal contents (Figure 8.9). The peritoneal cavity is an enclosed sac in male; however, in female it is connected with exterior via the cavity of uterine tubes, uterus, and vagina.

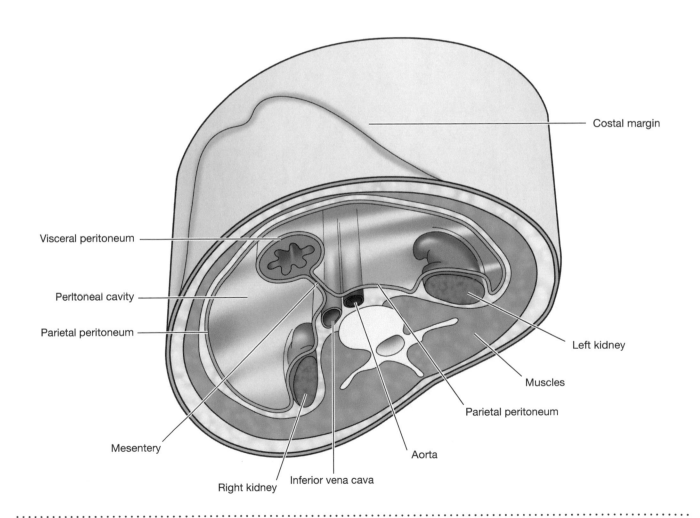

FIGURE 8.9

Peritoneum

The peritoneal reflections are double-layer peritoneal folds that carry blood vessels and nerves to the organs and are classified as:

1. The **peritoneal ligaments** connect the abdominal viscerae to the abdominal walls or other organs, for example, the **falciform ligament** connects the liver to the anterior abdominal wall and diaphragm.
2. The **mesenteries** connect the small intestine (except the duodenum), transverse colon, sigmoid colon, and appendix to the posterior abdominal wall (Figure 8.10). They are named mesentery, transverse mesocolon, sigmoid mesocolon, and mesoappendix, respectively.
3. The **omenta** are stretched between the stomach and other organs (Figure 8.12). The **greater omentum** connects the greater curvature of stomach to the transverse colon and like an apron covers the intestinal loops anteriorly. The **lesser omentum** connects the liver to the small curvature of the stomach.

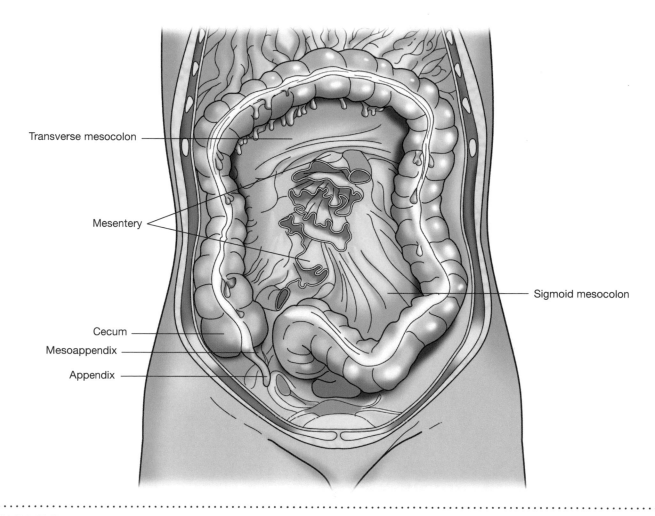

FIGURE 8.10
Peritoneal Reflections

···· Stomach

The stomach is the most dilated part of the alimentary canal with 1 to 1.5 liters of capacity. It is 25 cm long and 11 cm wide. It is located in the left hypochondrium, epigastric, and umbilical regions (Figure 8.11). This J-shaped part of the alimentary canal has a greater and a lesser curvature, an anterior and a posterior

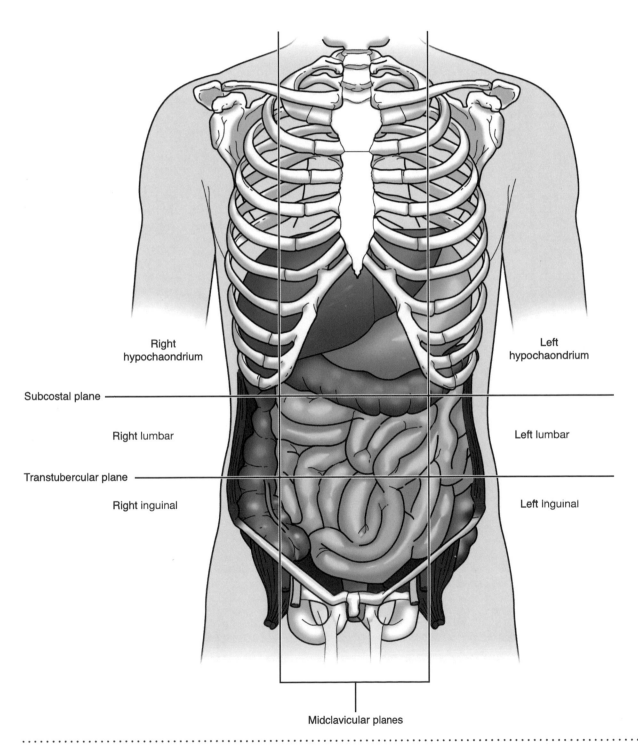

Right
hypochaondrium

Left
hypochaondrium

Subcostal plane

Right lumbar

Left lumbar

Transtubercular plane

Right inguinal

Left Inguinal

Midclavicular planes

FIGURE 8.11
Abdominal Regions

surface, two openings (cardia and pyloric). The stomach can be divided into the following regions (Figure 8.12):

The **fundus** is the dome-shaped part of the stomach, above the level of the cardiac opening.

The **body** is the funnel-shaped region located between the fundus and pyloric part.

The **pyloric part** is the narrow region of the stomach between the body and pyloric opening.

The **cardiac opening** and **pyloric openings** connect the stomach to the esophagus and duodenum, respectively. The pyloric opening is guarded by the pyloric sphincter.

The mucosal membrane lining the interior of the stomach is thrown into longitudinal folds known as the gastric **rugae**. These folds disappear when the stomach is full.

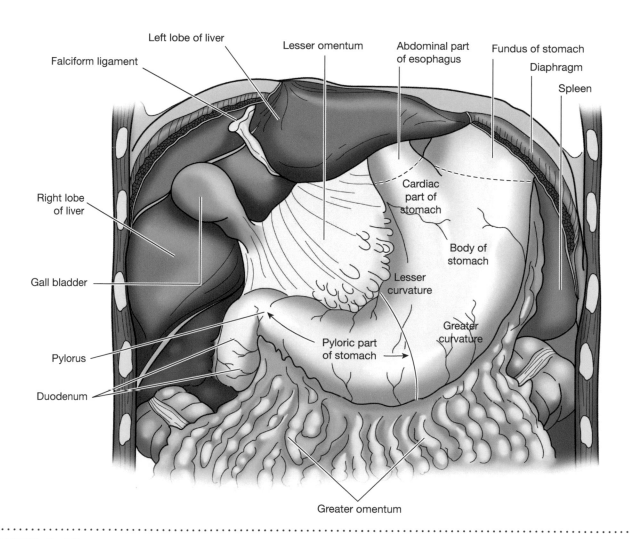

FIGURE 8.12

Stomach In Situ

· · · · Small Intestine

The small intestine starts from the pyloric opening of the stomach and ends at the **ileocecal junction**. It is about 6 meters long and is composed of the following parts:

Duodenum

The duodenum is the shortest and widest part of the small intestine (Figure 8.13). It starts from the pyloric opening of the stomach and ends at the **duodenojejunal flexure**. The duodenum is a C-shaped tube (25 cm) composed of four parts (**superior, descending, horizontal,** and **ascending**) that surround the head of pancreas. The **hepatopancreatic ampulla** opens at the summit of a mucosal elevation (**major duodenal papilla**) in the descending part of duodenum.

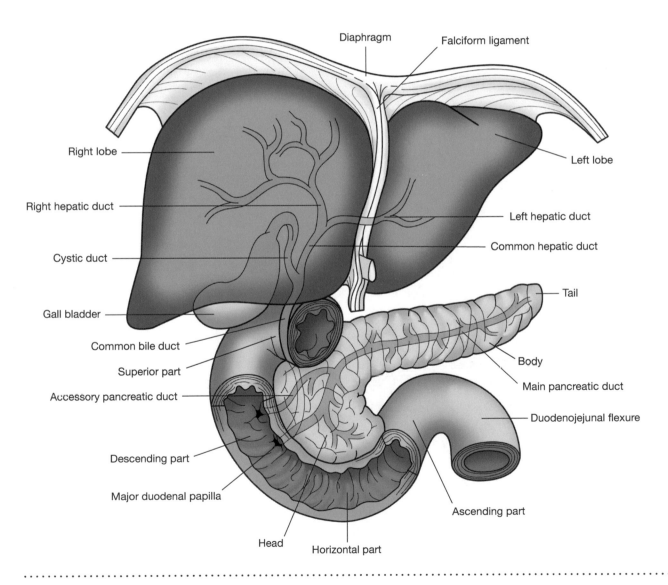

FIGURE 8.13

Duodenum, Pancreas

Jejunum

This part of the small intestine starts from the duodenojejunal flexure and constitutes about two-fifths of the proximal part of the small intestine. It is mainly located in the umbilical region of the abdomen (Figures 8.1 and 8.11).

Ileum

The ileum forms the distal three-fifths of the small intestine that opens into the large intestine at the **ileocecal junction**. This junction is internally guarded by the **ileocecal valve** (Figure 8.14). It is located in mostly the hypogastric region of the abdomen (Figures 8.1 and 8.11). The jejunum and ileum are intraperitoneal organs and attach to the posterior abdominal wall by the mesentery (Figure 8.10).

···· Large Intestine

The large intestine (1.5 m) extends from the ileocecal junction to the anus. The main characteristics of the large intestine include (Figure 8.14):

- **Tenia coli:** longitudinal bands of smooth muscle fibers.

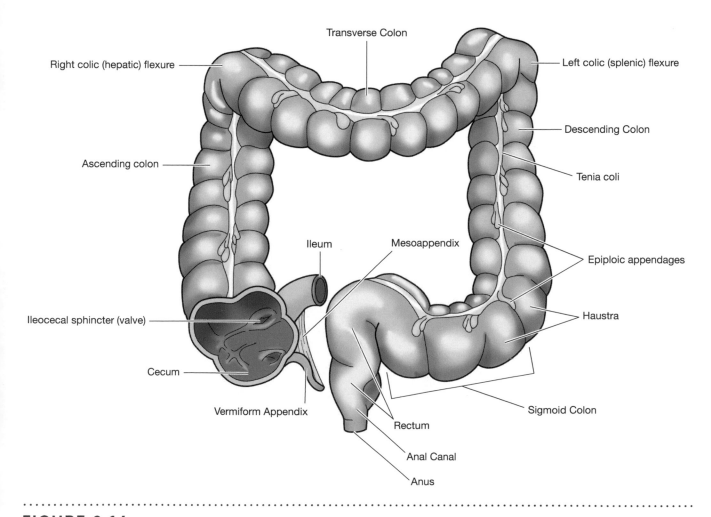

FIGURE 8.14

Large Intestine

- **Haustra coli:** pouches of large intestine produced by the contraction of the teniae coli.
- **Calibre:** the lumenal diameter is larger than the small intestine.

The large intestine consists of cecum, colon (**ascending, transverse, descending,** and **sigmoid**) **rectum,** and **anal canal** (Figure 8.14).

The **cecum** is the initial part of the large intestine located in the right inguinal region below the ileocecal junction (Figure 8.11). The **appendix** (9 cm), a worm-like appendage, attaches to the cecum inferomedial to the ileocecal junction (Figures 8.14 and 15). The surface marking of the base of the appendix is at the junction of the lateral third and medial two-thirds of the line joining the umbilicus to the anterior superior iliac spine.

The **ascending colon** (15 cm) starts from the cecum and ends to the right colic flexure. It is located in the right lumbar region (Figures 8.11 and 8.14).

The **transverse colon** (50 cm) extends between the right and left colic flexures and located in the right hypochondrium, umbilical, and the left hypochondrium regions (Figures 8.11 and 8.14).

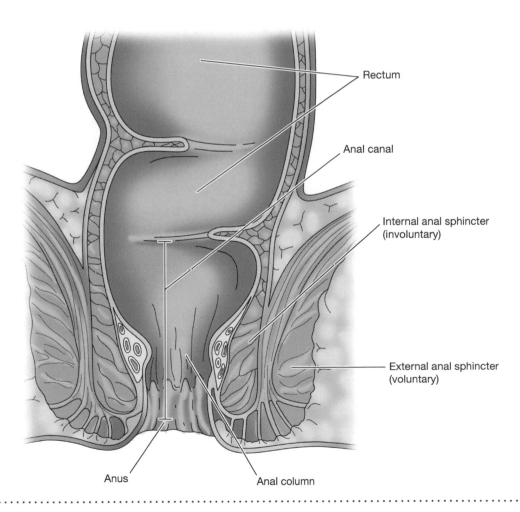

FIGURE 8.15

Frontal Section of Anal Canal

The **descending colon** (25 cm) starts from the left colic flexure and ends at the sigmoid colon in the left inguinal region. It is mostly located in the left lumbar region (Figures 8.1 and 8.14).

The **sigmoid colon** (40 to 80 cm) is S-shaped and starts from the left inguinal region and ends in true pelvic cavity in front of vertebra SIII (Figures 8.1 and 8.14).

The **rectum** (12 to 15 cm) starts at the level of vertebra SIII, passes though the pelvic diaphragm, and ends at the anal canal at the anorectal junction (flexure) (Figures 8.1 and 8.15). The distal part of the rectum expands to form the **rectal ampulla**. The longitudinal muscle fibers of the rectum do not form tenia coli.

The **anal canal** (4 cm) stretches between the **anorectal junction** and the **anus**. The distal part of the anal canal is guarded by two sphincters (Figure 8.15). The **internal anal sphincter** is involuntary, whereas the **external anal sphincter** is voluntary.

The appendix and transverse and sigmoid colons are intraperitoneal organs suspended from the posterior abdominal wall by their mesenteries.

· · · · **Associate Glands of the Digestive System**

Salivary Glands

There are three pairs of salivary glands associated with the oral cavity known as the parotid, submandibular, and sublingual glands (Figure 8.16). These glands secret about one liter of saliva per day.

- The **parotid gland** is the largest salivary gland located in front and below the external acoustic meatus and partially covers the masseter. The parotid duct drains the secretions of this gland into the vestibule of the oral cavity opposite to the second upper molar tooth.
- The **submandibular gland** is related to the medial surface of the body of the mandible. The submandibular duct carries the secretions of this gland to the floor of the oral cavity close to the lingual frenulum.
- The **sublingual gland** is an almond-shaped gland located underneath the mucosal membrane of the floor of the oral cavity. The secretion of this gland is drained by several short ducts to the floor of the oral cavity at the summit of the sublingual fold.

Liver

The liver is the largest (1.5 kg) gland of the body located below the diaphragm in right hypochondriac, epigastric, and left hypochondriac regions (Figure 8.11). It is mostly covered by peritoneum and is connected by the peritoneal reflections to the stomach (lesser omentum) and the anterior abdominal wall (**falciform ligament**) (Figures 8.12 and 8.13).

The liver has five surfaces (anterior, posterior, superior, inferior, and right), one inferior border, and four lobes. The inferior surface is related to the abdominal viscera (such as stomach, duodenum, and right kidney) and thus is termed as

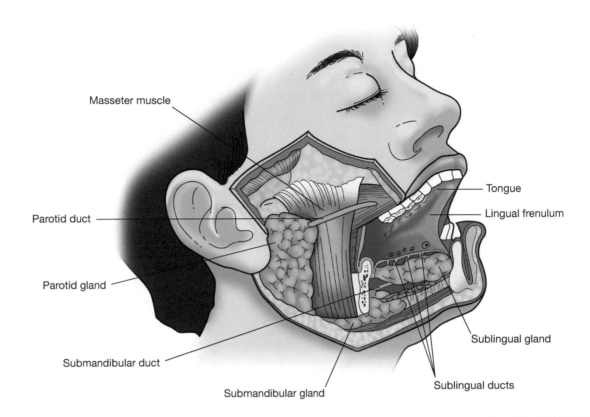

FIGURE 8.16
Salivary Glands

the **visceral surface**. The rest of the surfaces are related to diaphragm and are collectively referred to as the **diaphragmatic surface**.

The portal vein, hepatic artery, and autonomic nerves enter the liver, whereas the hepatic ducts and lymphatics leave the liver on the inferior surface at the **porta hepatis** (hepatic gateway).

On the visceral surface of the liver four lobes (**right**, **left**, **caudate**, and **quadrate**) are delineated by two impressions, two grooves, and porta hepatis (Figure 8.17). The impressions are occupied by the inferior vena cava and gall bladder and the grooves contain the **round ligament** of the liver and **ligamentum venosum**. The porta hepatis is horizontally located between the grooves (on the left) and the impressions (on the right).

Gall Bladder

The gall bladder is a small pear-shaped sac located on the inferior surface of the liver (Figures 8.13 and 8.18). It consists of the **fundus**, **body**, and **neck**. The fundus is round, protrudes from the inferior border of the liver, and is completely covered by peritoneum. The body is closely related to the visceral surface of the liver. The neck of the gall bladder is aligned with its body and is continuous with the S-shaped **cystic duct**. The cystic duct joins the **common hepatic duct** to form the **common bile duct**.

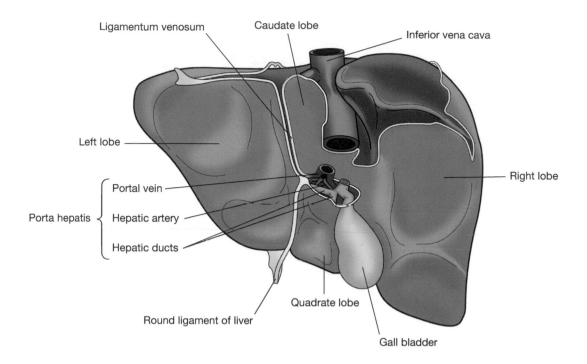

Ligamentum venosum

Caudate lobe

Inferior vena cava

Left lobe

Right lobe

Portal vein

Porta hepatis

Hepatic artery

Hepatic ducts

Round ligament of liver

Quadrate lobe

Gall bladder

FIGURE 8.17

Liver (viseral surface)

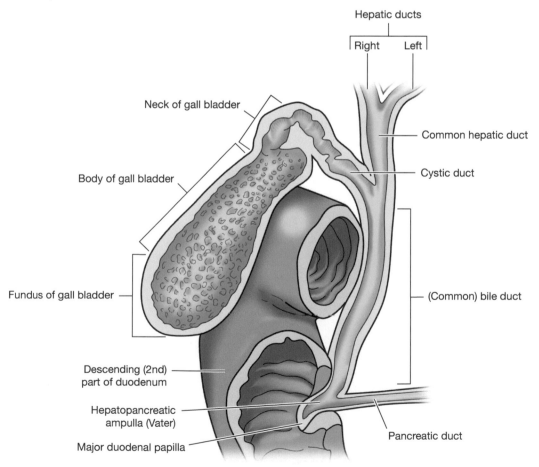

Hepatic ducts

Right | Left

Neck of gall bladder

Common hepatic duct

Body of gall bladder

Cystic duct

Fundus of gall bladder

(Common) bile duct

Descending (2nd)
part of duodenum

Hepatopancreatic
ampulla (Vater)

Major duodenal papilla

Pancreatic duct

FIGURE 8.18

Gall Bladder

Pancreas

The pancreas is a soft lobulated exocrine/endocrine gland located posterior to the stomach on the posterior abdominal wall (Figure 8.13). It is almost entirely retroperitoneal and consists of the **head, neck, body,** and **tail** (from right to left). The head is surrounded by the duodenum and the tail is related to the hilum of the spleen.

The secretions of the exocrine part of the pancreas are received by the **main** and **accessory pancreatic ducts** (Figure 8.18). The main pancreatic duct joins to the common bile duct to form the **hepatopancreatic ampulla** (of **Vater**) that opens into the descending (second) part of the duodenum. The accessory pancreatic duct usually drains to the main pancreatic duct.

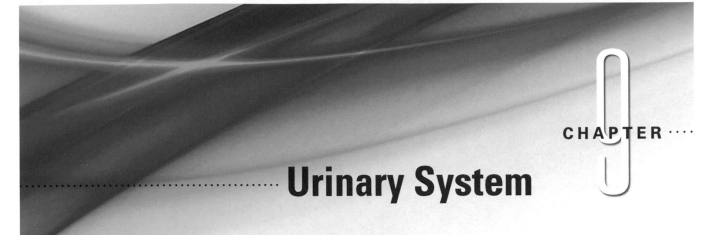

Urinary System

LEARNING OBJECTIVES
Upon completion of this chapter you should be able to:

1. Name the components of the urinary system.
2. Describe the external and internal features of the kidney.
3. Define the coverings of the kidney.
4. Explain the characteristics of the ureter.
5. Describe the external and internal features of the urinary bladder.
6. Discuss the characteristic differences between the male and female urethra.

The main function of the urinary system is to dispose of some of the waste byproducts of the metabolic reactions in human body. This system also plays a major role in fluid and electrolyte balance.

The different components of the urinary system include kidneys, ureters, urinary bladder, and urethra (Figure 9.1).

Kidney

The kidneys are two bean-shaped organs that are 12 cm long, 6 cm wide, and 3 cm thick. They are located behind the peritoneum on either side of the vertebral column at the level of vertebrae TXII to LIII (Figures 9.2 and 9.3). The right kidney is slightly lower than the left kidney due to the presence of the liver.

Each kidney has two surfaces (anterior and posterior), two borders (medial and lateral), and two poles (superior and inferior) (Figure 9.4).

The **anterior surface** of the right kidney is mainly related to the liver and duodenum, whereas the anterior surface of the left kidney is mostly related to the spleen and stomach.

The **posterior surface** of both kidneys is related to diaphragm, psoas major, quadratus lumborum, and transversus abdominis muscles.

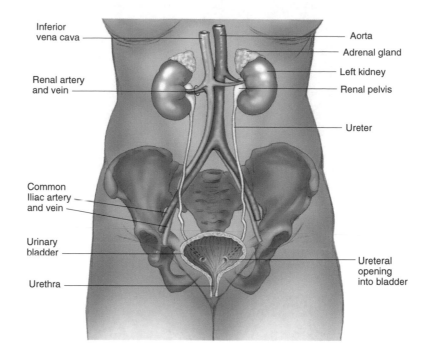

Inferior vena cava

Aorta

Adrenal gland

Left kidney

Renal artery and vein

Renal pelvis

Ureter

Common Iliac artery and vein

Urinary bladder

Ureteral opening into bladder

Urethra

FIGURE 9.1
Urinary System

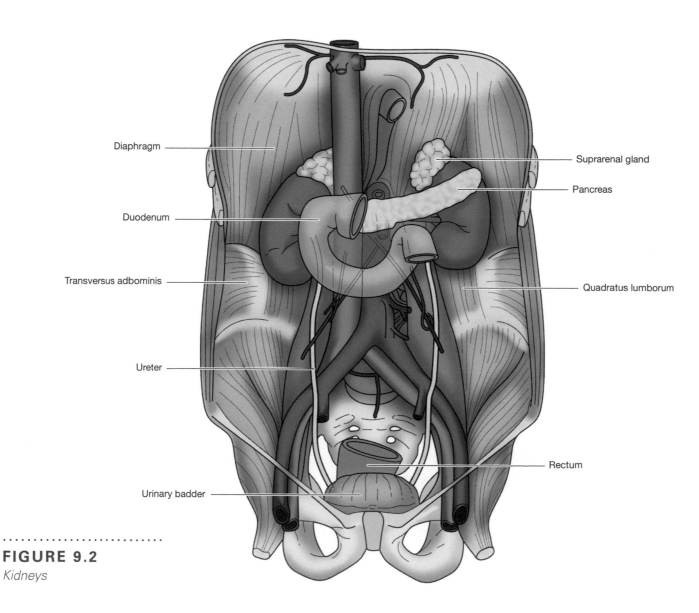

Diaphragm

Suprarenal gland

Pancreas

Duodenum

Transversus adbominis

Quadratus lumborum

Ureter

Rectum

Urinary badder

FIGURE 9.2
Kidneys

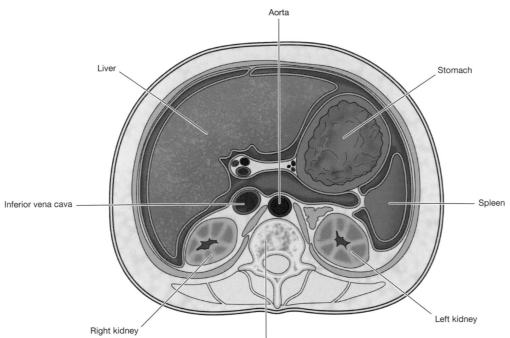

FIGURE 9.3
Kidney Relations (horizontal section of abdomen)

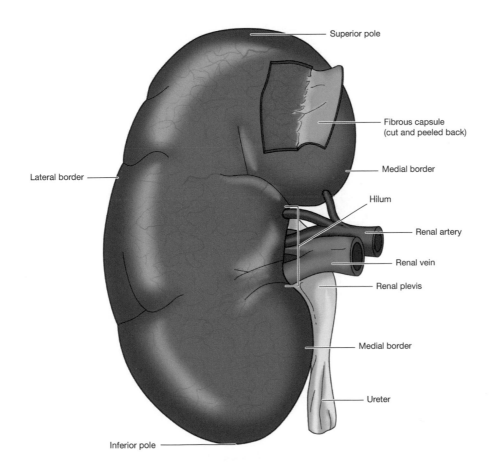

FIGURE 9.4
Right Kidney (anterior view)

The **lateral border** is convex but the **medial border** is concave and houses the **renal hilum**. The renal hilum is the entrance to a space, the **renal sinus**, which contains the renal vein, renal artery, renal pelvis, lymphatics, nerve fibers, and fat.

The **superior pole** of the kidney is in touch with the suprarenal (adrenal) gland, whereas the **inferior pole** is farther from the vertebral column and is round.

· · · · Coverings of the Kidney

1. The **fibrous capsule** is intimately attached to the surface of the kidney and partially extends to the interior of the renal hilum (Figure 9.5).
2. The **perirenal (perinephric) fat** invests the kidney outside the fibrous capsule.
3. The **renal fascia** surrounds the kidney and the suprarenal (adrenal) gland individually.
4. The **pararenal (paranephric) fat** is located behind the kidney and cushions it.

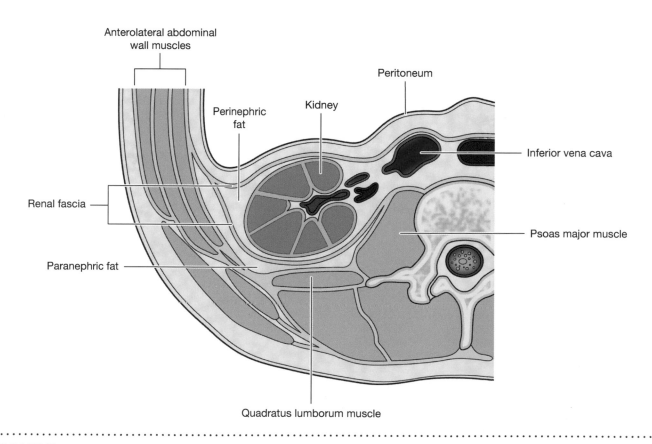

FIGURE 9.5

Coverings of Kidney (transverse section)

· · · · Internal Features of the Kidney

In a coronal section of the kidney a cortex (outer region) and a medulla (inner region) can be identified (Figure 9.6).

The medulla consists of 8 to 12 **renal pyramids**. The base of each pyramid faces the cortex and its apex (**renal papilla**) points toward the renal hilum.

The cortex is bounded between the renal capsule and renal pyramids. It extends between the renal pyramids and forms the **renal columns**. Each pyramid and the overlying cortex form a renal lobe.

The apex of each pyramid opens into a **minor calyx**. Every 3 to 4 minor calyces coalesce to form a **major calyx**. All major calyces join to form the **renal pelvis**, which ends to the ureter.

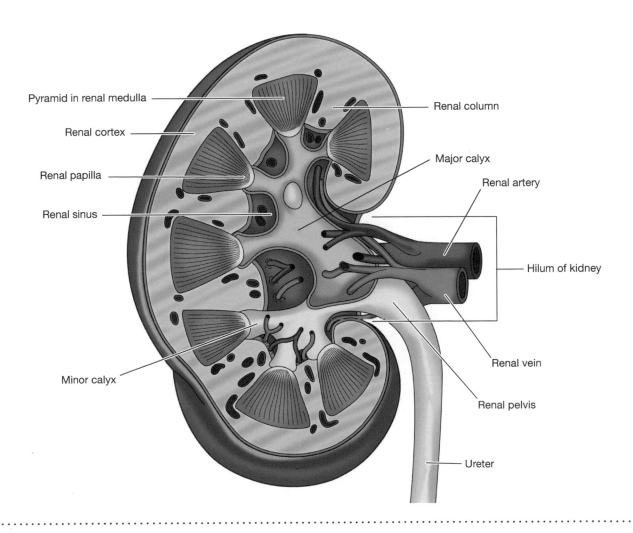

FIGURE 9.6

Kidney (internal features)

···· Ureter

The ureter is a muscular tube (25 cm) that starts from the renal pelvis and ends at the urinary bladder (Figure 9.2). It passes behind the peritoneum, in front of the psoas major muscle, and after crossing the common iliac artery enters the pelvis. The pelvic part of the ureter is crossed by the ductus deference in male and uterine artery in female.

The ureter has three constrictions in its course that are potential sites for obstruction by kidney stones. The first narrowing is at the junction of the ureter and renal pelvis. The second narrowing is where the ureter passes over the common iliac artery and the third one is at the entrance to the urinary bladder.

···· Urinary Bladder

The urinary bladder is a hollow muscular organ in true pelvis (when empty) behind the symphysis pubis (Figures 9.7A and 9.7B). It is located in front of rectum (in male) and in front of the uterus and vagina (in female). When empty, the urinary bladder is a pyramid with three surfaces (superior, right inferoleteral, and left inferolateral), a base, an apex, and a neck.

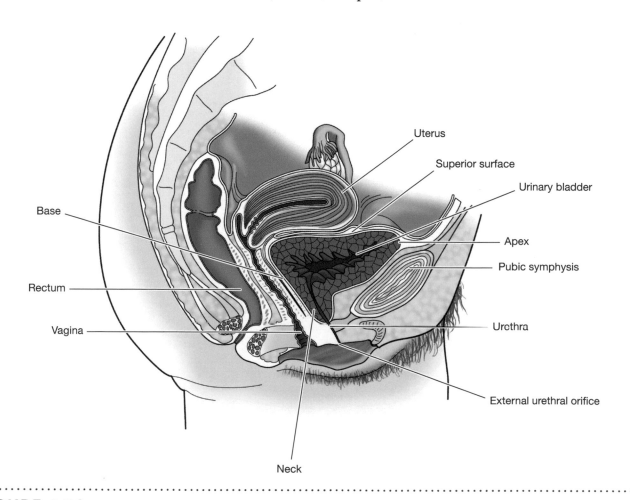

FIGURE 9.7A

Urinary Bladder in Female (sagittal section)

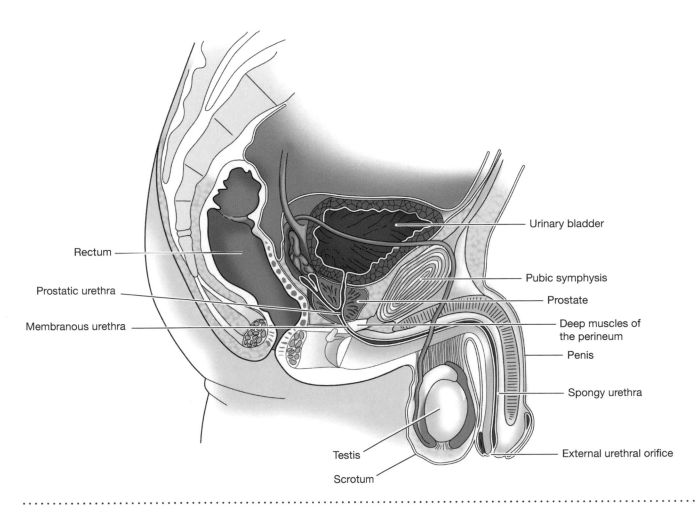

Rectum

Prostatic urethra

Membranous urethra

Urinary bladder

Pubic symphysis

Prostate

Deep muscles of
the perineum

Penis

Spongy urethra

Testis

Scrotum

External urethral orifice

FIGURE 9.7B

Urinary Bladder in Male (sagittal section)

The **superior surface** is covered by peritoneum and is related to sigmoid colon (in male), uterus (in female), and coils of the small intestine (in both genders). In males, the peritoneum covering the superior surface of the bladder reflects on the anterior surface of the rectum and forms a peritoneal pouch known as **rectovesical pouch** (Figure 9.7B). However, in females this peritoneal layer reflects to cover the body of the uterus and then reflects on the anterior surface of the rectum to form the **uterovesical** and **rectouterine** pouches respectively (Figuure 9.7A).

The **inferolateral surfaces** are related to the muscles of the pelvic wall and pelvic diaphragm.

The **base (fundus)**, triangular in shape, receives the ureters at its superolateral angles and gives rise to the urethra at its inferior angle. It is related to the ductus deference, seminal vesicles, and rectum in male, and to the uterus and vagina in female.

The **apex** is located behind the symphysis pubis and is connected to the umbilicus by the median umbilical ligament.

The **neck** is the most inferior part of the urinary bladder and is related to the prostate in male and external urethral sphincter in female.

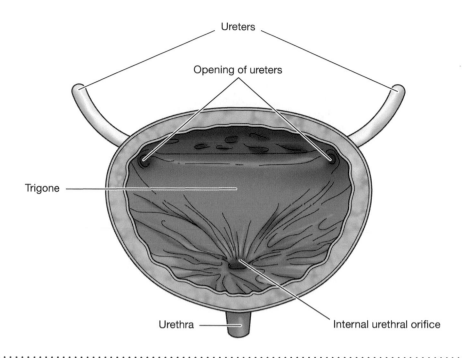

FIGURE 9.8
Urinary Bladder (interior view)

The mucosal membrane lining the interior of the urinary bladder is thrown into folds except on the base (fundus) of the urinary bladder that forms a smooth inverted triangular area known as the **trigone** (Figure 9.8). The ureters open at the superior angles, whereas the internal urethral orifice starts from the inferior angle of the trigone.

· · · · Urethra

The urethra is a passageway that starts from the neck of the urinary bladder and opens to the exterior.

The **male urethra** is about 20 cm long and is composed of four parts (Figures 9.7B and 9.9A).

1. The **preprostatic urethra** starts from the neck of the bladder at the **internal urethral orifice** and ends at the prostatic urethra. This part of the urethra is surrounded by the involuntary internal urethral sphincter (only in the male).
2. The **prostatic urethra** passes through the prostate gland and is the widest part of the urethra. The **prostatic** and the **ejaculatory** ducts open to this part of the urethra.
3. The **membranous urethra** passes through the anterior part of the pelvic floor and is surrounded by the voluntary external urethral sphincter. This is the narrowest and shortest part of the urethra.
4. The **spongy (penile) urethra** is the longest part of the urethra that passes through the bulb and corpus spongiosum of the penis and ends as the **external urethral orifice**. The **bulbourethral** glands open to the spongy urethra.

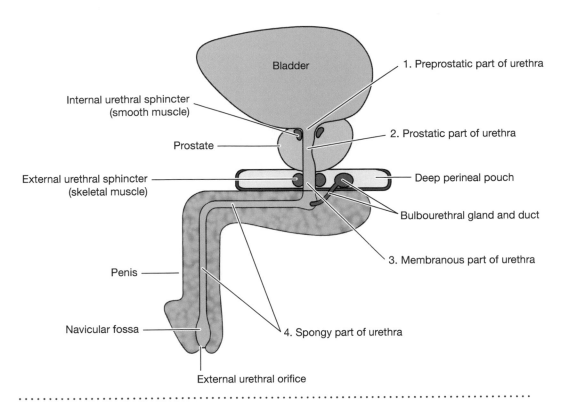

FIGURE 9.9A
Urethra in Male

The **female urethra** is about 4 cm long and starts from the internal urethral orifice at the neck of the urinary bladder and ends as the external urethral orifice to the exterior below the clitoris at the vestibule (Figures 9.7A and 9.9B). The female urethra descends in front of the vagina and passes through the anterior part of the pelvic floor where it is surrounded by the voluntary external urethral sphincter.

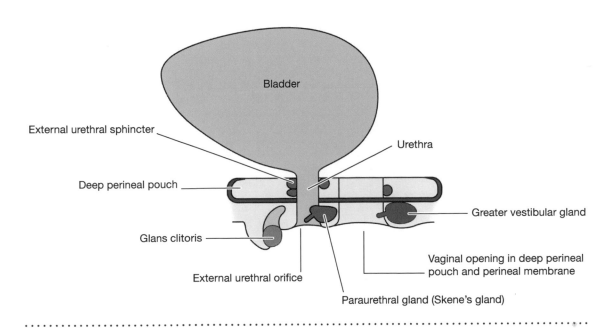

FIGURE 9.9B
Urethra in Female

CHAPTER 10

Reproductive System

LEARNING OBJECTIVES

Upon completion of this chapter you should be able to:

1. Discuss the main differences between the male and female reproductive systems.
2. Name the different components of the male and female reproductive systems.
3. Explain the characteristics of the testes.
4. Describe the position and characteristics of the epididymis and the ductus (vas) deferens.
5. Discuss the location and features of the seminal vesicles, prostate gland, and bulbourethral glands.
6. Describe the penis components.
7. Explain the characteristics of the ovaries.
8. Describe the position and characteristics of the uterine tubes, uterus, and vagina.
9. Discuss the supportive ligaments of the uterus.
10. Explain the female external genitalia.
11. Describe the mammary glands.

The differences between the male and female reproductive systems include:

1. The female reproductive system is anatomically related to the urinary system, whereas the male reproductive system is not only related but also shares parts of its ducts with the urinary system.
2. Most of the female reproductive system is located within the true pelvic cavity, whereas most parts of the male reproductive system are located outside the pelvis.
3. The female reproductive system connects the peritoneal cavity with the exterior as a conduit but the male reproductive system has no connection with the peritoneal cavity.

Due to all the above mentioned differences, the reproductive systems in both genders are discussed separately.

· · · · Male Reproductive System

The male reproductive system includes testes, epididymis, ductus (vas) deferens, seminal vesicles, prostate gland, bulbourethral glands, and penis (Figure 10.1).

Testes

The testes are two egg-shaped organs, 5 cm long, located in scrotum (Figure 10.2). The testes produce the sperms and testosterone. Each testis has two surfaces (lateral and medial), two borders (anterior and posterior), and two poles (superior and inferior). The testicular hilum is on the posterior border and the spermatic cord is attached to the superior pole of the testis. A fibrous capsule, **tunica albuginea**, covers the testis and invaginates into its posterior border to form the mediastinum of the testis. The testis is divided into about 250 lobules by the septa arising from tunica albuginea. Each lobule contains one to three tortuous **seminiferous** tubules. These tubules produce the sperms and eventually deliver them to the epididymis.

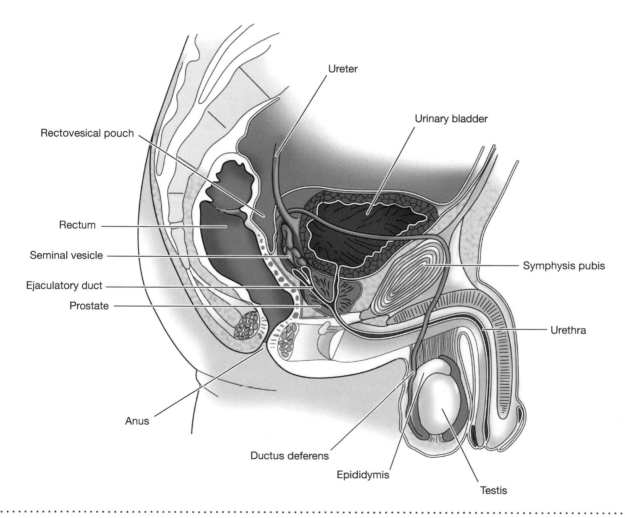

FIGURE 10.1

Male Reproductive System

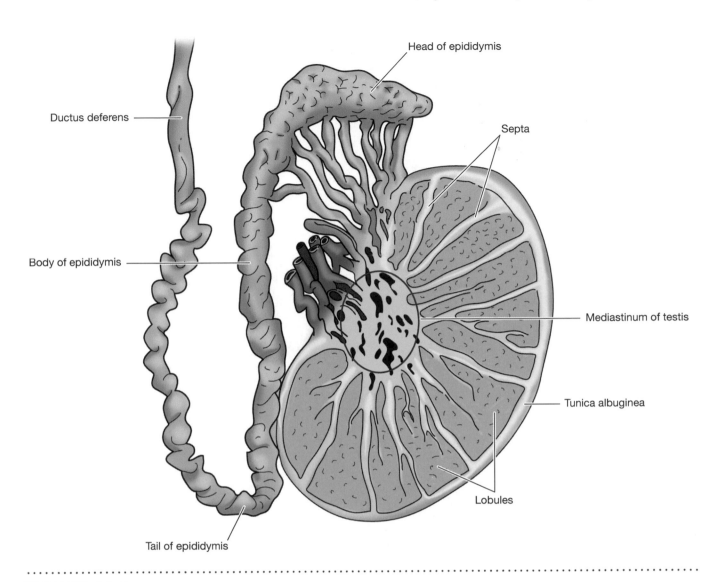

FIGURE 10.2
Testes

The testes develop in the abdominal cavity behind the peritoneum. They descend via the inguinal canal and enter the scrotum before birth. As the testes pass through the inguinal canal they carry parts of the abdominal wall layers with them thus surrounded by several layers. These layers along with the ductus deferens, testicular vessels, nerves, and lymphatics form the **spermatic cord** (Figure 4.23).

Epididymis

The epididymis is a convoluted muscular tube, 6 m long when uncoiled (Figure 10.2). It is composed of head, body, and tail parts. These are attached to the superior pole, posterior border, and inferior pole of the testis, respectively. The head of the epididymis indirectly receives the sperms from seminiferous tubules and its tail is continuous with the ductus deferens.

Ductus (vas) Deferens

The ductus (vas) deferens is a muscular tube, 45 cm long that starts from the tail of the epididymis and ends at the posterior surface (base) of the urinary bladder (Figures 10.1 and 10.2) It ascends through the spermatic cord and inguinal canal to enter the pelvic cavity. Inside the pelvis, it passes over the ureter and dilates to form the **ampulla** of vas deferens. It joins to the duct of the seminal vesicle at the end to form the **ejaculatory duct** (Figure 10.1).

Seminal Vesicles

The seminal vesicles are two coiled tubes at the base of the urinary bladder, lateral to the ductus deferens (Figure 10.1). The duct of the seminal vesicle joins to the ductus deferens to form the ejaculatory duct that opens into the prostatic urethra.

Prostate Gland

The prostate is a conical gland 3 cm high and 4 cm wide (Figure 10.1). It is located behind the pubic symphysis and in front of the rectal ampulla. The base of the gland is related to the neck of the urinary bladder and its apex lies on the external urethral sphincter. The prostate carries the prostatic urethra and the ejaculatory ducts pierce its posterior surface to open into the urethra.

Bulbourethral Gland

The bulbourethral glands are two small pea-sized glands on either side of the membranous urethra. The secretions of these glands empty into the spongy urethra to lubricate its lumen (Figures 10.1 and 10.3).

Penis

The penis has a root and a body (Figures 10.1 and 10.3). The root of the penis is fixed and is formed by three masses of erectile tissue, bulb (in the middle), and crus (on either side). The **bulb of penis** anchors to the membrane covering the inferior surface of the external urethral sphincter and carries the spongy urethra. The **crura** attach to the ischiopubic ramus. The root of the penis is covered by some of the perineal muscles.

The bulb and the crura continue anteriorly to form the body of the penis as the **corpus spongiosum** and the **corpora cavernosa**, respectively. These columns of erectile tissue are completely invested by a fascial sheet. The two corpora cavernosa are positioned on the dorsal aspect, whereas the corpus spongiosum is on the ventral aspect of the penis. The anterior end of the corpus spongiosum enlarges to form the **glans of penis** that reflects on the anterior ends of the corpora cavernosa. The spongy urethra passes through the corpus spongiosum and opens to the exterior at the glans.

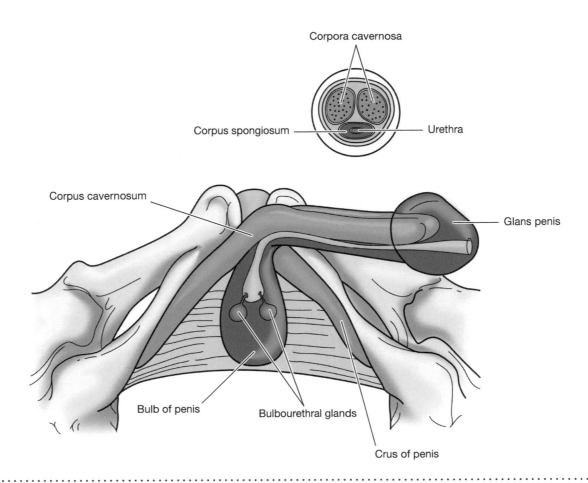

FIGURE 10.3
Penis

· · · · Female Reproductive System

The female reproductive system includes a pair of ovaries, a pair of uterine tubes, the uterus, the vagina, and external genital organs (Figure 10.4). The mammary glands or breasts may also be considered as parts of the female reproductive system.

Ovaries

The ovaries are two almond-shaped organs, 3 cm long, 1.5 cm wide, and 1 cm thick, located on the lateral wall of the pelvic cavity (Figures 10.5 and 10.8). The ovaries produce the female gametes (ovum) and female hormones (estrogen and progesterone).

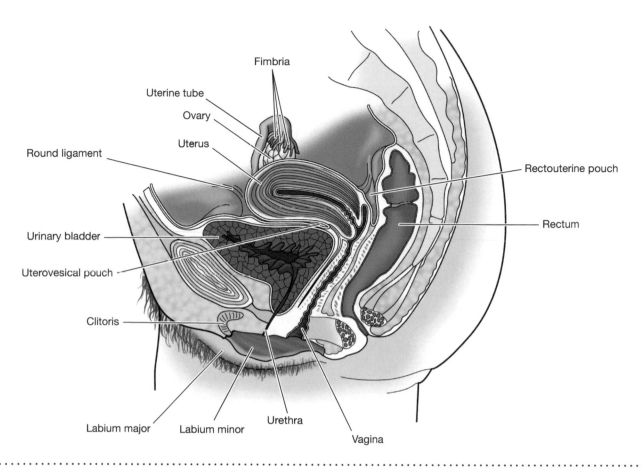

FIGURE 10.4
Female Reproductive System

Each ovary has two surfaces (lateral and medial), two borders (anterior and posterior), and two poles (superior and inferior).

The **anterior border** of the ovary gives attachment to mesovarium, whereas the **posterior border** is free. The ovary hilum is located on its anterior border.

The ovarian surfaces are smooth before puberty and become rough afterward due to ovulation.

Each ovary is held in place by the following ligaments (Figures 10.5 and 10.7):

The **ligament of the ovary** attaches the inferior pole of the ovary to the superior angle of the uterus.

The **suspensory ligament** is a double-layer fold of peritoneum that attaches the superior pole of the ovary to the posterior abdominal wall. This ligament carries the ovarian vessels and nerves.

The **mesovarium** is a double-layer fold of peritoneum that attaches the anterior border of ovary to the posterior layer of the broad ligament.

Fallopian or Uterine Tubes

These are 10-cm muscular tubes located on the superior border of the broad ligament on either side (Figures 10.5 and 10.7). The uterine tube connects the uterine
cavity to the peritoneal cavity and can be divided into four parts:

1. The **infundibulum** is the funnel-shaped lateral end of the tube that hangs
   over the ovary. The free margin of the infundibulum carries some finger-
   like projections known as **fimbriae**, one of which, the **ovarian fimbria**, is
   longer and attaches to the ovary. The infundibulum collects the released
   ovum from the surface of the ovary.
2. The **ampulla** is the most dilated part of the uterine tube forming the lateral
   two-thirds of it.
3. The **isthmus** is the narrowest part of the uterine tube that forms the medial
   one-third of it.
4. The **uterine part (intramural)** passes through the thickness of the uterine
   wall and opens into the uterine cavity.

Uterus

The uterus is a pear-shaped hollow organ with thick muscular walls that accom-
modates and nourishes the fertilized ovum (Figures 10.5 and 10.7). In a nul-
liparous adult the uterus is 7.5 cm long, 5 cm wide, and 2.5 cm thick. It has two

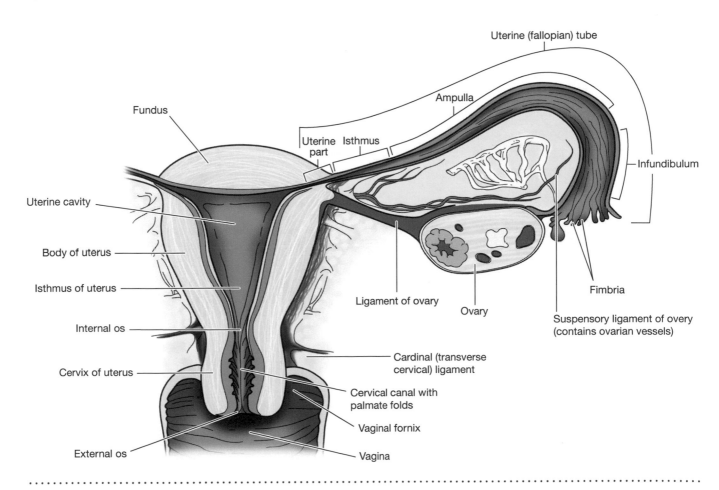

FIGURE 10.5

Uterus, Utrine Tube and Ovary (coronal section)

surfaces (superior and inferior) and two lateral borders. Both surfaces are covered by peritoneum and related to the sigmoid colon and small intestine loops (superior surface) and urinary bladder (inferior surface).

The uterus is divisible into the following parts:

1. The **fundus** is that part of the uterus located superior to the entrance of the uterine tubes.
2. The **body** is the middle part of the uterus located between the fundus and cervix (neck). The distal third of the body is known as the **isthmus**.
3. The **cervix (neck)** extends between the isthmus and vagina.

The uterine cavity is triangular in a coronal section and connects with the **cervical canal** via the **internal os** (Figure 10.5). The cervical canal in turn opens into the vagina through the **external os**.

The angle between the axis of the cervix and the axis of the vagina opens anteriorly and is known as **anteversion angle** (Figure 10.6). The angle between the axis of the uterus body and the axis of the cervix is known as **anteflexion angle**.

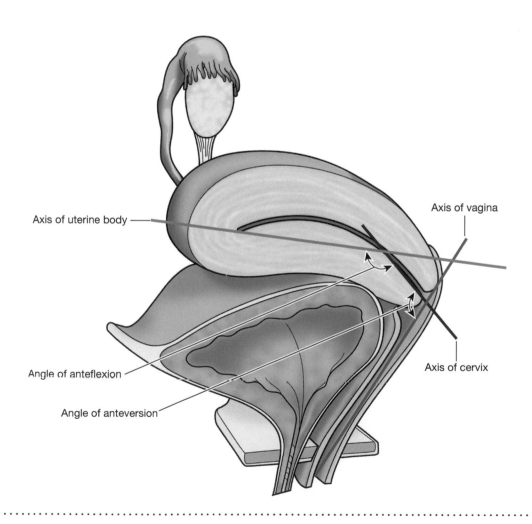

Axis of uterine body

Axis of vagina

Axis of cervix

Angle of anteflexion

Angle of anteversion

FIGURE 10.6
Uterine Angles

The Supportive Ligaments of the Uterus

The weight and position of the uterus is supported and maintained by the following ligaments on either side:

1. The **broad ligament** is a double-layer membrane made by the peritoneum that extends from the lateral border of the uterus to the lateral pelvic wall and floor (Figure 10.7). It contains the uterine tube on its superior border and the ligament of ovary and round ligament of uterus inferior to the uterine tube.
2. The **round ligament of uterus** starts from the superolateral angle of the uterus, passes through the inguinal canal, and blends with the connective tissue of the labium major (Figure 10.8).
3. The **transverse cervical ligament** connects the uterus cervix and the superior part of the vagina to the lateral pelvic wall (Figure 10.5).
4. The **pubocervical ligament** anchors the cervix of the uterus to the posterior surface of the pubis.
5. The **uterosacral ligament** extends from the inferior part of the sacrum to the cervix and the superior part of the vagina (Figure 10.7).

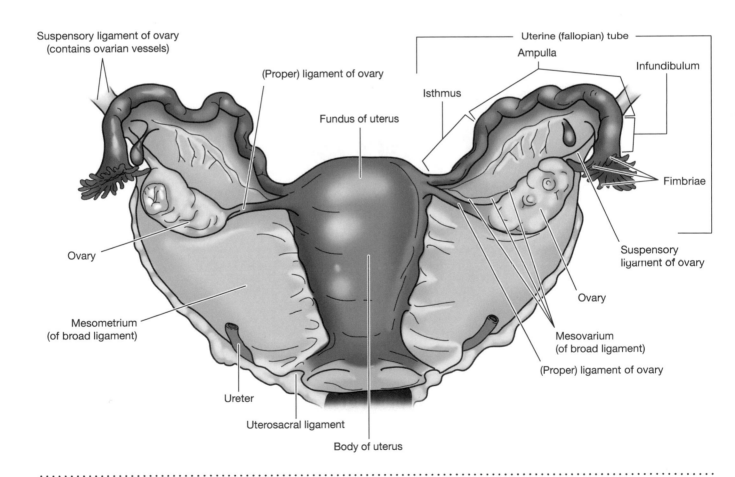

FIGURE 10.7

The Supportive Ligaments of the Uterus

Vagina

The vagina is a muscular tube that starts at the vestibule, runs posterosuperiorly, and ends to the cervix of the uterus (Figure 10.8). The **hymen**, a thin mucus membrane, partially closes the entrance of the vagina. The vagina is usually collapsed; thus, its anterior and posterior walls are in contact, except the proximal end where it surrounds the cervix of the uterus to form a circular space known as **fornix**. For descriptive purposes, the fornix is subdivided into the anterior, posterior, and two lateral parts.

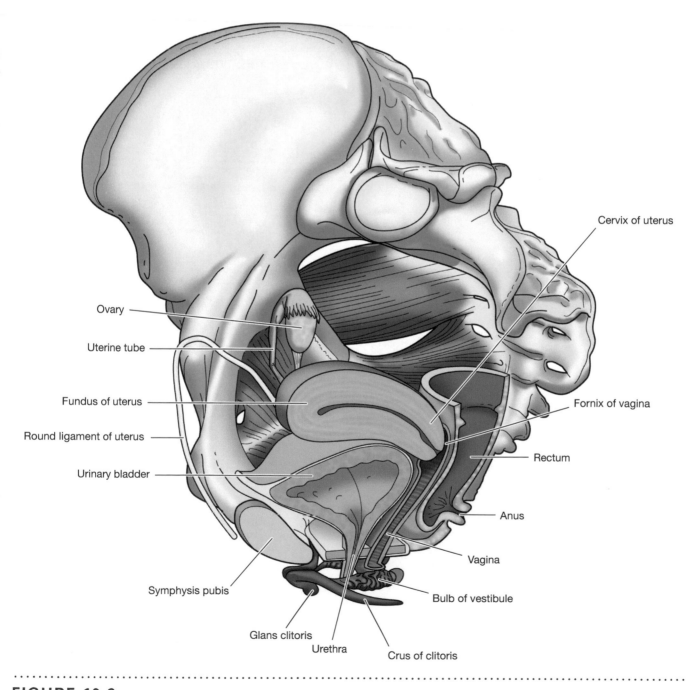

FIGURE 10.8

Female Reproductive System (sagittal section)

Female External Genitalia

The female external genitalia (**vulva**) include the mons pubis, labia major, labia minor, vestibule, clitoris and greater vestibular (Bartholin) glands (Figures 10.9 and 10.10).

The **mons pubis** is a skin prominence in front of pubis that contains fat.

The **labia major** are two skin folds that contain fat and are covered by coarse hairs after puberty. They are the equivalent of the scrotum in males.

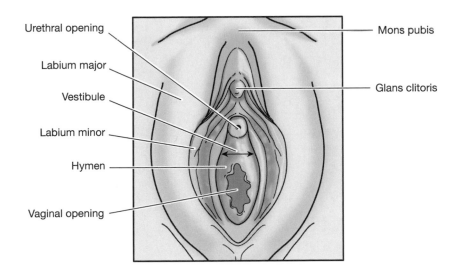

FIGURE 10.9

Female External Genitalia

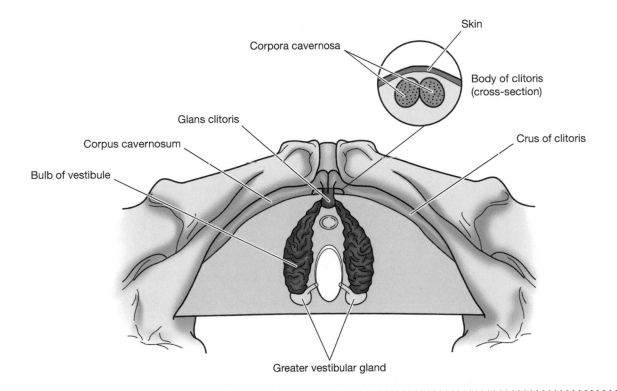

FIGURE 10.10

Female External Genitalia (deep dissection)

The **labia minor** are two hairless skin folds covered by the labia major from outside.

The **vestibule** is the cleft between two labia minor. It receives the urethra anteriorly and the vagina posteriorly.

The **clitoris** is homologous to the penis located at the anterior end of the vestibule. The clitoris has a **root** and a **body**. The root is formed by the left and right crura and right and left bulbs of vestibule. The crura and bulbs of vestibule continue anteriorly to form the corpora cavernosa and glans of clitoris respectively in body of clitoris.

The **greater vestibular glands** are a pair of glands deep to the skin and posterolateral to the vestibule. They release their secretion by means of small ducts into the vestibule posterolateral to the vaginal orifice.

Mammary Glands (Breasts)

The mammary glands are modified sweat glands located within the superficial fascia of the pectoral region (Figure 10.11). The relatively round base of each breast is extended vertically between the rib II to VI and transversely between the sternum and midaxillary line. The most prominent part of the breast, the **nipple**, is surrounded by a circular pigmented skin (the **areola**) and receives the lactiferous ducts of the mammary gland lobes.

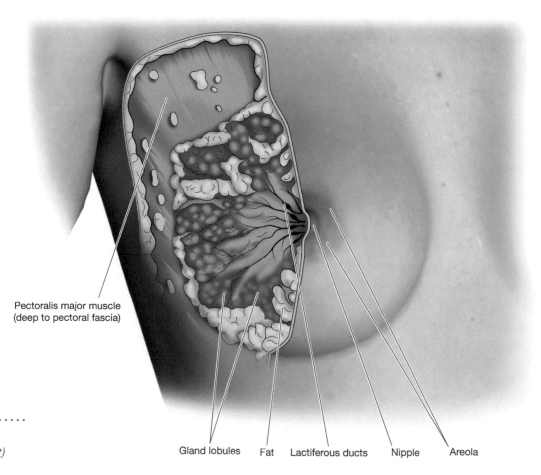

Pectoralis major muscle
(deep to pectoral fascia)

Gland lobules   Fat   Lactiferous ducts   Nipple   Areola

FIGURE 10.11

Mammary Gland (breast)

Endocrine Glands

LEARNING OBJECTIVES
Upon completion of this chapter you should be able to:

1. Name the major endocrine glands.
2. Compare characteristics of the endocrine and exocrine glands.
3. Explain the main features of the pituitary gland.
4. Describe the pineal gland.
5. Discuss the thyroid and parathyroid glands.
6. Explain the suprarenal gland.

The endocrine glands, along with the nervous system, regulate different functions of the other organ systems. The secretions of the endocrine glands, **hormones**, are directly released into the bloodstream, whereas the exocrine glands release their secretions via ducts either to the surface of the body or into the lumen of the other organ systems.

Pituitary (Hypophysis) Gland
The pituitary gland is an oval-shaped structure located in the hypophyseal fossa of the sphenoid bone in the middle cranial fossa (Figures 11.1 and 11.2). The hypophyseal stalk connects the pituitary gland to the diencephalon. This gland regulates the secretions of most of the other glands.

Pineal Gland
The pineal gland is a cone-shaped structure that attaches to the posterior wall of the third cerebral ventricle (Figure 11.2). Its secretions control the circadian rhythm and distribution of the melanin pigments in skin. This gland may calcify in the elderly people.

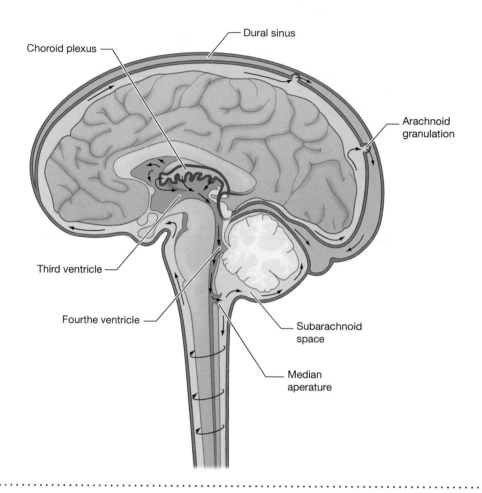

FIGURE 11.1
Pituitary Gland

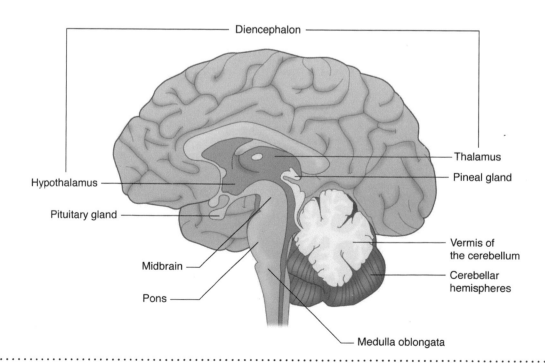

FIGURE 11.2
Brain (sagittal section)

· · · · **Thyroid and Parathyroid Glands**

The thyroid gland is situated in the neck in front of the trachea (Figure 11.3). It consists of two lateral pyramidal lobes connected together by isthmus. The lateral lobes relate to the thyroid and cricoid cartilages medially and common carotid arteries laterally. The isthmus passes in front of the trachea. The thyroid hormones regulate either the metabolic rate of the body or the blood calcium level.

The parathyroid glands are usually four in number and are embedded within the posterior border of the thyroid capsule. The parathyroid hormone cooperates with the thyroid hormone (calcitonin) in blood calcium level regulation.

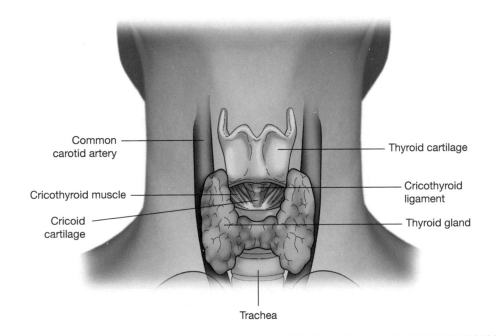

FIGURE 11.3
Thyroid Gland

Suprarenal (Adrenal) Glands

The suprarenal glands are located on the superior pole of the kidneys while surrounded by separate capsule (Figure 11.4). The right gland is pyramidal-shaped, whereas the left gland is crescent-shaped.

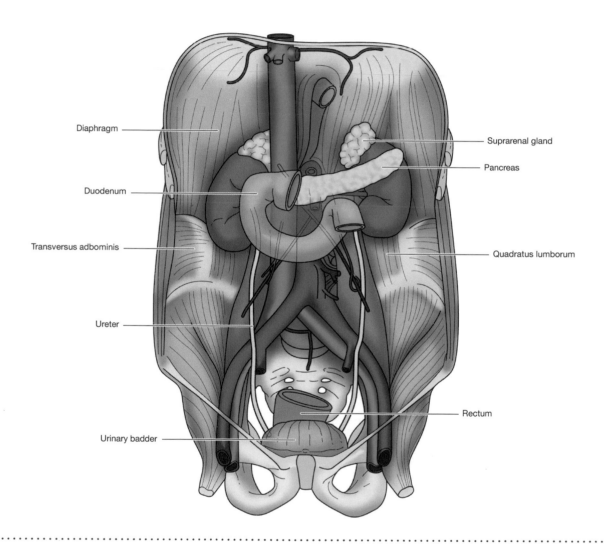

Diaphragm

Duodenum

Transversus adbominis

Ureter

Urinary badder

Suprarenal gland

Pancreas

Quadratus lumborum

Rectum

FIGURE 11.4
Adrenal Glands

CHAPTER 12

Special Senses

LEARNING OBJECTIVES

Upon completion of this chapter you should be able to:

1. Describe the different layers of the eyeball.
2. Explain the inner space of the eyeball and its subdivisions.
3. Discuss the structure of the eyelid.
4. Identify the lacrimal apparatus.
5. Describe the structure of the external ear.
6. Explain the main features of the middle ear.
7. Identify the major characteristics of the inner ear.

···· Eye

The eyeball and its associated structures (the eyelids, extraocular muscles, and lacrimal apparatus) occupy the orbital cavity (Figure 12.1).

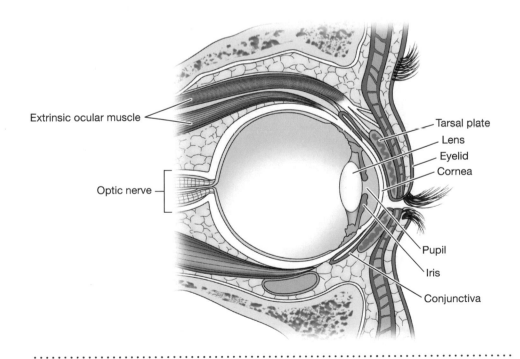

FIGURE 12.1

Eye (sagittal section)

Eyeball

The eyeball is surrounded by a layer of loose connective tissue that allows the eyeball to move freely. The structure of the eyeball consists of the following three layers (Figure 12.2):

1. The **fibrous layer** is the outermost layer and its posterior five-sixths, the **sclera**, is made up of dense, whitish connective tissue. The extra-ocular muscles attach to this layer and blood vessels penetrate it. The posterior part of the sclera is perforated by the optic nerve. The anterior one-sixth of the fibrous layer, the **cornea**, is thin, transparent, and without blood vessels. It is convex anteriorly and is covered by the **conjunctiva**.

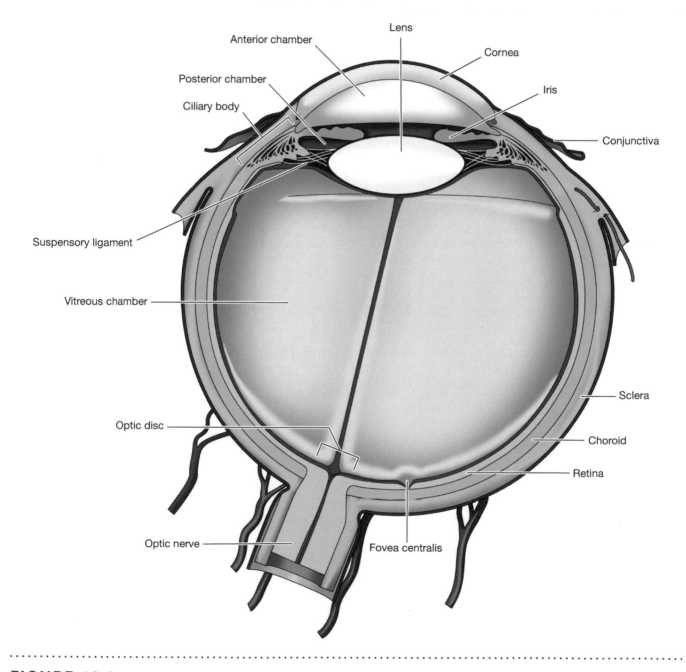

FIGURE 12.2

Eyeball (horizontal section)

2. The **vascular layer** is located deep to the fibrous layer and consists of:
   a. The **choroid**, the posterior five-sixth that lines the inner surface of the sclera and is highly vascularized.
   b. The **ciliary body** is the anterior continuation of the choroid which secretes the aqueous humor and modifies the convexity of the lens. The **suspensory ligaments** are delicate fibers stretched between the inner surface of the ciliary body and the circumference of the lens. The contraction of the circular smooth muscle fibers within the ciliary body changes the convexity of the lens.
   c. The **iris** is the anterior one-sixth of the vascular layer and forms a vertical circular plate in front of the lens and behind the cornea. The **pupil** is at the center of the iris. The smooth muscle fibers are arranged in a longitudinal and circular manner within the iris. The circular muscle fibers constrict the pupil whereas the longitudinal muscle fibers dilate it. The pigments of the iris determine the color of the eye.

3. The **nervous layer** is composed of two parts. The posterior three-fourths, the **retina**, carries photoreceptors that are sensitive to the light. The anterior one-fourth does not have any photoreceptor but carries pigments and lines the ciliary body and the posterior surface of the iris. The optic nerve leaves the retina at the **optic disc** (blind spot), which lacks the photoreceptors. The **fovea centralis (macula lutea)** is situated lateral to the optic disc and is very sensitive to the light due to an abundance of photoreceptors.

The inner space of the eyeball is subdivided into anterior and posterior parts that contain the aqueous humour and vitreous body respectively.

Lens

The lens is a transparent, biconvex, elastic body located posterior to the iris (Figure 12.2). It is held in place by the suspensory ligaments that act as the tendons of the ciliary muscles.

Aqueous Humor

The aqueous humor is a clear fluid produced and secreted by the ciliary body. It fills the posterior chamber (between the lens and iris) and the anterior chamber (between the iris and cornea). This fluid is picked up by the venous system at the junction of the sclera and cornea.

Vitreous Body

The vitreous body is a clear jelly-like substance that occupies the inner space of the eyeball posterior to the lens (vitreous chamber) and forms the shape of the eyeball.

Ocular Muscles

The ocular muscles are grouped as **intrinsic**—smooth muscle of the iris and ciliary body—and **extrinsic**—skeletal muscles arising from different parts of the orbit and inserting to the sclera (Figure 12.1).

Eyelids

The eyelids, or **palpebrae**, are thin skin folds in front of the eyeball that protect the eye (Figure 12.1). The core of the eyelid is formed by a fibroelastic plate, the **tarsus**, and skeletal muscles. The inner surface of the eyelids is lined by **conjunctiva**, a mucous membrane that reflects on the eyeball to cover the cornea. The eyelashes, sweat glands, and sebaceous glands are found at the free margin of the eyelids.

Lacrimal Gland

The lacrimal gland occupies the superolateral part of the orbital cavity (Figure 12.3). It releases the tears on the surface of the eye (cornea) that is collected by the **lacrimal sac** at the medial corner of the eye. The lacrimal sac passes the tears to the **inferior nasal meatus** via the **nasolacrimal duct**.

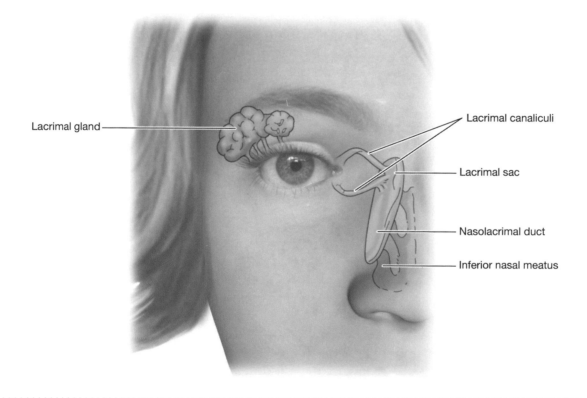

Lacrimal gland

Lacrimal canaliculi

Lacrimal sac

Nasolacrimal duct

Inferior nasal meatus

FIGURE 12.3

Lacrimal Apparatus

···· Ear

The ear can be divided into external, middle, and internal parts (Figure 12.4). The first two parts are mainly involved in reception and transmission of the sound waves to the inner ear where the sound waves are converted to electrical impulses and transmitted to the brain. The inner ear also contains the organ of balance.

External Ear

The external ear includes the auricle and external acoustic canal (Figure 12.4).

The **auricle** has a cartilaginous core covered by thin skin. It carries some contours to collect sound and transfer it to the external acoustic meatus. In the inferior part of the auricle, the **lobule**, the cartilage is replaced by connective tissue.

The **external acoustic meatus** is an S-shaped, 2.5-cm-long canal extending from the auricle to the tympanic membrane (ear drum). The lateral one-third of the canal is cartilaginous, whereas its medial two-thirds is bony. The thin skin covering the external acoustic meatus contains the ceruminous and sebaceous glands that secrete **cerumen** (earwax).

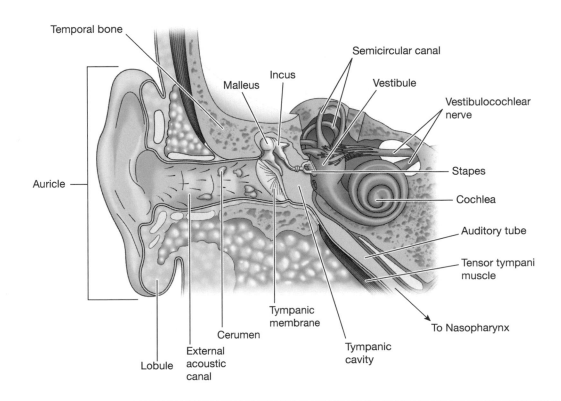

FIGURE 12.4

Ear (frontal section)

Middle Ear

The middle ear, **tympanic cavity**, is an irregular cubic space contained within the petrous part of the temporal bone (Figures 12.4 and 12.5). It is lined by the mucous membrane that is continuous with that of the nasopharynx. There are three ossicles (malleus, incus, and stapes) in the middle ear conveying the sound from the tympanic membrane to the inner ear. Two small skeletal muscles (tensor tympani and stapedius) are also contained in the middle ear and their function is to intensify or dampen the sound.

Here some of the walls of the tympanic cavity, including more distinct features, are discussed:

The **lateral wall** carries the tympanic membrane separating the middle and external ears.

The **medial wall** separates the tympanic cavity from the inner ear and has two openings, the **fenestra vestibuli** (ovale window) and the **fenestra cochlea** (round window) that are covered by the stapes and a membrane, respectively.

The **anterior wall** is connected to the nasopharynx via the auditory tube.

The **superior wall,** or the roof, separates the tympanic cavity from the middle cranial fossa.

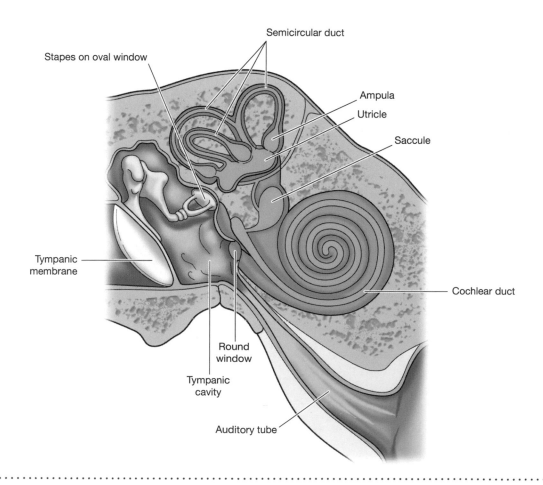

FIGURE 12.5

Middle and Inner Ear (coronal section)

Inner Ear

The inner ear, **labyrinth**, is housed within the petrous part of the temporal bone and includes the bony and membranous part (Figures 12.4 and 12.5).

The **bony labyrinth** includes the semicircular canals, vestibule, and cochlea.

The **semicircular canals** are three tubes that open into the vestibule.

The **vestibule** is connected to the middle ear (via the ovale window) and cochlea.

The **cochlea** is the shell-shaped part of the bony labyrinth. The lumen of this tube is partially divided into two sections by a bony septum (lamina). The **scala vestibuli** is located in the upper section of the lumen that ends with the fenestra vestibuli (ovale window). The **scala tympani** is located in the lower section of the lumen that ends with the fenestra cochlea (round window).

The **membranous labyrinth** is suspended in the bony labyrinth and is formed by a series of membranous sacs and ducts (Figure 12.5). The membranous labyrinth is filled with endolymph and is surrounded by perilymph. It includes the membranous semicircular ducts, utricule, saccule, and cochlear duct.

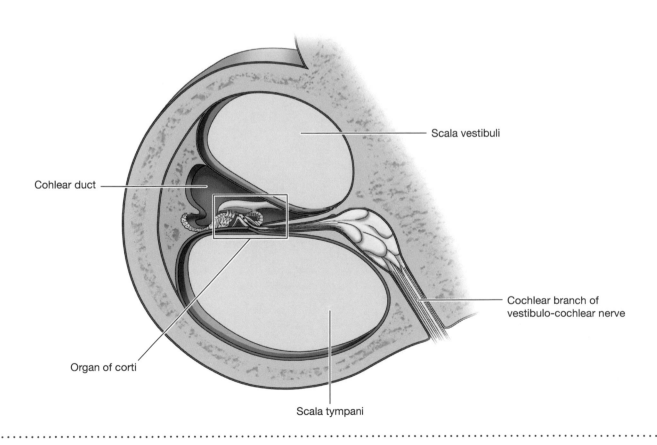

FIGURE 12.6

Cochlea (cross section)

The **membranous semicircular ducts** are located within the bony semicircular canals and open to the utricule (Figure 12.5). The dilated part of the membranous semicircular canals, the **ampula**, contains the **crista**. The crista carries the equilibrium receptors.

The **utricule** and **saccule** are located inside the vestibule and are connected to each other by a duct (Figure 12.5). The saccule is connected to the cochlear duct. The **macula** is an elevation on the floor of the utricule that carries the equilibrium receptors. The vestibular nerve arises from the crista and macula.

The **cochlear duct** carries the organ of hearing known as **organ of corti** that gives rise to the cochlear nerve (Figure 12.6).

Index